A HUNDRED YEARS OF SPEED WITH SAFETY

Dedicated to the memory of Ossie Nock and his beloved wife Olivia.
Ossie personified the spirit that made the company what it was.

A Hundred Years of Speed with Safety

THE INCEPTION AND PROGRESS OF THE WESTINGHOUSE BRAKE & SIGNAL COMPANY LTD.

1881 – 1981

O S NOCK

edited by
Stuart Angill, John Francis,
Mark Glover and Mike Stone

First published in the United Kingdom in 2006 by

The Hobnob Press,
PO Box 1838, East Knoyle, Salisbury SP3 6FA

British Library Cataloguing in Publication Data
A catalogue record for this book is available from the British Library.

ISBN 10: 0-946418-51-9
ISBN 13: 978-0-946418-51-0

Typeset in 10/12 pt Scala
Typesetting and origination by John Chandler
Printed in Great Britain by Salisbury Printing Company Ltd, Salisbury

Contents

The Editors recognise that there is a wealth of information about the subjects contained within this book held by a wide range of interested parties. We would welcome any corrections or additional information for inclusion in later editions. Please feel free to contact us via Hobnob Press.

Preface (1981)

IT IS A MOVING EXPERIENCE to look back over 100 years in the life of a great company, and then to set it down in a connected history. My great friend the late L T C Rolt did it most skilfully for the Hunslet Engine Company, while O R Hobson produced an equally fascinating work for the Halifax Building Society. Their tasks were however to a considerable extent simpler than mine in that they were outsiders, established authors it is true, but having no other connection with the firms than the commissions to write the Centenary Volumes. My situation is far otherwise.

Not only was I an employee of Westinghouse for 45 out of those 100 years, and a shareholder for the ten years since my retirement; but in the course of my work I was associated with men whose own service went back into the 'eighties' and 'nineties' of nineteenth century, and with others whose family connections extend to the very dawn of signalling and interlocking. The memory of them is as vivid today as when I worked for them, and with them 50 years ago, and that in a way could be a handicap. At my age it is easy enough to stray off into so much gossiping reminiscence, or at the opposite extreme, to allow the history to degenerate into a year-by-year summary of the Annual Reports.

In weighing up the prospects I recalled another centenary, that of the distinguished publishing firm of B T Batsford Ltd., which was celebrated in 1943 with a notable book. The then Chairman of the Company, the late Harry Batsford, to whom I shall never cease to be grateful for his masterly guidance when they were publishing one of the earliest of my books, asked, in connection with their centenary: 'Is it a story for anyone outside our immediate circle?' In our case, as with Batsfords, the answer is emphatically 'yes'. In many of my books on railway engineering, history and biography I have taken pride in putting in references to the work and products of our company, as a contribution to railway evolution as a whole; but now is the time for a little more direct blowing of the Westinghouse trumpet, in the modern alliance of brakes and signalling. My many friends in the other disciplines of engineering which have grown out of the basic brake and signal activities must forgive me if at times this book seems to be a little railway orientated; but I too was involved in the very dawn of rectifiers; with colliery work when it was still electro-pneumatic, and with the beginning of ticket machines.

My friends on the other side of the fence must also forgive me if I quote once again the famous Christmas admonition made by Mervyn Shorter, Managing Director of Westinghouse Brake & Signal Company from 1953, to one of our railway clients:

> If you must use GEC Signals, for God's sake use Westinghouse brakes!

The incorporation of Westinghouse in the massive Hawker Siddeley Group might have seemed to some to forecast a disappearance of our individuality, and merging of some activities with those of other members of the Group. But this is not so. Our contribution, which is a massive one amounting to an addition of nearly 10% to the annual turnout, is entirely complementary, and indeed an invaluable integral addition, for example, to the building of locomotives and passenger cars. In the past I have had occasion to write as

enthusiastically of British locomotives as I have of Westinghouse brakes and signals. Today the alliance between brakes and signals is as fundamental as that between brakes and locomotives, and it is on this background and its evolution to suit modern condition that the 100-year story of Westinghouse has been based. I write it in a spirit of deep gratitude: gratitude to the men who gave me my first opportunities, gratitude to those who worked with me, and in later years who worked for me. And not least, to those who invited me to write this book.

OS Nock
Batheaston
Bath
1981

Foreword

IN 1988 OSSIE NOCK very kindly provided, in his own inimitable style, the Foreword to a treatise I had written on the Westinghouse Style 'L' Power Frame. This was my first venture into publication, the work having been a labour of love, and I well remember the assistance and encouragement I received from many colleagues during the research stage. It was fitting therefore that Ossie, a Westinghouse man through and through, had no hesitation in writing the Foreword which, for me, sealed the completeness of the book. It is with great pleasure therefore that I am honoured to pen this Foreword to his latest book; a book that has lain dormant waiting the chance of publication since his death in 1994.

The original draft for this book was created on behalf of the Westinghouse Brake and Signal Company back in 1980 but, apart from a handful of photocopies which found their way into the possession of interested parties, the manuscript remained shelved, its completion and publication curtailed at the time the company was acquired by the Hawker Siddeley Group. Twenty years have passed since then with many subsequent changes to the make up of the company and even greater changes to the world of railways that it supplied. Today, the Brake and Signal Divisions of the company trade separately

as individual companies under the ownership of Knorr Bremse and Invensys respectively. The technology they employ reflects the modern era of electronics and microprocessors. Having put such significant effort into its preparation it is only right and proper that Ossie should now, at long last, be honoured by its final publication. Such was his professionalism he made no mention of the existence of the manuscript in either of his autobiographies despite including references to his other commissions.

Oswald Stevens Nock is well known in railway circles as the author of more than 140 books embracing a wide range of railway topics. He was also an extensive contributor to the railway press, including *The Railway Magazine* (RM) and *The Model Engineer*. He began writing for RM in 1932 and, following a series of articles during the early 1940s on Gresley locomotives, published his first book in 1945 entitled *The Locomotives of Sir Nigel Gresley*. He went on to consolidate his position at RM by taking over the regular 'Locomotive Practice and Performance' feature from Cecil J. Allen. Ossie always wrote in an engaging and entertaining manner, a style that is perpetuated in this new release which, I am sure, will be welcomed by a variety of readers, not just railway scholars and those interested in the history of one of Britain's great railway supply companies. He wrote enthusiastically for his subject and provides inspiration to the reader as he draws on the rich panoply of engineering skill that was so evident within the company.

He was of course a signal engineer by profession. This enabled him to write not just about locomotives and railways in general but about the specifics of railway signalling. A series of articles in *The Model Engineer* during 1940 covering semaphore signals was followed in 1946 and 1947 by a further series describing many of the fascinating styles of interlocking frame that existed at the time. He went on to write books about signalling including *British Railway Signalling* in 1969 having earlier, in 1962, to coincide with its Golden Jubilee, produced the history of the first 50 years of the Institution of Railway Signal Engineers (IRSE) in a work entitled *50 Years of Railway Signalling*. The IRSE featured highly in his professional life, acting as a stimulus for debate, learning and travel. He produced many learned Papers and, in 1969, he was honoured to be elected President of the IRSE.

Starting out as a draughtsman, Ossie spent his entire working life with the Westinghouse Brake and Signal Company rising to the position of Chief Mechanical Engineer. It comes therefore as no surprise that he accepted the pleasure of documenting the history of the company at is first Centenary. This book, *A Hundred Years of Speed with Safety*, covers the period 1881 to 1981 and follows the direction, setbacks and triumphs of a company that has been at the leading edge of innovation throughout its existence, a company whose name is synonymous with railway safety.

The book transports us on a journey from the 'Battle of the Brakes' and the establishment of the UK company at Kings Cross in London, to the end of the 20th Century, recording complicated manoeuvrings and company structures, the effects of two world wars and the drive for diversification. The text is not confined to technical or commercial history but highlights many of the personalities that brought life to the company. There is insight into the thinking of railwaymen, the worldwide influence of the company through its export and overseas operations and a portrayal of transatlantic know-how transfer that saw American ideas introduced on to the railways of the UK. The company has seen many successes and survived its share of failures and missed opportunities too. Diversification saw techniques and equipment put to good use in mechanisation of the collieries and other mines, and forays into road vehicle brakes, whilst early exploitation of the metal rectifier (or semiconductor) and electronic remote control systems spawned whole new Divisions and ultimately new companies in their own right.

Having been written in the 1980s, there are references to people, places and situations which, whilst factual at the time are now history. In first reading this book in the 21st Century the reader must make allowance for this time lag. The pictures that support the text are drawn from the extensive photographic archive which the company had the foresight to maintain and from the collections held in Chippenham Museum & Heritage Centre.

This record which charts, in visual form, the technology developed and applied by the company depicts in itself a fascinating story of enterprise and achievement. If only there were space to include every image. The safe keeping of many of the pictures from the Westinghouse archive is now in the hands of the Kidderminster Railway Museum which offers a reproduction service. Further extensive archives of Westinghouse related documents, photographs and items are held by the Wiltshire & Swindon History Centre, and Chippenham Museum & Heritage Centre.

Railway signalling and braking equipment has been manufactured in Chippenham since 1894. The industry is therefore part of that town's local heritage. It is fitting that O S Nock's work recording the first 100 years of Westinghouse Brake and Signal has been published 25 years after it was written, through the efforts of Mike Stone, the Curator at the Chippenham Museum & Heritage Centre. Mike's enthusiasm and perserverance has meant that Ossie's history of the company he was proud to work for is now available for all to read.

I have been pleased to work with Mark Glover, Stuart Angill and Mike Stone in the production of the additional explanation panels and footnotes, and in the selection of photographs. These we hope will add to the appeal of this book by illuminating the story for readers who have interests in railways, signalling and social history, as well as those who have connections with the companies and places mentioned.

J.D. Francis
Head of Research,
Westinghouse Rail Systems Ltd
President IRSE 2006

Oswald Stevens Nock (1905 - 1994)

Born at Sutton Coldfield in 1905, O S Nock was educated at Giggleswick School and Imperial College, gaining an honours degree in mechanical engineering. He joined the Westinghouse Brake and Signal Company as a draughtsman where he remained for his entire working life, rising to the position of Chief Mechanical Engineer. Professionally, after 40 years in the industry, he was honoured to be elected President of the Institution of Railway Signal Engineers in 1969.

Ossie, as he became known, is more famous for his writing than his engineering, having contributed countless articles to the railway press and penned more than 140 books. This previously unpublished work records the first 100 years of the company he worked for. It brings together his passions for the railway industry, the company in which he was immersed and the talent for writing that became his hallmark.

Acknowledgements

THIS BOOK has finally been published thanks to the efforts, great and small, of a large number of people. The editors would like to particularly mention (in alphabetical order!) the following:

Aerofilms Ltd
Rosemary Angill
Dr John Chandler
John Clark
Ernie Clayton
Rachel Francis
David Gillan
Unni Glover
David Hall
Anthony Howker
Paul Johnson
Don Little
Lloyd Plum
Barrie Shephard
Nick Smith
Cyril Stone
Richard (Dick) Wood
The staff of Chippenham Museum & Heritage Centre
The staff of the National Railway Museum, York
The staff at the Punch Library

and the thousands of staff who worked for the Westinghouse Brake & Signal Company at any time throughout its astonishing history – this is a record of their achievements throughout well over one hundred years of speed with safety.

1

Introduction
The Prelude to Automatic Continuous Brakes

IN JULY 1871 George Westinghouse made his first visit to England. Three years earlier, in the USA, the first-ever run with an air braked train began with a sensational incident that sold the brake more effectively than any modern sales promotion scheme could ever have done. For when the train so equipped, the Steubenville Accommodation on the Panhandle Railroad, emerged from Grant's Hill Tunnel, Pittsburgh, there on a level crossing just ahead was a pair of horses drawing a four-wheeled wagon.

In a trice all was panic and confusion. The terrified horses reared and bucked, completely out of control and for a second it seemed nothing could avert disaster; but the driver of the locomotive made a full application of the brake and the train stopped four feet clear. Never before had a train stopped so quickly and the news went round the country like wildfire. Railroad after railroad fitted its trains with the air brake and George Westinghouse came to Europe to set up manufacturing companies in Great Britain and on the Continent.

At that time the financial status of the British railways and the esteem in which they were held internationally was extremely high and to Westinghouse it seemed essential to get their support; but he found it extremely difficult to make any impression on their managers and he therefore sought the assistance of the editors of *Engineering*, then and for very many years subsequently a most influential journal.

Westinghouse's distinguished biographer, Henry G Prout, tells how, after several interviews, one of the editors, Dredge by name, handed him an editorial article he had written on the general subject of brakes. This article included this considered requirement: 'If a part of the train breaks loose from the rest, the brakes must come automatically into play; the failure of this brake apparatus on one or more carriages must not interfere with the action of the brakes on the rest of the train.' This was a vital stipulation that the original form of the air brake did not meet and Westinghouse was quick to appreciate the cogency of the argument.

Several articles about railway brakes, including a highly detailed account of the equipment on the Caledonian Railway did appear, but not one urging the introduction of this automatic feature. It would seem that Dredge, having sold the idea to Westinghouse, felt he had carried the point sufficiently far at that time. So having, as an audacious youngster of 27, 'invaded'

England with his still undeveloped brake, Westinghouse returned home to bring it very quickly near to perfection.

In 1869 the Westinghouse Air Brake Company was organised and, although a Pennsylvania Corporation, it set up a depot and works first in Liverpool and later a technical and sales force with offices in Westminster; but at first all brake equipment for the European market were made in the USA. Westinghouse's father, also named George, was still alive at the time and in consequence his name appears on the notepapers of the Continuous Brake Company as George Westinghouse Jr.

It is also interesting to know that he had as Vice President Sir Henry W Tyler, who for 23 years had been an Inspecting Officer of the Board of Trade in England and responsible for enquiring into many serious accidents. Tyler was also President of the Grand Trunk Railway of Canada; this latter was directed from England and was a fierce rival of the Canadian Pacific. It is significant that Westinghouse had secured the collaboration of a man who, by his past experience, was as much aware as anyone living of the shortcomings of British railway equipment. At the same time his position, currently as a manufacturer and head of a great railway, was somewhat invidious.

When Westinghouse journeyed to England for the second time, in 1874 it is recorded that 148 locomotives and 724 carriage equipments on European railroads had been supplied with the original 'straight air' brake; but by that time, thanks to the specification laid down by Dredge, successive inventions towards meeting this requirement for an automatic brake had brought the 'triple valve' into the general form that it held for many years subsequently.

His task was thus to sell this far better brake to European railways instead of the one originally introduced in 1871. Ordinarily it should not have been difficult,

Rather less formal than the traditional portraits of the great man, here Westinghouse looks relaxed surrounded by the mechanical engineering that meant so much to him

but in England he found a formidable competitor in the vacuum brake, which like the air brake also had its origin in the USA. It was based on a patent taken out by Nehemiah Hodge and others as early as 1860, but the form taken up in England was embodied in a patent taken out by John Y Smith in Pittsburgh in 1872. Smith created the vacuum by means of an ejector, in contrast to the vacuum pump driven off the locomotive machinery specified by Hodge.

Westinghouse had entered the vacuum brake field in opposition to Smith by securing assignment of the original Hodge patent and he followed this by taking out patents of his own for improvements. So that when he came to England for the third time in 1875 he was prepared to sell either air or vacuum brakes.

The first shots in what became known in Great Britain as the 'Battle of the Brakes' had already been fired and in June of that year the celebrated trials took place on the Nottingham – Newark – Lincoln line of the Midland Railway.

Regrettably, cost was a factor that influenced many managements and despite its American origin Smith's simple vacuum brake enjoyed a considerable spell of popularity, albeit while showing a very inferior performance. There were some strange contraptions demonstrated at the Newark trials, none more curious in retrospect than the Clark & Webb chain brake, strongly favoured by the largest and most influential of all the British railways, the London & North Western. The over-whelming superiority of the Westinghouse air brake was shown by comparison of stopping distances, of 1,477 ft from 50mph by the Smith vacuum brake and only 777 ft with the automatic air brake.

While in appreciation of this remarkable demonstration a few British companies adopted the automatic air brake, other inventors continued to try to equal, or nearly equal, its performances with their own forms of brake. Westinghouse himself spent some considerable time in England and in 1878 personally participated in the famous Galton trials on the London Brighton & South Coast Railway. This and subsequent ones in France and on the North Eastern Railway, were described in a remarkable series of papers presented before the Institution of Mechanical Engineers by Captain Douglas Galton FRS, first in Paris in June 1878, then in Manchester later that year and in London in 1879. But the opposition was strong, as could be discerned from the discussion at those meetings.

Charles Sacré, locomotive super-intendent of the Manchester, Sheffield & Lincolnshire Railway, under financial pressure no doubt from the dour and soulless chairman, Sir Edward Watkin, was one of them; so was C Fay whose form of the vacuum brake was in limited use on the Lancashire & Yorkshire Railway. In the discussion in Manchester, in October 1878, Fay is reported thus:

> Mr C Fay agreed with Mr Sacré that there were other things to be considered in a brake besides its rapid stopping of a train. There was the question of keeping it in repair and of the certainty of its acting when required – not, like some country-town fire-engines, being out of order when the emergency occurred. From a lengthened experience he could assure the meeting that the most simply constructed brake was very difficult to keep always in order: much more a very complicated apparatus. It was not the experience of two or three years alone that would enable it to be judged which brake was the most efficient or the best, taking everything into consideration; it required a very lengthened time to form an accurate judgement . . .

In the course of several discussions on Captain Galton's papers the work of George Westinghouse came in for frequent commendation and much interest was shown in the air brake. The accompanying reproduction of an original letter of August 1878 is typical of the times when Westinghouse was working hard to get the brake launched in England. To what extent the address Pittsburgh on the letter heading or the fact of the equipment coming from America prejudiced his chances it is not possible to say; but in this particular case, although the locomotive committee of the London & South Western agreed to have one train fitted up for trial, the company eventually decided to use the vacuum brake.

The time was evidently approaching for an English based company and

This view is an artist's impression of the Westinghouse Brake Company's offices in 1894.

manufactory to be set up and in 1881 the Westinghouse Brake Company was incorporated, with offices and works in York Road, Kings Cross, overlooking the station yard. One of the earliest users of the air brake in Great Britain was the Midland Railway, which had fitted up a local train running between Leeds and Bradford as early as 1873. This, of course, was with the straight air brake, but after the formation of the Continuous Brake Company the Midland was regarded as the most important customer.

When the far-famed Settle and Carlisle line was opened in 1876 and the joint Anglo-Scottish services with the North British, to Edinburgh and with the Glasgow and South Western Railway were put on, these trains were Westinghouse fitted and by the time the English based Westinghouse Brake Company was incorporated it seemed likely that the automatic air brake would be adopted generally on the Midland. Had this step

been taken, by a railway of such prestige and traffic, it is probable that the brake would, eventually, have become standard on all railways in the United Kingdom. So close was the association at one time that the diagram illustrating the brake in the Westinghouse advertising literature showed a Midland 2-4-0 locomotive.

Nevertheless, the association, though close, was not always cordial and Westinghouse was not pleased with the way that the locomotive department moved the air pumps from one locomotive to another. He was never reconciled to the British railway philosophy whereby the engineering department worked generally on the 'do-it-yourself' principle and felt free to modify or develop purchased equipment as they wished.

So, from one cause or another, friction grew between the Brake Company and the Midland Railway. They had a number of trains fitted with Smith's simple vacuum brake, but a more serious competitor to

Westinghouse was the Sanders & Bolitho vacuum brake, from which the standard automatic vacuum brake was eventually evolved. The occasional intransigence of the Westinghouse Brake Company only served to increase the determination of Midland Railway Engineers to develop a satisfactory alternative of their own.

In the same year that the Westinghouse Brake Company was incorporated, when the 'Battle of the Brakes' was at its height, there was an important conference held at Euston to consider the brake question. It was a time when the air and vacuum factions were indulging in a war of leaflets and articles in the technical press, running down their opponent's systems and claiming all the virtues for their own.

The Euston conference, very largely sponsored by the London & North Western Railway and attended by representatives of eleven of the principal British railway companies, voted in favour of standardising the vacuum brake. Those railways already using Westinghouse did not attend the conference and took no notice of its findings; but the others accepted the majority decision and ordered vacuum brake equipment accordingly; using two-inch brake pipe and the Clayton universal coupling. As previously mentioned however Westinghouse had his own patents for vacuum braking and when the

company was incorporated in England he made it clear he was prepared to supply either air or vacuum, the latter using the one-inch pipe system developed from the original Hodge patents. But in 1881 he was too late to beat the advances of the system well established and consolidated by the Vacuum Brake Company and manufactured by Gresham & Craven.

Instead he went into the attack on another line. In 1882 he issued writs against three railways, the Lancashire & Yorkshire, the London & South Western and the Midland, all of which had some locomotives and trains fitted up with Gresham & Craven, or Hardy automatic vacuum brake accusing them of infringement of Westinghouse patents. He claimed that the addition of reservoirs and ball valves to render the vacuum brake automatic infringed the principle of the triple valve. He demanded that they should cease fitting ball valves immediately and remove and destroy those already installed. He also claimed a large sum in compensation for loss of profits.

Naturally the three British railway companies were very upset at this attitude and after consultation with the Vacuum Brake Company and Gresham & Craven, and taking legal advice they decided to take it to the courts. The proceedings were long and complicated and continuing through the years 1883 and 1884 many innocent railway engineers were called upon to give evidence. One by one Westinghouse's claims were demolished and in the end he lost the case completely.

Relations became increasingly strained between the Westinghouse Brake Company and the Midland Railway, but the event that hastened the final breaking off of relations and the disappearance of the Westinghouse Brake from the Midland Railway was the invention by Mr Holt, the Works Manager at Derby, of his sanding gear, by which sand was blown on to the rails by compressed

The Front Door of the York Road Offices, c. 1970

air supplied by the brake pump. Westinghouse most emphatically did not approve. His pump was there to supply the brake apparatus, not for anything else; and relations became so strained over this matter that Holt modified his invention to use steam instead of air for sanding, and no more locomotives and trains were fitted with the Westinghouse brake on the Midland Railway. By the year 1889 use of the brake had ceased on what was one of the largest of the English railways.

In the meantime the 'Battle of the Brake' continued with unabated vigour. The Board of Trade had certainly laid down, in the most unequivocal terms, the features recommended for a satisfactory brake; but as yet those terms were not mandatory and some of the company managements seemed to take a positive delight in flouting them. Those who used Smith's simple vacuum brake were the most flagrant sinners in this

respect and one manager in particular stated that he would rather have an occasional disaster and pay the com-pensation for death and injury, than go to the expense of a brake that he did not want.

But public opinion against such an attitude was steadily hardening and the disaster on the Manchester, Sheffield & Lincolnshire Railway at Hexthorpe, near Doncaster in 1887, in which 25 persons were killed and 94 seriously injured, had a sensational sequel. The driver and fireman of the colliding train were arrested and committed to trial for manslaughter; but the proceedings at York Assizes, before the Lord Chief Justice of England, not only found the two men 'not guilty', but earned a severe reprimand for the railway company.

The Lord Chief Justice said: 'He could not but think that the railway company was seriously to blame for having had in use a

York Road viewed from above

Armagh Accident, 12 June 1889

A special excursion train of school children, carrying some 940 passengers, stalled on a steep gradient. Instead of waiting for a following train to assist, the driver chose to divide the train in an attempt to lighten the load. The excursion train was fitted with a non-automatic brake, which meant that as soon as the train was split, the brakes did not function. The train crew understood this, applied the hand-brake and chocked the sixth carriage with stones, but during the operation of uncoupling the train lurched back, with sufficient force to start the rear portion running down the hill out of control. Despite the frantic efforts of the footplate crew, the runaway train hit the following train at high speed, and 80 lives, mostly of young children, were lost. Locking the carriage doors was a contributory factor as, probably, was passengers playing with the guards hand brake. Much more can be found in The Runaway Train Armagh 1889 *by J R L Currie, published by David & Charles in 1971.*

brake which not only was not the best in existence, but which was known to be insufficient and liable to break down.'

Yet despite this stern indictment it was not until two years later, after the catastrophe of Armagh (see panel), that Parliament stepped in and made automatic continuous brakes compulsory on all passenger trains in the United Kingdom.

At that time, although there were some railways like the Great Northern of Ireland, on which Armagh occurred, that were still using non-continuous, non-automatic brakes, the automatic was well established as the main competitor to Westinghouse. At the time that the Regulation of Railways Act of 1889 was passed there were those who thought that the requirements then made compulsory did not go far enough, and that a single type of brake should have been specified as standard throughout the Kingdom. As it was however, the Westinghouse and the automatic vacuum were left in a state of co-existence.

At the turn of the century, six out of the sixteen main line railways of Great Britain had standardised on the Westinghouse automatic air brake, namely the Caledonian, Great Eastern, Great North of Scotland, London Brighton & South Coast, North British & North Eastern, with one important local railway in South Wales, the Rhymney.[1] All the Irish Railways used the automatic vacuum. Against Westinghouse was the Vacuum Brake Company, whose products were manufactured by Gresham & Craven Ltd in Manchester.

[1] In fact the London Tilbury and Southend railway was also 'Westinghouse' and remained so through Midland ownership into LMS days. The Isle of Wight and Isle of Wight Central were also so equipped and remained so until the end of steam traction. The London Chatham and Dover component of the South Eastern and Chatham was slow to convert to the dual brake, whilst the North British Railway started a switch to vacuum between 1906 and 1911.

2
Interlocking Diversity
The Signalling Constituents

Although the centenary that is being commemorated by the publication of this book is that of the incorporation of the first Limited Company in the Group, the signalling interests extend back many years prior to 1881. Beginning with Saxby & Farmer in 1860 and followed by McKenzie, Clunes & Holland in 1862 they were however trade partnerships rather than formally incorporated Limited Companies. It is rather curious that the first limited company in the signalling business, Dutton & Co Ltd, incorporated in 1889, was formed by an employee of McKenzie & Holland, who wished to branch out on his own. But the origin of the signalling interests of Westinghouse goes back even earlier than the formation of the firm of Saxby & Farmer; because it was in 1856 that John Saxby took out his first patent, for the simultaneous pulling off of the signal with the points over which that signal read.

The very word 'patent', with all that became involved with counter claims, infringements and long drawn out lawsuits became synonymous with interlocking apparatus in the 20 years following that first patent of Saxby's and in his Presidential Address to the Institution of Railway Signal Engineers in 1934, R S Griffiths, son of one of the partners in

McKenzie & Holland, and a Westinghouse man, named no fewer than fifteen different inventors, some of whom like Saxby produced many variations of their basic ideas.

The majority of these had quit the field by the time the Westinghouse Brake Company was incorporated in 1879; one at least of Saxby's strongest competitors had been eliminated by the cost of unsuccessful litigation. In Westinghouse circles the story is often told of the famous case between Saxby and Farmer and McKenzie & Holland. Whereas Saxby had introduced simultaneous working in his patent of 1856, McKenzie used separate levers and put a primitive form of interlocking between the two, Saxby claimed that he

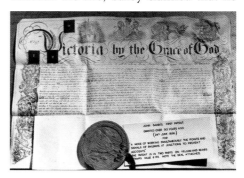

Saxby's Original Patent, carrying the seal of Queen Victoria.

held the master patent for the whole principle of interlocking and took McKenzie to court.

He did the same with Stevens & Sons, over an alleged infringement of a patent of 1860. The latter case was disposed of fairly quickly, to Saxby's discomfiture, when it was disclosed that the Board of Trade Inspecting Officer, Colonel Rich, had inspected and passed an interlocking frame of Stevens' manufacture, installed at Yeovil Junction on the London & South Western Railway four months before the date of the Saxby patent!

Against Easterbrook in the late 1860s however Saxby was running neck and neck in producing virtually the same kind of actuation. The Easterbrook 1868 locking frame used the catch handle locking and rocker principle and although Saxby's claim for a patent preceded that of his rival by three days, Easterbrook's was sealed first and he claimed prior right. It became an historic test case, involving far more than interlocking frames, because it postulated the principle of whether the initial disclosure of an invention and claim for a patent established priority, or whether the date of sealing was the arbiter. The case lasted for more than five years and ended in favour of Saxby.

Apparently it finished Easterbrook because he was not heard of again; but an unexpected souvenir of the affair came into the possession of the author in the 1940s. At that time the Westinghouse works at Chippenham was being scoured for scrap metal to be melted down for wartime salvage and from the dark corner of an old store there emerged a one-eighth full-size scale model of a 20-lever locking frame. My offer to purchase it for a token sum was accepted by an astonished storekeeper and with the aid of some improvised, non-mechanical wartime transport I got it to our Chippenham house.

It was thoroughly rusted up and none

John Saxby. In the 1956 Brochure, A Century of Signalling, *this photograph was captioned: 'John Saxby (1821-1913). In the service of the Locomotive Department of the London, Brighton and South Coast Railway he resigned from it in 1862 and in partnership with J S Farmer founded the business known as Saxby & Farmer at Kilburn. At the termination in 1888 of their agreement, he directed the factory established in 1878 at Creil (Oise), France, until his retirement in 1900.'*

of the locks were moveable, but as I came to examine it more closely my interest and surprise grew. It was not any Saxby or McKenzie product, but nothing less than an Easterbrook '1868'. No one I spoke to at the time knew of the existence of the model, still less how and by whom it came to be made. One can only imagine that it formed a piece of evidence in the lengthy Saxby versus Easterbrook case of 1868 – 1873.[1]

The circumstances of the still more famous Saxby versus McKenzie case were picturesquely described by Captain B H Peter, when Managing Director of Westinghouse, in a talk to the Supervisor's

Discussion Group at Chippenham in 1946. Speaking of the early days of interlocking he said:

> Saxby claimed to hold the master patent of the whole principle and in characteristic fashion, he started action after action against anyone whom he thought was infringing, almost to the extent of taking proceedings against anybody who operated a signal by a lever at all!
>
> This situation had come to a head and, from old documents, we see now that he met his Waterloo when he brought an action against McKenzie & Holland.
>
> Actions are slow things, as we all know. That action was fought out very slowly in the Courts and Saxby lost. Not satisfied, he took it to the Court of Appeal and again lost the day. Still refusing to give in, Saxby took the matter to the House of Lords and the whole thing drifted on for six solid years in all (which would not be unusual in these days).
>
> That action meant life or death for McKenzie & Holland. If they had lost, they would have been broken and put straight out of business as, for the six years since the beginning of the action, they had been continuing taking orders from all over the world and so would have been liable for heavy damages. Thus, it was really a matter of life or death on that famous Monday when they went to the House of Lords.
>
> Not only were McKenzie & Holland personally concerned, but also the whole town of Worcester, where their business was one of the staple industries. So, Worcester was taking the keenest interest and we have, I am glad to say, the original account from a local newspaper of the events of that Monday when the announcement was made in the House of Lords that McKenzie & Holland had successfully defended their action and won the case.
>
> When McKenzie and Clunes, who were in London to hear the result of the case, arrived back in Worcester, they were met by a vast crowd of 6,000 people, employees

and other inhabitants of the town. They all proceeded to celebrate the occasion – to say the least of it. First, they turned to the Station Hotel, which soon ran dry, whereupon they found other places which had not. There were fireworks, the whole place was beflagged and they generally had a real night out. Finally, round about midnight, Clunes and Holland were taken to their respective homes in open carriages, hauled by men with ropes.

> The description of the final phase of the celebration is most touching. The next morning, 300 workmen took an open carriage to the house of Mr Holland to take him to work, however Mr Holland was 'somewhat indisposed' and was unable to appear!!

Litigation apart, both firms had, by the year 1874 produced interlocking frames of such soundness of principle and good workmanship as to become world leaders in their respective spheres. The Saxby 'rocker and grid' and the McKenzie 'cam and soldier' were, as can be seen from the accompanying cross-sectional drawings, vastly different in their means of achieving the desired result; but both gained an outstanding record of dependability in service. The Saxby 'rocker and grid' became the standard form of interlocking frame in North America. Even after later products of the firm in England superseded the original design of 1874 the latter remained the strong favourite in the USA.

The McKenzie 'cam and soldier' dating from 1873 was extensively used in Australia and New Zealand. Studying the two cross-sectional drawings surprise may be expressed at the relative complexity of these machines and the extraordinary if dissimilar mechanisms used to achieve the same basic results. But it must not be forgotten that the two firms were then the most dogged of opponents, and any vestige of similarity would have been seized upon as ground for litigation!

McKenzie and Holland 'Cam and Soldier' system of Lever Locking

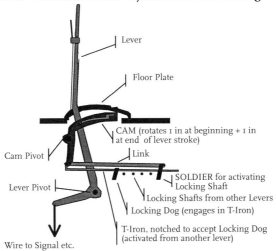

Pulling the Lever rotates the CAM, causing the Link and T-Iron, which are both attached to the CAM, to move horizontally. Movement of the Link causes the SOLDIER, and thereby the attached Locking Shaft, to rotate. Locking Dogs, attached to this shaft, will cause other levers to become locked as appropriate by engaging in notches in their T-Irons. If a Locking Dog is engaged in the T-Iron, the Lever cannot be moved. The Catch Handle has no connection to the locking, serving primarily to locate the lever position relative to the Floor Plate.

Saxby and Farmer 'Rocker and Grid' system of Lever Locking

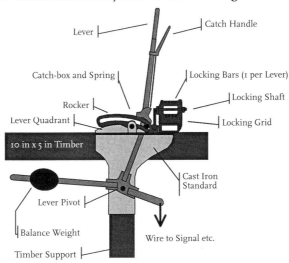

The Catch Handle is pulled to release the Lever. This rotates the Rocker via a stud attached to the catch-rod, thereby imparting a 22½° rotation to the Locking Shaft via a vertical linkage from the rear of the Rocker. The lever can then be pulled (but imparts no further movement to the rocker). At the end of the stroke, the Catch Handle snaps home in the notch on the Quadrant, thereby rotating the Rocker a further 22½° in the same direction. This Locking Shaft is fitted with a fork to impart a horizontal movement to the related Locking Bar, which is itself fitted with 'dogs' to interlock with the Shafts of other Levers, and thereby prevent their movement as appropriate. The Locking Grid extends across the back of all the Levers in the Frame and can have as many Locking Bars as are needed.

It was in this atmosphere that the oldest of all the signalling firms, Stevens & Sons, cut between them in 1870 with the simplest of all interlocking mechanisms, the straight tappet. Unfortunately for the firm, the management of Stevens & Sons seemed curiously indifferent to the fierce cut and thrust of competitive business; and although the principle of tappet locking was patented in the first place it was soon allowed to lapse. Needless to say both Saxby & Farmer and McKenzie & Holland swooped on to it and both produced new designs of locking frame in which it was incorporated. The Saxby version was the '1888 Duplex', while McKenzie & Holland simply substituted tappet action for their complicated rocker actuation. Both naturally adhered to their principles of driving the tappets by the action of the catch handle by Saxby and by indirect lever drive by McKenzie. Stevens continued with the simplest method of all – direct lever drive.

S T Dutton, having broken away from McKenzie & Holland and formed his own company in 1889, produced a most original form of catch handle actuation, doubtless in an attempt to avoid conflict with Saxby interests. In 1888 however the partnership between Saxby and Farmer was ended and with Farmer left in sole charge at Kilburn the attitude of the firm became notably less aggressive! In his 1889 patent Dutton pivoted the lever handle and made it combine the function of catch handle as well.

It was an interesting example of the way inventors worked, at a time when one had to produce something different from everyone else or go out of business. Four years later he reverted to the normal type of catch handle but used a highly distinctive shape of quadrant plate in which the lever worked. His venture into independent business was not successful however and he sold out to J F Pease & Co Ltd, general engineers, also in Worcester, while being retained as Manager of their signalling interests. It was during this time that an interesting sidelight upon the business of signalling took place: the first ever catalogue of material was compiled and circulated.

This was entirely a labour of love on the part of a young assistant, Thomas E Haywood by name. No fewer than 370 items, covering all detail parts were drawn individually and precisely to scale.

On the flyleaf is inscribed:

> I made this catalogue entirely in my own time at home and presented it to Mr S T Dutton with a complete set of negatives, from which several hundred copies were printed and bound in the drawing office at Shrub Hill, Worcester, Mr Dutton kindly gave me a 10 inch by 8 inch camera in appreciation of my work, June 1898, TEH.

A little before that time there had been important developments elsewhere in the signalling business. Farmer died in December 1892 and in the following year Saxby & Farmer was incorporated as a limited company with Charles Hodgson as Managing Director and later Chairman of the Board. Hodgson, when a pupil in the Locomotive Department of the London Brighton & South Coast Railway had met Saxby and when he and Farmer went into partnership and opened the works at Kilburn, Hodgson joined them and remained in the firm for the rest of his life.

Then, in 1894, J P O'Donnell, a well known patent agent, who had been representative in London for Dutton & Co. joined A G Evans to form yet another signalling manufacturing firm, Evans, O'Donnell & Co Ltd; this had particular significance for the future because the new firm set up their works alongside the Great Western Railway main line at Chippenham, Wiltshire. That the new firm soon obtained large orders, including their own particular pattern of catch-handle interlocking frame, is indicative of the amount of business then available.

At the turn of the century the following firms were all active in signalling business that was almost entirely based on the use of mechanical interlocking frames:

Saxby & Farmer Ltd – Kilburn
McKenzie & Holland – Worcester
J F Pease & Co Ltd – Worcester
Stevens & Sons – London and Glasgow

Charles Hodgson, (1841 – 1912) Managing Director and later Chairman of the Board of Saxby & Farmer until his death in 1912.

Evans, O'Donnell & Co Ltd – Chippenham
The Railway Signal Co Ltd – Liverpool
W R Sykes Interlocking Signal Co – London

By that time the Westinghouse Brake Company in London had also entered the signalling field, introducing the electro-pneumatic equipment of the Union Switch and Signal Company of Swissvale, Pennsylvania, one of the Westinghouse companies in the USA. This new development was accompanied by a business alliance with McKenzie & Holland, who manufactured some of the equipment. It was then that a very important merger of interest took place by the incorporation on August 16 1901 of the Pneumatic & Electric General Engineering Co Ltd.

This company, the name of which was changed to the Consolidated Signal Company Ltd in December 1903, was formed to acquire a controlling interest in

John Stinson Farmer (1827-1892). In the brochure, A Centenary of Signalling, *this photograph was captioned: 'Originally in the service of the London, Brighton and South Coast Railway he was appointed Assistant Traffic Manager in 1849 and in 1862 resigned in order to join John Saxby in manufacturing signals and interlocking apparatus. On the dissolution of the partnership in 1888 he managed the works at Kilburn until his death four years later.'*

This photograph shows Evans O'Donnell's Chippenham factory at some point between 1895 and 1900. The factory sign reads 'Manufacturers of Roller Bearings for Railways, Tramways, Shafting etc.'.

Evans, O'Donnell & Co, all the issued share capital of Saxby & Farmer Ltd. and all the issued share capital of a company to be called McKenzie & Holland Ltd. Until that time the latter had been a trade partnership of Walter Holland, William Griffiths, Sidney P Wood and William T Page. The Railway Signal Company was also taken over, likewise the signalling business of J F Pease & Co Ltd (except for pulleys and wheels), which was merged with that of McKenzie & Holland.

To outward appearances there was not a great deal of change. Except in the case of Pease & Co Ltd who still carried on their non-signalling business at Worcester, the well established names of Saxby & Farmer, McKenzie & Holland and The Railway Signal Co continued as separate entities with their own Boards of Directors. They were however under the very strict control of the Board of the Consolidated Signal Company. This control went so far as authorising salary and wage increases for comparatively minor staff and the approval of all items of capital expenditure, no matter how small.

The case of Evans O'Donnell was different from that of the rest, in that the company was not taken over in its entirety. 'Consolidated' had only a controlling interest and there were outside shareholders for a further 19 years.

The original directors of the 'Consolidated' were:

Walter Holland, Chairman
William Griffiths
Charles Hodgson
William T Page
Sidney P Wood
George Terrell
William Wingfield

The representation was thus the entire partnership of McKenzie & Holland and only one, Charles Hodgson, from Saxby & Farmer. It is interesting to add that sons of three out of those five original directors came to hold distinguished positions in the Westinghouse group. R S Griffiths has already been mentioned[2]. P F Hodgson became Managing Director of Saxby & Farmer, while R Wood became Assistant Secretary of the Westinghouse Brake & Signal Company. Nothing seems to be known of Wingfield, but Terrell later became Member of Parliament for Chippenham.

As a result of these amalgamations the Dutton type of interlocking frame, which had been extensively used on the Great Northern Railway, became, for a time, a standard product of McKenzie & Holland, and its manufacture was transferred to the Vulcan Iron Works at Worcester. The most important outcome of the formation of the 'Consolidated' was however the amalgamation of Evans O'Donnell with Saxby & Farmer, and the decision in 1902 to move the smithy and foundry of the Kilburn works to Chippenham.

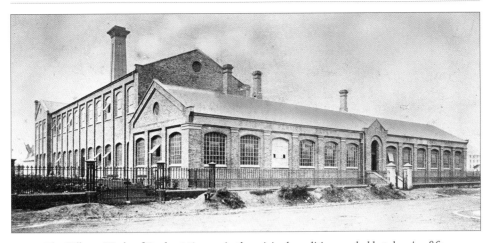

The Kilburn Works of Saxby & Farmer in the original condition, probably taken in 1863.

A group at the Kilburn works, taken after the second floor had been added to the office building in the early 1870s.

The two companies seem to have continued a separate existence, though Evans O'Donnell no longer carried on independent manufacture. Just as Dutton's frame became a standard stock-in trade of McKenzie & Holland, so the Evans O'Donnell frame was adopted as a standard Saxby product. There was good reason for this, because the Evans O'Donnell frame had become a standard and much appreciated machine in South America. In the new era Saxby's remained faithful to

The Old Foundry, 1896.

catch handle actuation of the interlocking, though the famous rocker mechanism became obsolete.

The standard frame went through two phases before reaching what was virtually its final form, in the 1914 apparatus. These two stages of the rocker mechanism were

the '1883 duplex' and the '1905'. This latter was designed by T E Haywood and its description in the final form of the Saxby catalogue was 'spring catch 1905 type'. It is extremely interesting to record that Haywood, after his first gratuitous compilation of the signalling catalogue for Pease & Co Ltd., also did the post-amalgamation catalogues for both McKenzie & Holland and Saxby & Farmer. In the latter the rocker type, with grid locking, continued to appear, but designated 'Belgian State Railways Standard Pattern'.

By the turn of the century the interlocking frame, essentially the centrepiece of the safety signalling system, had reached a very high degree of reliability in its provision for the safe movement of traffic; and although there were many different varieties – six in current production among the firms embodied in

London Bridge North. On the London, Brighton and South Coast Railway, the sheer size of the mechanical interlocking provided for London Bridge North signal box is very apparent from this magnificent photograph.

the Consolidated Signal Company alone – they were all means of achieving the same end. Some of the larger British railways, like the London & North Western and the Great Western had designed and were manufacturing interlocking frames of their own, while improvements subsequent to 1905 by both Saxby & Farmer and McKenzie & Holland were in detail rather than principle.

The basic difference between the products of the two firms remained, namely that McKenzie & Holland used lever actuation of the locking, having the catch handle as no more than a means of registering the lever in position on the quadrant, while Saxby & Farmer actuated the locking by means of the catch handle: one could not lift the catch out of its notch on the quadrant if the lever was locked. There were varying preferences among the railways of the United Kingdom and the fact that the honours were divided fairly evenly is enough to show that it was a matter of individual choice rather than a fundamental advantage one way or the other.

On the main line railways of the United Kingdom the main running signals were universally of the semaphore type working in the left hand lower quadrant, but of an astonishing number of designs. No two of the main line companies used the same pattern and if one included the smaller railways, like the Furness and the local lines in South Wales, one would find many more. I became very much aware of this in 1940, when the weekly journal *The Model Engineer* asked me to write a series of articles, with full working drawings, describing them. That series ran to nearly twenty instalments.

Some of the railways made their own, as they did the interlocking frames; but Saxby & Farmer, McKenzie & Holland and the Railway Signal Company made many of them, while Stevens & Sons, outside the 'Consolidated' group – made several more.

Easily the most distinctive of all the individual railway patterns was that of the Southern Division of the North Eastern Railway. In earlier semaphore days some railway signals were based upon the old Admiralty design on which the arm worked in a slot in the post. One particular indication, which on certain railways at one time signified 'line clear', was provided in a negative way by the arm hanging vertically down and completely obscured. This form of construction was generally abandoned after the serious accident on the Great Northern Railway at Abbots Ripton in

The exterior of Brighton North signal box on the London, Brighton and South Coast Railway, erected in 1862 and believed to have been in use for around 20 years. The practice of mounting all the signals over the signal box and operating them by direct rod connections continued in favour for a long period.

January 1876, when in blizzard conditions the arms of several signals became clogged up with frozen snow accumulating in the slots and preventing the arms being moved. The North Eastern Railway however retained this design as a standard in its Southern Division to the very end of its independent existence in December 1892. In combination with the 4ft high McKenzie & Holland pinnacle it made a striking ensemble.

The signal box at Charing Cross terminus, London, South Eastern Railway, in service from January 1864 to February 1888. The signals are of the type favoured by the Brighton Railway with the coloured glasses inside the lamps. The arched stone buttresses can still be seen today (2006), but sadly the flamboyant lamps have long disappeared.

In 1902 it was felt that the W R Sykes Interlocking Signal Company should be brought into the Consolidated fold, as will be referred to in more detail in the following chapter. McKenzie & Holland were becoming increasingly associated with the electric and electro-pneumatic signalling activities of the Westinghouse Brake Company and a link up with Sykes, including the important additional safety principles of 'Lock and Block' (See Panel) seemed a natural and potentially advantageous development. An approach to Sykes was however rebuffed. The powerful 'Consolidated' thereupon authorised McKenzie & Holland to enter into direct competition with Sykes, and in 1903, following some evidently intense engineering work at Worcester, T E Haywood produced one of his inimitable catalogues covering:

McKenzies & Holland's
Improved
S Y X
Electric Block Interlocking
For safe railway working

I have that original draft of this catalogue before me and it is a remarkable document, in the beauty of the original drawings of complicated electrical apparatus and in the incredible neatness of the handwritten text, so scaled down as to occupy approximately the same space as the eventual printed pages.

Commercially it was an audacious enterprise, not least in calling it 'improved S Y X', because 'S Y X' was part of the trade mark of Sykes; and it was a pretty cool act to muscle in on what had been a product of an old-established firm, albeit a variation of the standard Sykes 'Lock and Block', design something similar and call it an improvement.

McKenzie & Holland had been licensees of the system known as Electric Block Interlocking. Furthermore 'Consolidated' were not content with throwing McKenzie & Holland into the fray. It was arranged that the other companies should give support and to offer instruments at 20% less than Sykes' price list. The struggle went on for several years, but it is significant of the status and esteem of the Sykes organisation that during this difficult period they secured contracts for and successfully installed two of their largest and most spectacular plants – at Glasgow St Enoch, the city terminus of the Glasgow & South Western Railway and at the rebuilt and greatly enlarged Victoria, of the London Brighton & South Coast Railway. During

Lock and Block

In the 1870s the concept of 'lock and block' was implemented by a number of manufacturers, but notably Sykes. Patent number 622 of 1875 was an important milestone. This set about linking the signalling to the logical progress of the train, through the block section and from signal to signal. The system found widespread use, particularly on some of the heavily trafficked lines around London. The 'union of lock and block' was finally enforced by legislation in the form of the 1889 Regulation of Railways Act following the disaster at Armagh in the same year.

Many variants existed with nuances to suit individual layouts, but in essence a sequence of operations linked to the actual movement of the train forced sequential locking and integrated it with the operation of the block instruments (devices used to determine whether a section of track was clear for a new train, occupied by a train or blocked – meaning neither).

all this period W R Sykes, the founder, remained in active control, ably assisted by his three sons, W R Junior, J C, and F J. It is sad to recall that his eldest son, W R Sykes Junior, who was in charge of the Victoria Station installation, died in 1908, before the work was completely finished.

There is no doubt however that the severe competition from firms in the 'Consolidated' group put a strain upon

Sykes and in May 1907 the firm was forced to a financial reconstruction. The records that remain do not make it clear when the W R Sykes Interlocking Signal Company eventually came into the Consolidated group, but in January 1912 27,100 'A' 10% shares in Sykes were acquired by Consolidated. The founder, the veteran W R Sykes, remained head of the firm until his death in 1917. Apart from the period

The mechanical frame provided for Glasgow St Enoch.

The 'Hole in the Wall' Signal Box installed at Victoria in 1860 by Saxby and Farmer. This was the forerunner of all signal boxes and later control centres, and was replaced in around 1900.

of strenuous opposition, from 1902 to 1907, Sykes were on friendly terms with both McKenzie & Holland and the Westinghouse Brake Company and when preparations began for the latter to take in the electric-pneumatic signalling interests of the Union Switch & Signal Co Ltd, it was a young Sykes engineer, Walter Allan Pearce by name, who was selected as the future design draughtsman.

---

1 Detailed description of the work of Easterbrook and his fight against Saxby is provided in the British Railway Journal Winter 1992, in an excellent article: "Walter Easterbrook Signalling Contractor" by John Dixon and Peter Kay.
2 On page 8.

3
The Dawn of Power Signalling

I N OPENING this chapter I cannot do better than quote a passage from Henry G Prout's biography of George Westinghouse (see Panel):

When Westinghouse became interested in interlocking and block signalling those arts were well developed in Great Britain, but were almost unknown in the United States. Block signalling began in England about 1846 and interlocking began in 1856. By 1890 all British railways doing passenger business were thoroughly signalled and interlocked. The first interlocking machine seen in the United States was an English machine brought over in 1876 for the Centennial Exposition. By 1900 many big railroad-yards, junctions and crossings were interlocked, but many more were still unprotected. Block signalling had begun on a few railway systems, but hardly more than begun. Even yet we have not reached the completeness of protection of the British railways, but in mechanical methods of signalling and interlocking we have gone far beyond the rest of the world, and this is due in great degree to the impulse and direction that Westinghouse gave to the art.

When Westinghouse entered this field in 1880, he found it entirely unoccupied here. He had not only to design and make apparatus, but he had to create his market, and the market grew very slowly. For twenty years the company which he organised, the Union Switch & Signal Company, struggled along in the tedious process of educating the buyers of its products, and then it came into great prosperity. Westinghouse had supported it through these lean years by his personal credit, and he laid the foundations of its success by his perception of the future course of the art and by his own contributions to its technical growth.

A basic contribution by Westinghouse to the signalling and interlocking art was the development of the use of power. He was not the first inventor to take out patents in power interlocking and signalling; probably he was not the first to conceive the idea. He was, however, the first inventor to conceive and develop methods and apparatus that went into actual and lasting use, that laid the foundations of general practice, and that are still in use substantially as he first worked them out and installed them in the railroads.

Henry G Prout's Life of George Westinghouse *was originally published in 1921 and is seen as the definitive biography of the great man. At least two versions are still in print today, a reprint of the original work, ISBN 0766167275, published by R A Kessinger, and the other, rather more recent version ISBN 158798104 published by Beard Books.*

Despite the completeness with which the British railway system was signalled, Westinghouse felt there was an opening for power operation and before even the twenty lean years of the Union Switch & Signal Company had passed, active preparations had begun towards the introduction of the electro-pneumatic system into Europe. Retaining vividly enough in mind the opposition put up against the air brake, simply because it was American,[1] it was considered essential to give the electro-pneumatic system an English façade even though its early fundamentals had been thrashed out in the USA; and for that reason an engineer familiar not only with the principles but with the finer points of British signalling practice was needed to adapt where necessary the American equipment. The choice fell on W A Pearce who had been trained under W R Sykes and in 1889 at the age of 26, he joined the Westinghouse Brake Company in London. It was shortly after that Westinghouse himself relinquished direct control of the English company and that Albert Kapteyn was appointed General Manager and Secretary.

The company was indeed fortunate in its choice of a designer for power signalling. Pearce, as I came to know him personally in later years, was a remarkable man. He had a natural flair for finding a neat and elegant solution to the most baffling of design problems and in his 48 years of service with the Westinghouse Group, including 35 in Management of the power signalling section of the drawing office and a further seven as consultant until his retirement in 1937, his contribution was indeed a massive one.

In preparation for the entry of the Brake Company into the signalling field, he was sent to America in 1893 and for two years was in the service of the Union Switch & Signal Company. On his return in 1895, he began the preparation of a complete set of drawings of the electro-pneumatic system of signalling ready for English or Continental use. The majority of the early drawings were made by him personally and every one is a masterpiece of perfect draughtsmanship. The engineer put in charge of signalling in the Westinghouse Brake Company was Mr E de M Malan and it is his initials rather than Pearce's that appear on the earliest drawings.

At first the Westinghouse Brake Company acted only as designers and manufacturers of the equipment rather than overall signalling contractors and an arrangement was made for McKenzie & Holland to do all the work in the field and supply the required items of purely mechanical equipment. It was in this partnership, not yet advanced to the point of a formal agreement, that the first-ever installation of power signalling in Great Britain was made in 1899.

In retrospect, it is rather curious why the particular installation was made. It is true that McKenzie & Holland had not long previous put in some very large mechanical interlockings on the Great Eastern Railway and that the junctions at Spitalfields Goods Station gave an opportunity for some coordination of control by replacing two mechanical boxes by one new power plant. But whys and wherefores apart, the new box at Granary Junction was a milestone in the history of British railway signalling and that of the Westinghouse group of companies. It controlled the complicated track layout where the line from Spitalfields Goods Station connected with the freight line from Bethnal Green West Junction to Bishopsgate Goods terminal. Operation was all the more awkward and complicated because traffic for Spitalfields Goods had to reverse direction when arriving from Bethnal Green Junction.

The interlocking frame installed was of the standard Union Switch & Signal Company's type, with rotating handles

The McKenzie & Holland Power Frame at Granary Junction, Bishopgate, on the Great Eastern Railway

The interior of Whitechapel Cabin on the Metropolitan and District Railway.

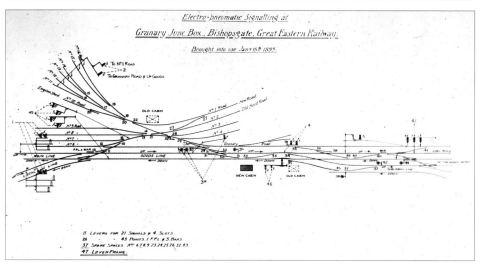

The layout of Granary Junction, as referred to in this chapter.

mounted on a vertical board in front of the signalmen and with the mechanical interlocking in a horizontal tray just behind the levers. In one respect however, American practice was not followed. In many large installations in the USA a track diagram was mounted vertically on the frame, immediately beyond the inward end of the tray containing the locking. On this diagram the lie of every set of points was indicated by a mechanical connection to the shaft on which the operating levers were mounted. It was an ingenious mechanism and Pearce included it on his earliest drawings of the Union Switch type of interlocking machine.

At Granary Junction however it was not considered necessary to have this indication of the setting of the point levers and the signal box had a track diagram in the contemporary British style – at that period in signalling history not animated in any way. It is interesting to see from photographs taken at the time of installation that the diagram was labelled 'White-Chapel Box'. This was curious because it was generally referred to as either the Bishopsgate or the Spitalfields installation in early days. Whitechapel was

some little distance away and had no station, goods or passenger, on the Great Eastern Railway. All the mechanical work and installation of the electro-pneumatic equipment was carried out by McKenzie & Holland for whom Mr W J Griffiths, one of the partners in the firm, was engineer in charge.

The interlocking machine for Granary Junction was imported from the USA and it was the only one of the American design to be installed in Great Britain.[2] Very many years later, when I was one of his senior assistants, Pearce told me how British railway officers objected to the oscillating handles and how he had to redesign the mechanism to include a miniature lever working in an orthodox manner. This he put out in front in a characteristically neat design. But in rearranging the frame, particularly in view of some considerably larger installations for which it was hoped to secure the contracts, the horizontal tray method of accommodating the interlocking seemed likely to be something of an embarrassment in the width of tray that would be required, resulting in a much wider apparatus than the traditional British mechanical locking frame. So Pearce put the locking trays vertical. He used to recall, with amusement, the horror expressed in America when his friends in the Union Switch heard of this development and how he would never be able to prevent the locking falling out. All the subsequent English built frames were designed in this way, including the great plants at Glasgow Central (374 levers) and London Bridge (311 levers) and, as he dryly remarked to me once: 'The locking hasn't fallen out yet!'

The year 1902 was a crucial one in Westinghouse history. For some time previously the air of London had been thick with rumours and counter-rumours about impending electrification of the Inner Circle Railway. Much of the speculation and back-stage manoeuvres arose from there being two separate companies involved, the Metropolitan on the north side and the Metropolitan District. They had been controlled by two celebrated railway 'barons' whose bitter antagonism had sustained the ruinous railway warfare in Kent between the South Eastern and the London, Chatham and Dover Companies – Sir Edward Watkin, and James Staats Forbes; and each had in turn tried to engulf respectively the Metropolitan and the Metropolitan District in to their strangely unprofitable enterprises.

Neither succeeded and while Watkin eventually retired, Forbes remained to carry on the 'war' in the tunnels of the Inner Circle. It developed into a major row as to what system of electrification should be used. The Metropolitan wanted the Hungarian Ganz alternating current system, while Forbes out of cussedness rather than any logical reasoning, opposed it on principle and with floods of his usual rhetoric. Not for nothing was he once described as 'The Master of Bunkum'!

It is difficult to imagine how this deadlock might have been resolved if Forbes had remained in control, but in 1901 the whole situation was changed by the sudden appearance on the scene of a prominent American tycoon by the name of Charles Tyson Yerkes. He was head of a syndicate that had, among other major projects, completely reorganised the transport system of Chicago and he saw in London the opportunity to do more big business. In a matter of weeks he secured virtual control of the District Railway by the simple process of buying up large blocks of shares and, while the management, the staff and the remaining shareholders were wondering what had hit them, he flung down the gauntlet on the matter of electrification and flatly refused to have anything to do with the Hungarians. The Metropolitan were furious and appealed to the Board of Trade and eventually the case was submitted to arbitration. The Tribunal sat for two months in the summer of 1901 and then declared in favour of direct current. It was a triumph for Yerkes and in no time he had ousted Forbes from the Chairmanship of the District Railway.

This situation had of course been closely watched at Westinghouse. John Wills Cloud, who had been appointed Vice President and Managing Director in 1899, was himself an American and was familiar with the activities of Yerkes in the USA. It was clear that electrification of the Inner Circle would involve new signalling on a large scale, and while he had Malan and Pearce neither of them was sufficiently versed in the latest electrical techniques to sell the system in England. So, in 1902, it was arranged for him to go to the USA to find the man for the job. It was perhaps no more than natural for him to go to one of the most spectacular of the Yerkes railways, the Boston Elevated. The signal engineer on that line was Harold Gilbert-Brown, then no more than 27 years of age, but already having displayed a remarkable flair for electrical invention.

He had, among other things, perfected a system of track circuiting (see Panel) for

Track Circuiting

Train detection, or more properly 'train absence detection', whereby electronic or mechanical systems are used to determine whether a train is within a certain area of track, is still a vitally important element of the majority of modern railway signalling systems. The more traditional means of executing this is the use of the 'track circuit', an electrical system using the electrical circuit through the running rails and the axles of the train to determine whether or not a train is in a section.

In its simplest form the railway is split up into sections by placing insulated rail joints in either rail, at either end of the track circuit section. At one end a battery (feeding through a resistor to limit current) is connected to the rails. At the other end of the section a relay (an electrical switch) is connected. If there is no train in the section, then current from the battery can flow through one rail, through the relay which is thereby operated or energised and back to the battery through the other rail. If there is a train in the section, then the axle acts as a short circuit, preventing current reaching the relay, causing the relay to de-energise. Switch contacts of the relay can be used within the interlocking system so that signals cannot be cleared, nor points moved, if there is a train in a certain location.

More modern systems use variations on this theme, largely dealing with different types of electrical traction system, or using tuned circuits so that insulated rail joints are not needed.

electrified railways using the polarised form of relay which bore his name. It seemed certain that the Metropolitan District Railway in London would be equipped for electric traction in the same way as the Boston Elevated and 'HGB' as we always knew him in later years, seemed the ideal man for the job. At less than a fortnight's notice he packed up home and family and sailed for England to become Signal Engineer of the Westinghouse Brake Company in London. In that same year of 1902, a formal agreement was concluded between the Brake Company and McKenzie & Holland for marketing and installing electro-pneumatic signalling.

It was not however on the London Underground Railways that the next developments took place. Neither was there any extension of the electro-pneumatic signalling or indeed of any form of power signalling on the Great Eastern Railways. For many years previously McKenzie & Holland had enjoyed close and cordial associations with the North Eastern

Railway. That company had done much towards partial mechanisation of the working at one of its most modern coal shipment ports, Tyne Dock near Jarrow, by the use of gravitational running of railway wagons onto and off the loading staithes; and by the year 1900 traffic had grown to such an extent that it was decided to install power signalling on the approach lines. The situation was complicated by the main approach crossing the important passenger line from Newcastle to Sunderland at right angles at Pontop Crossing. To control the extensive group of lines three new signal boxes were installed, each equipped with Pearce's anglicised version of the Union Switch interlocking frame and having 35 levers at Pontop Crossing, 71 levers at Green Lane and 35 levers at Bank Top. To these was added, shortly afterwards, a fourth box at Harton Colliery with 23 levers.

It will now have been noted that up to the year 1903 all the British installations of electro-pneumatic signalling had been made on non-passenger lines; but by the end of 1903 an important new plant at Bolton on the Lancashire and Yorkshire Railway was in course of construction to control the southern entrance to the busy passenger station. When that installation was brought into service preparations were also advancing towards the signalling on the electrified Inner Circle in London. In that same year of 1903 a young Cornishman of 17, Bernard Hartley Peter by name, joined the staff of the Metropolitan District Railway. In its steam days that railway was mechanically signalled with a form of Sykes 'lock and block' and Peter, young as he was, became entrusted with the preparations for electrification.

Westinghouse secured the contract for the signalling and so he became closely associated with Pearce and H G Brown. In 1904 when the preparations reached their greatest intensity Peter, even then no more than 18 years of age, was very much the 'baby' of the trio. H G Brown was 29 and Pearce 31. In such a way were three of the leading personalities of the future Westinghouse 'group' brought together.

At first their association was rather a strange one. Peter for all his youth and towering stature, was after all the customer; and while 'HGB', forthright as he could be on occasions, was a diplomat of diplomats, it was sometimes far otherwise with Pearce.

A clear view of Pontop Crossing shortly after its signalling described in this chapter.

From much later times, but a good photograph to show the arrangement at Pontop Junction, as a steam-hauled ore train passes through.

As I came to know only too well in later years, he had a fiery disposition that concealed a warm-hearted nature; he also had a high pitched voice that got higher and more squeaky as his temper shortened. Many years later when making a presentation to him on his retirement from Westinghouse, Peter admitted that in the early days he was unashamedly frightened of Pearce! Fright or not, he must have been a master of tactful persuasion for how otherwise could he have put across to that irascible designer, who did not take readily to innovations, the ideas of two novelties that became 'world firsts' in railway signalling: the automatic train describer[3] and the illuminated track diagram, both of which were installed on the Metropolitan District Railway at the time of the electrification.

The Westinghouse business in electro-pneumatic signalling developed rapidly, to such an extent that in 1907 the collaboration with McKenzie & Holland ripened to the point of forming a new company, the McKenzie, Holland & Westinghouse Power Signal Company Ltd, generally known afterwards as 'The Power Company'.

Sidney P Wood, one of the partners in McKenzie & Holland at the time of the formation of the Consolidated, became Managing Director, and H G Brown was appointed Chief Engineer. Pearce, of course, transferred to the new company but he never seemed to have any official title.

He remained **the** Designer, though in the 1915 List of Members of the Institution of Railway Signal Engineers (IRSE), T E Haywood is listed as 'Engineer and Chief Draughtsman'. There would appear however, to have been some confusion in the early listing of titles in the IRSE between McKenzie & Holland proper and the McKenzie, Holland & Westinghouse Power Signal Company, very likely because the Power Company and the other members of the consolidated group occupied the same block of offices in Victoria Street, London. From all accounts, Haywood was concerned only with mechanical signalling. Two other important changes in personnel came with the formation of the Power Company. Charles E Strange, who had been Signal Engineer of the Metropolitan District Railway, joined the company as Business

Manager and with his transfer B H Peter stepped up to become Signal Engineer of the Metropolitan District Railway at the age of 21!

Going back a few years to the time when the electro-pneumatic signalling activity began and manufacture of the equipment was undertaken in the brake works at York Road, Kings Cross, it was not long before a strong move to obtain export business was launched and important orders were obtained from Germany. In Imperial days the railways were not unified although a degree of standardisation in practice had been achieved between the various State systems.

One peculiarity of German operation at the time, specified for the installation at Cottbus on the Prussian State Railways, was the use of route levers. The regulations laid down that before a signalman could clear the signal for any incoming or outgoing train he must not only set the necessary points but also lock them by means of a route lever. This latter was however locked until released by the movement of a similar lever in the stationmaster's office. That official was required to choose the route for the train and then release the route lever in the signal box by pulling over his control lever. The route lever, on being pulled, released the signal lever and was itself backlocked[4] until released either by the stationmaster or by the train passing over an appropriately sited treadle. It all sounds rather complicated and restrictive and resulted in many more levers being required than for a comparable layout in Great Britain. The make-up of the 90 lever frame at Cottbus was 48 point levers, 15 signal levers, 14 route levers and 13 spare spaces.

This German practice, in its complication and its bringing the work of the signalmen under direct subservience to the stationmaster by positive interlocking, in some ways nullified the advantages of power working. The contrast was to be seen in two other large export orders obtained not very long after those on the Prussian State Railways. The earliest form of the Style 'B' locking frame, designed by Pearce in 1903, had most of the signal levers standing normally halfway over on the quadrant. When pulled towards the signalman they controlled one signal,

The Peter automatic train describer (left), and shown with the cover removed (right).

and they controlled another when pushed away. As such they could be used for signals that were related as those reading over the alternative routes at a junction. By this technique the total number of levers in a frame could be much reduced. At Howrah Station box for example, the Calcutta terminus of the East Indian Railway, the make-up of the frame was:

- 24 levers for 64 signals and 15 slots
- 31 levers for 60 points and 52 facing point locks
- 3 levers for point controls
- 9 spare spaces
- 67-lever frame.

The contrast between this and the Prussian frame at Cottbus was very striking. In another early Style 'B' apparatus for Cairo Egyptian State Railways, the proportions were very similar with a 47 lever frame to work 39 signals, 43 points, 30 facing point locks, 6 fouling bars and 2 indicators. All these installations, which were based on British practice, included a number of the spectacular signal gantries and arrays of semaphores that were characteristic of all McKenzie & Holland's work. The arms were all actuated by the very neat electro-pneumatic signal motors.

While it was no more than natural that the Westinghouse Brake Company and the McKenzie, Holland & Westinghouse Power Signal Company should have been strong advocates of the electro-pneumatic system, in view of the competition that was arising in the field of power signalling it was decided to develop an all electric system. Rivalry between the northern and southern halves of the Inner Circle in London, which had been so bitter over the system of electrification to be adopted and the Yerkes coup d'état, showed itself in a milder form when the Metropolitan Railway adopted all electric rather than electro-pneumatic signalling. The Power Company scored an early triumph over their 'all-electric'

competitors in 1910 by securing what was termed the 'Neasden Contract' for all-electric automatic signalling on the 'Extension Line' over the heavily worked five miles between Baker Street and Neasden. The equipment was however not quite all-electric, because at the two extremities and at the four intermediate points where there were siding and crossover connections, the points were mechanically worked. On the daylight section between Finchley Road and Neasden the semaphore signals, both elevated and dwarf, were all electrically operated and all of the upper quadrant type.

This feature created much interest and not a little criticism at the time, but from the Westinghouse point of view interest centres round the electric machines for signal operation and for the co-acting automatic train stops. In America the Union Switch & Signal Company had a cumbersome and complicated mechanism for electric operation of semaphore signals. A full set of manufacturing drawings was made in London: but it looked more like a laboratory 'hook-up' and when the Neasden contract was obtained from the Metropolitan Railway, Pearce, while adopting the basic principles, turned it into a beautifully neat and compact machine which lasted the company for as long as semaphore signals were required. On the Neasden contract the signal machines were mounted at mast top with the arm carried directly on the driving shaft; but there were variations for operating lower quadrant signals and also for those clients who wished to mount their signal machines at the base of the post and connect to the semaphores by a down rod.

Although none were called for on the Neasden contract, Pearce made an equally neat and successful adaptation of the first Union Switch electric point machine. In the latter, the constituent parts, motor, gear box and driving worm were strung out longitudinally on a steel bed plate extending over four sleepers, each of which had to be cut down to half its normal thickness in order to position the machine correctly in relation to the point operating rods. In the British version, no cutting of sleepers was necessary at all. It spanned three longitudinally, but was supported on the two outer ones. The worm drive and the gear train were neatly accommodated in a casting nicknamed in the shops 'the boat', extending well below sleeper level. It required a separate facing point lock mechanism and electric point detector.

---

1 When E C Sharpe checked Nock's manuscript he commented on this section as follows: 'Untrue. Our folklore. This was more an objection to Westinghouse's methods than his nationality. EP brake used on trial in 1887 (Burlington) to prove idea possible at least, but G Westinghouse not in favour.'

2 This frame is now preserved at the National Railway Museum in York.

3 A device, still in common usage, to allow signallers to identify individual trains, allowing them to control them in the appropriate manner.

4 Backlocking is simply a technique for keeping a route locked until certain conditions – usually confirmation of train position – are met. With the route locked, conflicting routes cannot be set and safety is ensured.

4
The First Alliance of Brakes with Signals

THE ENTRY of the Westinghouse Brake Company into the field of signalling and the subsequent setting up of the Power Company in 1907 was the result of an association of business interests rather than a technological link up between the separate arts of braking and signalling. On the railways of Great Britain and Ireland the two were usually included in the activities of two entirely separate departments: braking by the Chief Mechanical Engineer or Locomotive Superintendent; signalling by the Civil Engineer. The time had not yet arrived when the Signal Engineer was an independent officer. In the early 1900's however events were moving to influence the first changes in this situation.

Concern was frequently expressed at the number of occasions on which accidents occurred through drivers running past adverse signals or failing to observe regular speed restrictions; and the need was felt for some more positive link between the indications displayed by the signals and the means of interpretation in the locomotive cab, having particularly in mind the frequent incidence of fog on some of the busiest areas around the great cities.

In December 1914 the Institution of Mechanical Engineers (IMechE) broke new ground by having five brief papers under the title of Audible and other Cab signals

on British railways. Two of these, by engineers from the Midland and from the Caledonian railways, were purely theoretical, but the other three were descriptions of systems and apparatus already in use. The fact that two of these latter were by distinguished locomotive engineers and the third by a Chief Civil Engineer ensured a variety of approach and philosophy. That of Mr W A Stanier, as he then was, when Assistant Manager of the Great Western Railway Locomotive works at Swindon (later Sir William Stanier, and Chief Mechanical Engineer of the London Midland & Scottish Railway), was highly significant. It embodied, from the inception of the system in 1905, principles that were subsequently accepted as standard by the nationalised British Railways.

In his contribution to the group of papers presented to the IMechE, Stanier stated that:

> . . . any device proposed must provide the following features:
> 1. An audible warning on the footplate of the engine to indicate to the engineman the position of the signal he is approaching.
> 2. The warning must be separate and distinctive for STOP or DANGER position and the PROCEED or ALL-RIGHT position of the signal.
> 3. The STOP or DANGER warning must

be independent of any electric connexions either in the line or the engine and must be given, even if the electric connexions fail.

4. Each signal must be acknowledged by the engineman in some tangible way.

5. It must be possible to apply it to any engine and to any line, whether single or double.

6. There should be no moving parts on the line.

That was the original remit, to which Stanier added: 'Latterly it has been decided that in the event of the signal being at DANGER, the brake must automatically be applied.'

The systems, of which the details were worked out and manufactured by the Swindon locomotives works and the Reading Signal Works of the GWR, had been installed to no more than a limited extent when war broke out in August 1914; the licence to manufacture this equipment for sale elsewhere had been granted to the Power Company. There is however no record of it being installed other than on the Great Western Railway.

The need for having some means of alerting a driver who, through inadvertence, bad visibility or pure negligence, was running through signals, was highlighted by the terrible disaster near Ais Gill summit on the Midland Railway in September 1913.

It was terrible not so much in the magnitude of the death toll, but in the harrowing manner in which the victims perished and by the knife-edge on which safety and disaster were balanced until the very last minute. No one occurrence would have done more to hasten the introduction of automatic train control, but for the onset of war in the following summer. More details are given in the text panel. The need was felt not only in Great Britain and perhaps to an even greater extent in America, where the accident record was infinitely worse. The Interstate Commerce Commission of the USA, when visiting England in 1908, reported on their return:

> Of the cab signal devices in use on English railways and forming the chief object of the Committee's investigations, only one, namely that of the Great Western Railway, is believed to be worthy of consideration.

That the Power Company quickly obtained a licence to manufacture it is significant; but as things turned out Westinghouse did not receive any orders until 1930 and then it was from the Great Western Railway itself.

In Australia a system was developed by 'The Ideal Locomotive Cab Signalling Syndicate' which was described as 'A method of Automatic Railway Signalling, in which full information of all the outdoor

Ais Gill Accident, September 2, 1913

This accident occurred on the Midland Railway Settle & Carlisle line. One passenger train ran into the back of another which had stalled due to the use of poor quality coal. Fourteen passengers died in the fire that followed in the first train and a further 38 were seriously injured in the second. In the inquiry, conducted by Colonel Pringle, it was found that the second train had run through signals at danger, due to the footplate crew being pre-occupied with other duties necessary to keep the locomotive running. The crew of the stalled train, despite having time, did not lay detonators in rear of their train. Colonel Pringle suggested the adoption of automatic train stops as introduced on London's Underground and even the 'wireless control of trains'. Pringle additionally referred to the GWR's system of automatic train control and said that he thought that this system deserved 'wider notice and trial.'

A series of photographs of the Automatic Train Control Equipment designed and implemented by the GWR and later provided by WB&S Co.

The Contact Shoe arrangement of the GWR system of Automatic Train Control

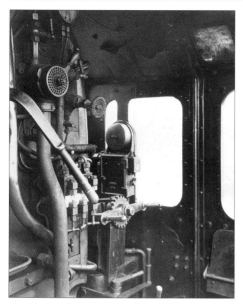

The in-cab equipment of the GWR system

Signals together with Speed Limit Notices, is given to the driver in the Engine Cab.' It had the intriguing sub-title 'Interlocking the Engine with the Signals.' This system was taken up by Saxby & Farmer, who issued a comprehensive brochure on the subject. It was a remarkable document. Certain paragraphs in the preamble tilt at the existing systems in limited use on the Great Western and North Eastern Railways, thus:

> Now, several such schemes have and are still being tried on different railways in England and abroad, but they are hardly likely to prove quite satisfactory on account of the liability to fracture of the parts attached to an engine travelling at an express speed when these are arranged to strike something in the permanent way . . .

The preamble continues:

> The present device goes much further than anything yet suggested and, as all the signals are picked up by a continuously running wheel engaging with an ordinary rail or its equivalent, all shock or hammering between

the parts on the locomotive and those in the permanent way is eliminated . . .

Interest in the system can be no more than academic today, because there is no record of its ever having been put to a practical test in Great Britain; but it is important in the present saga as showing the extent to which the member firms of the Consolidated were 'with it' towards the evolving needs of modern railway operation. For the 'Ideal Cab Signalling' system, for example, it was claimed:

> . . . our system covers many important points that have not hitherto been attempted. For example we remind a driver, by uncovering a notice in his engine cab, that over any special section he is coming to, a speed limit restriction prevails. This notice will be shown to him about one and a half miles before he reaches such a section, in order to give him time to obey it. At the same instant his engine begins to automatically time its speed for the next mile and at the end of that distance, if he has not obeyed the required speed limit, his engine will be checked automatically.
>
> In fact, in any case where a signal is disobeyed either intentionally or otherwise, the brake will be automatically applied and the train pulled up before any damage results.

It would have been extremely interesting to see how this very comprehensive system would have been worked out in practice, particularly in those features that involved a link up between signalling and brakes. In the McKenzie, Holland & Westinghouse Power Signal Company the two principal forms of power signalling enjoyed a peaceful co-existence, though the management itself was always strongly on the side of the electro-pneumatic; but in the Brake Company proper it was far otherwise. For some years after the turn of the century it was 'war to the death' with the Vacuum Brake Company. As recorded in Chapter One, the railways in the British Isles using the air brake were in a minority, though this was not the case in the rest of the world. But the Vacuum Brake Company sought to push their advantage home further by some vigorous publicity for their 'Rapid-Acting Vacuum Brake.'

Though both the Air and Vacuum as used on the British railways fully met all the safety requirements of the Board of Trade, the air brake was quicker in its action. The Vacuum people nevertheless were doing their best to catch up, no doubt in the hope that eventually one brake would be standardised – theirs.

What touched off a war of pamphlets was a series of trials made on the heavily graded Arlberg route of the Austrian State Railways.[1] It is certainly a terrain to test any kind of brake. Going eastwards from Bludenz there is a climb of 15½ miles on gradients of around 1 in 36 to Langen at the entrance to the 6½ mile long Arlberg Tunnel, and then another 16½ miles of equally precipitous descent to Landeck, in the Tyrol. In the latter part of the 19th Century when the 'Battle of the Brakes' was being fought out to its conclusion in Great Britain, the railways of Continental Europe were all closely watching the progress of events here; and although the majority of railways decided at once for the air brake, a number fitted up many locomotives and trains with the automatic vacuum.

By the end of the century however it was evident that the vacuum was losing ground. The Northern Railway of France, the Strade Ferrate Meridionali in Italy and two lengthy private railways in Russia, had changed to the air brake, though the vacuum remained in full possession on the various railways of the Austro-Hungarian Empire. It will thus be appreciated with what annoyance the Vacuum Brake Company learned, in the spring of 1901, that the Austrian State

Railways had asked Westinghouse to fit up a locomotive and train of 30 coaches for trial on the Arlberg route. It was evident that one of their last remaining footholds on the continent of Europe was threatened.

The trials were highly competitive and as in many such events on railways before and since, favouritism for one side or the other tended to load the dice. The Vacuum brake representatives, already well established in Austria, pulled every string they could lay hold of to make difficulties for and discredit the Westinghouse brake. If there was anything that was vital in working trains of any kind over a route like the Arlberg it was intimate road knowledge. How it was contrived that the Vacuum fitted train was worked by a regular man of long experience, while the Westinghouse train had a man who not only did not know the road but had only a few days experience of working the air brake, was not divulged!

Much store was set upon the maintenance of a very steady speed on the long descending gradients and it is not surprising that the man strange to the road did not do too well in that respect. The Vacuum Brake Company stressed every deficiency of its rival in a pamphlet entitled 'The Rapid-Acting Vacuum Brake and its Successes', in which they set out to prove that the Westinghouse quick-acting brake was not only inferior but positively dangerous.

This brought a rejoinder from Westinghouse in a pamphlet entitled 'Railway Brake Trials' which began with an account of some carefully conducted trials with both passenger and express goods trains on the North Eastern Railway. They were made to compare the performance and efficiency of three forms of the air brake as follows:

- The ordinary automatic;
- The quick-acting;
- The high speed.

Class of Brake	Initial Speed (mph)	Distance to Stop (ft)	Time of Stop (s)
Ordinary	56	1,160	23
Quick Acting	54 ½	945	21
High Speed	56	708	16
Ordinary	66	1,740	30
High Speed	66	1,200	22

The test train consisted of ten 8-wheel coaches and a 6-wheel testing van containing Kapteyn's automatic recording apparatus, representing a load of 263 tons. The recording apparatus, at the rear end, was a distance of 600 ft from the cab of the locomotive. The latter was a standard North Eastern Railway express passenger 4-4-0 of Class 'R'. The table (above) gives typical results and shows the different performance achieved with the three varieties of brake.

The report was supplemented by reproductions of the diagrams made by Kapteyn's apparatus.

The trials with the express goods train, consisting of 29 four-wheeled fish vans and two six-wheelers were perhaps even more satisfactory. Tests were made with the vans both tightly coupled and loosely coupled, although all were fitted with the quick-acting brake. The train was run at speeds up to 62mph and the stops made with the train loosely coupled were, in particular, highly satisfactory. Although in these conditions the buffers stood more than six inches apart when the train was running, it was stopped repeatedly under these conditions without shock or recoil. When the train came to a stand it was found that the buffers in each case were only slightly compressed, demonstrating the almost instantaneous action of the brake through-out the train. The total weight, exclusive of engine and tender, was 342 tons and from an initial speed of 62mph this train was stopped in a distance of 1,620 ft.

After setting out the general results of these tests on the North Eastern Railway

the Westinghouse pamphlet then went into the attack thus:

With the foregoing record of facts automatically recorded, it is impossible to reconcile many of the statements contained in a pamphlet recently issued by the Vacuum Brake Company Limited, entitled 'The Rapid-Acting Vacuum Brake and its Successes.' The row centred upon the quick-acting feature.

From the time the Westinghouse Brake Company first introduced the 'quick-acting' brake, the Vacuum Brake Company has endeavoured to produce similar results with the Vacuum Brake, the first attempt being in 1889, or the year following the issue of the Westinghouse patent. It has invariably failed to show that its 'rapid-acting' Vacuum Brake can be AT THE SAME TIME a practical brake for the ordinary handling of trains and it is believed to be impossible that it can ever accomplish these two features of this service, because the range of pressures available in the Vacuum Brake, which is limited to one atmosphere, is not great enough for the two results, with a sufficient margin between them to enable either to be employed at will on modern railway trains.[2]

The Westinghouse 'Quick-Acting' Brake was designed for practical railway service and its extended use is due to the fact that it meets all the conditions of service. It is not only available as an ordinary automatic brake to control trains promptly and effectively in ordinary service, but is available to give a rapid action when needed in cases of emergency. There is a sufficient margin between the two actions of the brake to enable the driver to obtain the ordinary graduated action when desired without producing the quick and consequently full action of the brake. He can, however, at will produce a full and quick action of the brake in case of emergency.

Any quick acting brake, to be useful in controlling trains, must have these two distinctive features of operation with sufficient margin between them, so that the one may be employed without the other, as needed. If a brake cannot be used partially and by graduated steps with sufficient promptitude to be useful in ordinary traffic without the quick-acting ensuing thereupon, that brake is useless for practical railway service. Such is believed to be the case with the 'rapid-acting' Vacuum Brake as employed in the Austrian railway trials.

When the programme and published results of the Austrian trials are considered, it will be observed that no runs were made to show that the brake was suitable for ordinary service. If the Westinghouse 'Quick-Acting' Brake were made so sensitive as to make it unsuitable for ordinary service, it would propagate rapid action beyond a much larger number of piped vehicles.

The Vacuum Brake Company tried to make capital out of certain incidents in the Arlberg trials when the test trains parted, and tried to make a case that the Westinghouse was a dangerous brake and our Company's reply was remarkably restrained, thus:

> The Vacuum Brake Company assumes a large undertaking when it tries to prove that the Westinghouse 'Quick-Acting' Brake is a dangerous appliance and when it is considered that the Vacuum Brake Company has nothing practical to offer instead, the position becomes peculiar.

In England the association between the North Eastern Railway and Westinghouse was very cordial and it is interesting to recall that when the Railway Company's Chief Mechanical Engineer, Mr Wilson Worsdell, reached the retiring age in 1910, having held the office with great distinction for 20 years, he was invited to join the board of the Westinghouse Brake Company, where he remained a director until his death in 1920. It was during his tenure of office on the North Eastern Railway that quite an elaborate system of cab signalling was developed (Raven's Cab Signalling), with its associated control of the brakes in the event of a signal being passed at danger. Although it came in for some criticism at the time of the symposium of papers at the IMechE in December 1914, its record of service was a good one and it was one of the earliest examples of carefully coordinated working of signalling with brakes. It remained in operation on the North Eastern Railway until after the grouping of the railways in 1923 – in fact, a number of locomotives built afterwards by the London & North Eastern Railway had the equipment added to them for a time.

It was however the principle of the automatic train stop on what would now be called Rapid Transit Railways, exemplified in the early 1900s by the Inner Circle in London and the extension lines of both the Metropolitan and District Railways into the outer suburbs, that established the outstanding feature that forms the very cornerstone of operation today, not only on the London Underground but on similar railways in many parts of the world.[3] It differed fundamentally from that of the Great Western in that the train stops were placed at every stop signal. While the Great Western system and that of British Railways developed from it, was a *warning* system and as such applied at the distant signals, the system introduced on Rapid Transit lines made an irrevocable emergency application of the brakes if a stop signal was passed, or overrun, in the danger position. On the Metropolitan, the train stops were of the all-electric type, another of W A Pearce's designs, consisting of a neat rearrangement of his electric signal machine to be mounted at the track side in the confines of the Inner Circle tunnels.

A description of the working was included in the five-paper symposium on 'Locomotive-Cab Signals' at the IMechE in December 1914. At that time the responsibility for signalling on the Metropolitan Railway was that of the Chief Civil Engineer, then W Willox, and he subtitled his paper: 'Signalling on Railway Trains in Motion.' There was a disposition among senior officers of the main line railways at that time to regard the London Underground lines as so many third-rate tramways and I shall always remember the scorn with which a very old servant of Westinghouse received the news that further sections of the Brighton line were to be electrified. He declared that all the old drivers were to be sacked and their places taken by ' . . . a lot of bloody LCC tram drivers!' Much the same sentiments were indicated, though in more restrained language, in the discussion at the IMechE, when a high officer of the Midland Railway said:

> He thought the train-stop question had nothing whatever to do with the cab signalling question and to his mind it was rather regrettable that both questions should have been dealt with at the same time.
>
> He did not think any railway man present would challenge his opinion when he said that for a high speed railway, whether steam or electric, train stops were of no value whatever. They were useful to a certain extent on moderately low speed railways and they had been found useful in America both on urban and inter-urban electric railways, but they were entirely

useless when the speed exceeded a certain minimum limit . . .

And so he continued, getting more scathing as he went on. I wonder if he came afterwards to eat his words when the Midland's great rival, the London & North Western, electrified their suburban line to Watford and the beautiful new trains would often 'pace' the main line express between stations, on a line equipped with electric train stops and on which speeds regularly approached 60mph.

Apart from matters that formed the early basis of automatic train control it was evident that the status of the Metropolitan District Railway stood high among the signal engineers generally and when the question arose, in 1910, as to the desirability of forming an association of those engaged in signalling work, B H Peter was invited to attend a meeting with seven other senior signal engineers. The other railways represented were the London & North Western, Midland, Great Western (2), Great Central, North Eastern and Lancashire & Yorkshire. Peter, then no more than 25 years of age, was very much the 'junior' of the gathering, though the work for which he was responsible was among the most advanced in the country – if not the whole world.

When a few months later the 'Institution of Signal Engineers' as it was first known was formed, the membership was confined to railway men; and so, in November 1911, when Peter was invited to join the McKenzie, Holland & Westinghouse Power Signal Company, as Assistant Engineer, he had to resign his membership of the Institution. His absence was not for long, because when the Institution was re-constituted, and received its seal of incorporation in November 1912, members of manufacturing firms were admitted. In later years Peter did more than anyone else to secure the gradual welding together of the signalling and brake interests of the Westinghouse Group of companies.

1 When E C Sharpe checked Nock's manuscript he commented that this section needed rewriting in view of statements by foreign experts 'unknown to O S Nock' – but the editors have been unable to identify what was being referred to.

2 When E C Sharpe checked Nock's manuscript he highlighted this entire section and referred to the contents as 'sheer propaganda'!

3 Trainstops are indeed still used widely on the London Underground network today (2006), on all lines except the Central Line and Victoria Line. They will gradually be replaced as the major form of train protection on all lines except the Piccadilly and Bakerloo as part of the current network upgrade.

5
World War I and Just After – The Great Amalgamation

T HE OUTBREAK OF WAR in August 1914 retarded the development of electric and pneumatic equipment on railways in a number of ways. The nation was wonderfully united in its resolve to support our allies on the Continent and in the first wave of intense patriotism men of every estate and profession left their peacetime occupations and flocked to volunteer for service in one or other of the armed forces of the Crown. There were no such things as reserved occupations in 1914; the men just went! As a result, the railways and the supply industries were at first denuded of their key personnel. The fact that railways were soon to become a vital factor in the national war effort and needed top class men, was not at first fully appreciated. The all-round urge was to 'join up'. Nevertheless, the first stage in the extension of the Bakerloo 'tube', in London, was complete in 1915 to come to the surface at Queens Park and connect with the London and North Western mainline at Willesden Junction. This was fully equipped with electro-pneumatic signalling.

The year 1915 was an important one for the Power Company in another respect, in that it saw a substantial American investment in it. The Union Switch & Signal Company acquired an equal number

The flat roof, Kings Cross, 1917. This area can be clearly seen in the aerial photograph of York Way in Chapter 1.

of shares with those held by McKenzie & Holland and by the Westinghouse Brake Company. H G Brown was appointed Managing Director of this re-constituted joint signal company and B H Peter became Chief Engineer, although in the later years of the war he was on active service in the Royal Engineers. During the war the electro-pneumatic system of remote control was adapted to the fore-bridge firing gear used for discharge of torpedoes on many ships of the Royal Navy, but for the most part activities were in a relatively minor key in the Power Company. In the works at Kings Cross, Chippenham and Worcester female workers were employed for the first time. The flat roof of the North Block at Kings Cross was a favourite place for group photographs to be taken in my own time with the Company and in its issue of

January 1917 *The Railway Magazine* reproduced a massive assembly of 170 girls, of all ages up on that same roof, while many years later our own *Westinghouse Review* in January 1955 had a picture of the Capstan Lathe section at Chippenham, during the war when, except for the two chargehands, everyone of the total workforce of 28 were female.

Although its members became very much involved in wartime duties, either on active service abroad or in multifarious tasks on the home railways, the Institution of Railway Signal Engineers (IRSE) found time to indulge in some interesting discussions, a few of which had a considerable bearing on future practices and on the welfare of the Westinghouse group. In 1916, for example, H G Brown read a paper on 'The Relative Merits of

A view of the staff during World War I. This picture was presented in the October 1951 Westinghouse Review with the staff identified as follows: Left to right, standing. Mr F Griffen, Miss T Mustoe, Miss Perry, Miss Baker, not identified, Miss Platts, Mr J Griffen, not identified, Miss Mustoe, Miss Tanner, Miss Kidd, not identified, not identified, Mr F Wheeler. Seated: Miss Davis, Miss Granger, Miss Bishop, not identified.

Whilst we have no information on this photo, it is fairly certainly a picture of some of the female workforce at Chippenham at some point during the First World War.

Track Circuits and Bars for Fouling Point Protection' (see text panel) at a time when track circuiting had been but little used in the largest power signalling plants in Great Britain.

Another paper that aroused much interest and controversy was by one A H Rudd, Signal Engineer of the Pennsylvania Railroad, describing current and evolving American practice. It was not so much the *practice* that stirred things up but the three position upper quadrant signal, the merits of which were extolled by some British engineers and lambasted by others. One otherwise distinguished railway signal superintendent ridiculed the idea of replacing the traditional slotted home and distant assembly by a single three-position semaphore as like trying to tell the time by a one armed clock!

The American investment in the McKenzie, Holland & Westinghouse Power Signal Company had nevertheless come at a very opportune moment – war or no war; because it was evident that the normally very conservative Great Western Railway was becoming distinctly three-position minded – if it may be expressed so. Drawings of the Union Switch electric upper quadrant signal mechanism were sent to London and a sample American-made signal was installed at Paddington as

Fouling Points

The Fouling Point is the position beyond which a train at a diverging set of points must be standing, or have passed, in order that a train passing it on the adjacent line does not collide with it. Put more simply, if two trains are meeting at a converging junction, it is important that the stationary train is out of the way of the moving train, otherwise there is a very good chance that one will 'side-swipe' the other with considerable force.

advanced starting signal on the main departure line. Competition was growing in this field also. The war traffic on the South Eastern & Chatham Railway from Victoria to the Channel ports had grown to such an extent that installation of power signals was authorised including use of three position upper quadrant signals. The contract was secured by the British Power Railway Signal Company, including the supply of a General Railway Signal Company 'pistol-grip' interlocking frame with dynamic indication. It is curious that at such a time the choice of equipment should have been thus, because there were then no facilities for manufacturing the interlocking frame in Great Britain and it had to be ordered from America. As if to emphasise this hazardous proceeding, the frame never arrived in England. The ship bringing it was torpedoed and lost and a replacement had to be made. It was not until nearly a year after the end of the war that the installation at Victoria was brought into service.

A much more important project so far as Westinghouse was concerned was the Ealing and Shepherds Bush line of the Great Western, planned as early as 1905 and on which most of the civil engineering constructional work had been completed by August 1914. From its western terminus at Ealing Broadway to its end-on junction with the Central London tube line at Wood Lane its length was 4¼ miles; but in addition to the proposed extension over it of the electric tube service from the City, it made several important links with other surface railways and was used to great advantage for freight traffic during the war. So far as signalling was concerned however, as *The Railway Gazette* emphasised in 1920:

> it has long been a foregone conclusion that the success which has attended the use of the three-position upper quadrant signal

fixed in 1914 outside Paddington Station, would lead to that type of signal being adopted elsewhere on the Great Western system.

So it certainly was on the Ealing and Shepherd's Bush line, and its installation the first in Great Britain of three-position automatic signalling, formed a notable conclusion to the independent existence of the McKenzie, Holland & Westinghouse Power Signal Company. Actually of course the Australian branch of McKenzie & Holland (established at Melbourne in 1884 and Brisbane in 1886) had a much earlier association with three-position upper quadrant signalling, because the Australian railways generally and the State systems of New South Wales and Victoria in particular, were much more inclined towards American than British practice and the three position upper quadrant type was coming into vogue in the USA before the important contract for electro-pneumatic signalling at Sydney Central was received in 1910.

Before the notable installation on the Ealing and Shepherd's Bush line of the Great Western had been brought into commission, H G Brown had initiated discussions for the take-over by the Westinghouse Brake Company of the signalling interests of the Consolidated Signal Company. He had, since 1915, become Managing Director of both Consolidated and McKenzie & Holland, in addition to the appointment he held in the Power Company. The arrangement ultimately concluded in November 1920 was that the Brake Company would acquire the signalling interests of Consolidated for the sum of £416,112. This sum was used to subscribe for 416,112 shares at £1 each in the Westinghouse Brake Company, 25,000 of which were allotted to H G Brown for his services in arranging the merger. Consolidated retained the balance of

ELECTRO PNEUMATIC POINT VALVE

RELAY CASES

ELECTRO PNEUMATIC DISC SIGNAL

ELECTRIC TRAIN STOP MACHINE

E. P. POINT LAYOUT

L 10 ᴬ ᴮ

POINT CYLINDER

POINT & LOCK MOVEMENT

POINT & LOCK DETECTOR

INSULATED ROD

A series of Ealing and Shepherd's Bush pictures.

(top) Ealing Broadway on the Ealing and Shepherd's Bush line – now part of the Central Line of the London Underground network. All equipment is marked McKenzie Holland and Westinghouse Power Signal Co Ltd. (left) Wood Lane signal cabin. (centre right) McKenzie & Holland pneumatic point operating equipment. (bottom right) Trackside location boxes with single element vane relays mounted in each one.

391,112 shares. The name of the company was then changed to the Westinghouse Brake & Saxby Signal Company Ltd.

The Board of the new Company was:

- J W Cloud, Chairman
- H G Brown, Managing Director
- Lt Col M Craddock, Director
- J H Luke, Director
- J F Miller, Director
- D E Norton, Director
- Lord Southborough, Director
- H H Westinghouse, Director[1]
- W Wingfield, Director
- S T Wood, Director
- R Payne, Secretary

B H Peter – since his war service always known as Captain Peter – was appointed General Manager and Chief Engineer.

A considerable tidying up of the organisation and streamlining of the manufacturing resources followed. The secretarial, accounts and sales departments of the various sections of the group were brought under single heads and centred at Kings Cross. The exact time-sequence in which the engineering activities were re-grouped is not directly relevant, but the Vulcan Iron Works of McKenzie & Holland at Worcester was closed and the premises sold.[2] All manufacture of mechanical signalling equipment was concentrated at Chippenham, both of Saxby and McKenzie designs, while all power signalling equipment previously assembled in the Signal Shop in the North Block of the King's Cross premises was also transferred to Chippenham. Only the purely pneumatic parts were left in London. The former Signal Shop was adapted to accommodate the drawing offices and engineering departments of all three principal activities, Brakes, Mechanical Signalling and Power Signalling, and the offices in Victoria Street, Westminster, previously occupied by the constituents of the Consolidated, were vacated.

One important feature of the organisation must be emphasised. Except in the case of the Brake Company, the Sales and Design Departments of the constituent companies had been apart from their associated works and had no direct responsibility for production. They were required to provide drawings and technological detail, but manufacture was the responsibility of the respective works managers. This arrangement continued after the amalgamation and with developing technology the amount of detailed information required on drawings and in specifications became increasingly comprehensive and required some expansion of the technical staff. The drive for new business was also strong. The first steps towards the mechanisation of working in coal mines were seen in the application of the principles of electro-pneumatic interlocking to the decking of coal tubs into and out of the pit cages, while the techniques of steam heating in railway carriages were applied to the heating of small individual industrial premises. And then, when the new organisation was not yet a year old, there loomed up a momentous change in the management structure of the British home railways.

The circumstances that led to the Grouping scheme of 1921, of which Sir Eric Geddes was the principal architect, are well enough known (see Panel), but so far as Westinghouse was concerned it was clear that three out of the four groups proposed would have to decide whether to standardise on the air or the vacuum brake. The dice seemed loaded in favour of the vacuum, because among the major constituents of the Southern, London Midland & Scottish (LMS), and London & North Eastern (LNER) groups the existing usage was 1:2; 1:5, and 4:2, Westinghouse against vacuum. On the LMS the air was outnumbered 5 to 1, and it was only on the

1921 Grouping Scheme

Prior to the First World War, there was a large number of railway companies operating in the British Isles. Many of these competed against each other and there was little national, or even regional coordination between these companies, most of them set up during the Victorian era as part of the explosion in public transport. Whilst there were several big players, notably the Great Western Railway, the situation was confused, and standardisation of equipment, operation and safety was extremely limited.

During the First World War the British Government took over control of the railways, although ownership remained with the original companies. The 'Railway Executive Committee' was formed as early as 1912, as a precaution.

This Railway Executive was highly efficient in its organisation, offering a far more integrated and successful transport system than the uncoordinated arrangement that had existed before the war.

As a result, the Government passed the Railways Act in January 1921 which in turn established four new companies in 1923, the only one retaining its original name being the legendary Great Western Railway. The Southern Railway, London & North Eastern Railway and London Midland & Scottish Railway were newly created.

Not Nationalisation, but an amalgamation, this organisation led to a railway system that remained largely unaltered until the Nationalisation into British Railways in 1948.

LNER that Westinghouse, in the Great Eastern, North Eastern, North British and Great North of Scotland was in a majority. As to the fourth group, the Great Western was a vacuum line; and although there were some Westinghouse users among the local railways in South Wales that were to be amalgamated with it, conversion there was inevitable. It was clear that Westinghouse stood to lose a good deal of business on the brake side if, as was to be expected, the LNER followed the trends that were obvious elsewhere.

A decision to enter the field of vacuum braking was not to be taken lightly. The Vacuum Brake Company, in association with Gresham & Craven Ltd of Manchester, was strongly entrenched; but Westinghouse were fortunate in securing the services of Louis J LeClair, as Sales Engineer for the Vacuum Brake. Despite his name, Le Clair was a Glaswegian Scot by birth, who, ironically enough had received his engineering training on a 'Westinghouse' railway, the Caledonian. Subsequently,

however, he had held a variety of posts of high responsibility and, what was more, displayed an innate capacity for making friends in industry. But again it was clear that an entry into the vacuum field was likely to involve conflict with many existing patents and to reinforce Le Clair an ingenious inventor by the name of Aloysius Brackenbury was engaged to join the Brake Department.

In referring to personnel in the amalgamated company however I have begun with the newcomers rather than the old stalwarts. H J Winter was Brake Engineer, with Kenneth H Leech as Chief Draughtsman. Leech, whose name will be familiar to many railway enthusiasts for his photographs of trains in motion, had his practical training on a 'Westinghouse' railway, albeit a small one – the London, Tilbury & Southend – and after war service with the Railway Operating Division had joined the Brake Company in 1919. The Brake team was completed by A W Simmons, from 1923 technical assistant to Mr Winter.

On the mechanical signalling side, A G Kershaw (who had been Chief Engineer of Saxby & Farmer) became design engineer in charge of the former Saxby and McKenzie & Holland activities, and R S Griffiths (son of William Griffiths, a partner in McKenzie & Holland and one of the first directors of the Consolidated) became Sales Engineer. One of the greatest personalities of the newly established section of the drawing office was W F Burleigh, one of the country's greatest experts in the design of mechanical interlocking frames. He had been Engineer to the oldest of all railway signalling firms, Stevens & Sons, but when their business dwindled to negligible proportions around 1910 he joined McKenzie & Holland as a draughtsman and it was as a draughtsman just topping 70 years of age (!) that he came into the new organisation at King's Cross. For a further *seventeen* years he continued to work out the locking diagrams for Saxby, McKenzie and even Evans O'Donnell frames that were still in current production and it was not until 1937, when he was in his 86th year and still apparently fighting fit, that he was eventually persuaded to retire. His fund of reminiscence was colossal.

On the power signalling side with H G Brown as Managing Director of the enlarged company and Captain Peter as General Manager, the top-level set-up was of course very strong. Pearce remained as Design Engineer and to take charge of electrical engineering there came in Peter's younger brother, Leslie Hurst, fresh from an exciting career as a fighter pilot in the Royal Air Force. Major Peter (see panel), as we knew him, proved an exceptionally far-seeing executive, as will be told in later chapters of this book. On the customer-liaison and installation side the Power Company had been strong, with H M Proud in charge of construction on site and Major C H W Edwards recently returned from service in the Royal

Engineers. Against this T E Haywood left the Company to take up business on his own account, while C E Strange left to become Managing Director of the Railway Signal Company in Liverpool, which by the amalgamation of 1920 became a subsidiary of Westinghouse, as did the W R Sykes Interlocking Signal Co Ltd and the two overseas companies, Saxby & Farmer (India) Ltd and McKenzie & Holland (Australia) Ltd.

The relationship between the technical departments in London and the manufacturing activities has been briefly mentioned, but the works management had a very important part to play after the amalgamation when the works at Worcester was closed and its activities transferred to Chippenham. In this particular move William Howard Powell played a vital part. Son of Mr W Powell, Signal Engineer of the Taff Vale Railway, he had joined McKenzie & Holland in 1900 and after a varied experience representing the company in Wales, Ireland and the North he was appointed Works Manager at Worcester in 1916. He was transferred to Chippenham in a similar capacity in 1919 and so, with a knowledge of both works and their personnel, he was particularly well fitted to supervise the merger of the two after the amalgamation of 1920. This work was completed in 1922, after which he was moved to London as General Business Manager. He was succeeded at Chippenham by F C Brittain.

Such was the strong, if somewhat fragmented team with which the 'new' Westinghouse faced the changing business situation of the 1920s. While H G Brown, 'The Skipper', remained a father figure to some of the older men, as Managing Director of so much larger a concern he was becoming more remote and the more immediate leadership delegated to Captain Peter. The Company was indeed fortunate at that time in having in the dual role of

Major L H Peter

Arguably more than anyone else mentioned in the book, the name of Leslie Hurst Peter appears as a guiding light to the Company through some of the most successful years and through some of the most impressive developments. In the Westinghouse Review *of March 1951, a detailed resumé of Major Peter's life was given.*

Peter was born at Launceston, Cornwall, on November 9, 1891 and was educated at Blundells School at Tiverton. He was married with two children and at the time of the publication of the article he had three grandchildren. Peter received his technical education at Finsbury Technical College (set up in 1878 by the livery companies of the City of London to become the City and Guilds of London Institute for the Advancement of Technical Education). He undertook technical training at Ferranti at Manchester, during which time he also took a post-graduate course at Manchester School of Technology.

After eighteen months working with Ferranti he joined the Electricity Department of the Lancashire and Yorkshire Railway (L&YR) where he worked on the electrification of Goole Dock and the maintenance of all electrical equipment from Leeds to Wigan. He subsequently moved to the Telegraph Department of the railway, where he installed the first track circuit at Manchester Victoria Station.

He left the L&YR in 1912 for London Underground where he remained until offered a job by the McKenzie Holland and Westinghouse Power Signal Company in 1914.

The Westinghouse Review *goes on to state 'The Kaiser interfered with these plans however and on the day he should have reported for duty he was mobilized as a member of the Cornwall (Fortress) Royal Engineers and stationed at Falmouth.'*

Finding the war a little too slow, 'LHP' volunteered for the Royal Flying Corps in 1915 and after a course at Reading University he was sent to learn flying at Turnhouse, near Edinburgh, where he was the first pupil. 'The flying school consisted of a hut and two fields, half of which were planted with potatoes, and no aircraft. Two planes which were sent could not climb over the Cheviot Hills but eventually a Maurice Farman Longhorn did arrive and his training started. The plane, which had a wing-span as wide as that of a Lancaster Bomber, had, of course, only one engine of 80 h.p.. The only seating accommodation was one wicker basket chair and, since those were the days before dual control, the pupil sat on the instructor's lap. After 35 minutes' instruction, LHP learned to fly.'

Peter was soon sent to fight in France, where he did not miss flying duty for a single day, being twice mentioned in despatches, awarded the Military Cross and, later, the Air Force Cross. He was posted back home in 1917 where he was promoted to Major and took up duties of testing pilots and setting up Training Schools. After a short while he asked to be given a squadron to take overseas, but whilst they travelled to France the Armistice was declared.

So it was that after a short while Peter returned to take up his job at McKenzie Holland and Westinghouse, some four years late. He joined the Signal Engineer's Department and was one of the first engineers to be involved in Colliery installations, working at Thurcroft Colliery in 1919. In the 1920s he made Metal Rectifiers a special study and drove this technology through for many years. When unable to find suitable staff for his projects he gave lectures in Power Signalling to post-graduate City & Guilds students and was in turn Chief Electrical Engineer, Chief Engineer and Chief Development Engineer. Other achievements that were largely down to Major Peter included the development of optical systems for colour light signals, being a member of the original British Standards Institute committee for the standardisation of colours in lenses. He designed the first hand-generator signal produced by the Company and the associated point machine and he was closely involved in developments including all sorts of relays, route indicators and the resonated impedance bond.

General Manager and Chief Engineer a man in whom a warm humanity was combined with outstanding business and technological acumen. In the first years after amalgamation his talents in those directions were certainly needed.

The gathering of all the London staff of the constituent companies in the premises at King's Cross was by no means popular. H G Brown may, with a touch of characteristic American sentiment, have rejoiced in having, as he once expressed it: 'One great family under one great roof', but those who worked in the new amalgamated drawing office, on the top floor of the North Block beneath the unshielded glass roof during the sweltering dog days of the 1921 summer, were not inclined to family feelings towards their new colleagues!

My own awareness of Westinghouse as a Company, as well as the name of one of the standard forms of railway brake, came at about the same time, although I did not join the staff until four years later. It was in the autumn of 1921 that I began my engineering studies at Imperial College, City & Guilds (Engineering) College; and

pursuing the very detailed syllabus of work that lay ahead and drawn irresistibly to the post-graduate course in 'Railway Engineering' I noted that one of the visiting specialist lecturers was 'Captain B H Peter, of the Westinghouse Brake & Saxby Signal Co Ltd.' From fellow students who were a year, and two years ahead of me I learned, well in advance, of the subject matter of those lectures and of the personality of the lecturer. However, when my own turn came, in the 1924–25 college year, Captain Peter's increasing responsibilities had led to his delegating the actual lecturing to Ralph Griffiths for the mechanical side and to Major Peter for the power. The contacts made over the years between Westinghouse and that most famous training ground for professional engineers, together with the adjacent and associated Royal College of Science have provided the Company with some of its most distinguished men of later years including one Chairman of the Board, several Divisional Managers and a galaxy of Division Engineers, not to mention one Managing Director of Saxby & Farmer (India) Ltd.

---

1 Henry Herman Westinghouse, George Jr's younger brother and long-term business associate.

2 The Editors' research finds that other sources suggest closure in around 1921.

6
A Time of Many Developments

THE AMALGAMATED COMPANY was formed at a time when the country in general was looking forward to a resurgence of the spirit of business enterprise and the volume of export trade that had been enjoyed before the war; and in both brakes and signalling a variety of new developments was introduced. Reference was made in the previous chapter to the application of electro-pneumatic signalling techniques to the control of pit cage operations in collieries. Coal mining in Great Britain had hitherto been a labour-intensive industry, but in the post-war era the first steps towards mechanisation were taken and one of these was to apply power to the loading and unloading of the tubs into and out of the pit cages, previously done by human push-power. Westinghouse developed pneumatic rams for this purpose, but the power inherent in these and the speed of operation, made it essential to introduce various safety features and interlocks on the control mechanisms of the rams.

It was like the locking of an intricate railway junction. In the case of operations at the pit top, the normal procedure was to leave empty tubs waiting on the approach track to the shaft and on arrival of a cage full of loaded tubs an equal number of empty tubs would be pushed forward, buffer up with those inside and the pushing continued until the empty ones were in the cage and the loaded ones had been pushed out of the far side. In using pneumatic rams for the pushing operation a number of safeguards had to be installed. First of all the cage, on arrival, had to be proved exactly in line with the approach and departure tracks; then the gates had to be proved open. For these proving functions, circuit breakers similar to those used for proving the position of signal arms were used. In the cages the tubs were correctly positioned by specially designed tub controllers at the front and by detecting back-axle stops at the rear. When all was ready for decking to begin the tub controller in the cage would be released by a striker mechanism on the surrounding structure, but the 'release' would allow only the loaded tubs that had been brought up in the cage to pass out. The controller would then re-lock to prevent the empty tubs that were being decked from running completely through the cage and out on the far side.

There were many other safety features and interlocks included in the system as a whole, with variations and elaborations at different pits; but enough has been mentioned to indicate the scope of activities generally. The control in all the earlier installations was electro-pneumatic, in that the interlocking between the working of the various junctions was effected through

Decking Plant at Orgreave Colliery.
United Steel Companies Ltd.
(Note the Power Operated Gates)

Electro-Pneumatic Safety Appliances for Collieries

This photograph of the Decking Plant at Orgreave Colliery is particularly interesting since it is in fact one side of a postcard from Westinghouse Brake & Saxby Signal Co to acknowledge receipt of correspondence to the company.

circuit breakers and relays, feeding magnet valves to control the air supplies to the appropriate cylinders and pneumatic rams. At the outset the work was undertaken by the men of the former 'Power Company', under the superintendence of Donald Fullerton Brown, son of the Managing Director of the Company. In the field, from the very first installation at Thurcroft Colliery near Sheffield, the work was for many years subsequently always commissioned under the supervision of one of those inspectors whose services to the Company in liaison and general customer relations were incalculable – Fred J Raymer. He had been a power signalling man, but from the outset he espoused the colliery business and made it his very own. Whether the situation was tense or hilarious, it was always an education to work with him.

Donald Brown was also concerned with the beginnings of the road brake business. At the end of World War I it was evident that road transport generally was going to play a very much larger part in the commercial, industrial and social life of the country and with heavier vehicles something more than hand brakes was going to be necessary, even though speed on the highways was then severely inhibited by law. The first vehicle to be fitted up with air brakes was the Company's own lorry at King's Cross – an AEC vehicle – and Donald Brown carried out the tests. At first, when attempts were made to interest the users of road vehicles, headway in this new field was slight.

The publicity was at times diverting to those of us who were not directly involved in the business. The Publicity Manager of

Pictures from a 1927 brochure of vehicles fitted with the Westinghouse Brake, to demonstrate its adaptability to all types of vehicle. AEC Electric Trolley Bus, Bradford (top); 'Merryweather' Fire Engine, Johannesburg (centre); 55 HP Leyland-Carrimore Brewer's Wagon (bottom)

Fig. 4.   BRAKE EQUIPMENT (automatic) for TRACTOR AND TRAILER USING AIR COMPRESSOR

Brake applied automatically on trailer when couplings are parted accidentally

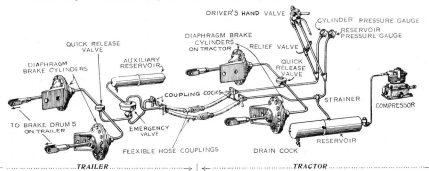

*Brake diagram (above) and Westinghouse logo
(right) from the 1927 brochure*

the Company, a former 'brake' man, was O J C Thorpe. A cantankerous old character, he had nevertheless a picturesque way of describing our products, as when he likened the precision building of mechanical interlocking frames and the alignment of the levers to guardsmen on parade. Who invented the following limerick I do not know, but he swooped on it and attached it to a photograph of four bright young things in a large open touring car, somewhere in the Lake District:

> You see these young ladies so gay,
> On steep hills no tremors display,
> Yet no risks do they take
> For the Westinghouse Brake
> Makes controlling a car mere child's play.

Nevertheless, in the early 1920s, the great days of the road brake were still a long way ahead.

Another new development, of much more immediate and lasting success was the introduction of the daylight colour light signal. This type had been gradually coming into use in America for some years previously, with an important contract awarded to the Union Switch & Signal Company on the highly competitive line of the Milwaukee Road to the Pacific North-

West, on which contracts for electrification had been let in 1912. The heart of the day colour-light signal is of course the doublet-lens combination, which not only results in a highly concentrated beam of light, but enables a long range beam to be projected from a very small lamp. On the original Union installation on the Milwaukee the main lamps were 6V, 28 W, and with them it was reported that they had a range of vision from 2,500 ft, in more favourable conditions. The outer lens of the doublet-lens combination was clear and the inner one coloured.

An important feature of the lamps was the concentrated filament and because it was necessary for the lamps to be interchanged without disturbing the alignment of the signal, very accurate basing of the lamp was required. In the

USA, at the time colour light signals were introduced, it had been found that when new lamps were fitted into an automobile the headlight needed re-focusing. This, it was realised, could not be done on a railway signal, unless two experienced men were employed every time a lamp burnt out. Even so, it would have been to do in the field what was normally done in a dark room. So, the lamps for the new colour light signals were re-based in a special jig. This was a technique that had to be developed in Great Britain when the colour light signals were installed. When at first quantities required were small, the lamps, as with the special lenses for the doublet combination, had to be obtained from America.

The first British installation of day colour light signals was on the Liverpool Overhead Railway, itself an enterprise of great historical distinction as the first overhead electric railway in the world. When it was opened, in 1893, the only other electric railway in Great Britain was the City and South London tube! Originally the signals at the intermediate stations were operated automatically by the collector shoes on the trains. The signals were put to danger mechanically and held in the 'off' (clear or proceed) position electrically, so that in the event of a failure of current all the signals would immediately go to the danger position. The arrangements by which the signals were released after the passing of a train and the safeguards provided were simple, but they worked well, and during the years of World War I nearly 12 million passengers were being carried annually on this short line of some 7½ miles, entirely without mishap. It was when the signalling equipment needed replacement that colour light signalling of the two-indication type was put in, with train stops co-acting automatically.

The fact of the line being on overhead structures introduced some design problems. It was, of course, track circuited throughout, but limited depth below rail level precluded use of the train-stop mechanism that had been installed on those sections of the Metropolitan Railway fitted with automatic signalling. So on the Liverpool Overhead the simple expedient was adopted by mounting one of the standard electric signal machines on a short post alongside and instead of driving upwards to a semaphore arm at the top of a tall post, the drive was downwards and then across the track to the trip arm part of the train-stop. Pioneer though it was however, this first installation of colour light signalling did not make the impact that it deserved, because among the men of the main line railways the Liverpool overhead was regarded as no more than a glorified tramway. Nor, when in 1923 the Mersey Railway was re-equipped with colour light signals – in this case of the tunnel type – was more than passing attention paid to a pioneer instance of automatic point operation at Liverpool Central Station.

The crossover road beyond the island platform was normally set for a crossover movement. When a train came to rest on the arrival side of the platform and was proved there by track circuit, a time-element control, which gave a delay of about 25 seconds, caused the points of the crossover road to operate and the signal to clear for the train to draw ahead into the siding. Once proved there the points were restored to normal and the appropriate signal cleared to enable the train to draw into the departure line and load passengers for its return trip. That this operation was commissioned as early as February 4, 1923, was a point of inestimable value to Westinghouse when the celebrated law suit over centralised traffic control principles was fought in the late 1930s, as will be told later.

The real break-through in colour light signalling came later in 1923 when the

Reliostop Mechanical System of 1916

Track equipment outside the running rails was fitted at both distant and home signals. This engaged with equipment on the loco to give an audible warning and an automatic brake application. The Great Central Railway equipped the lines out of Marylebone by 1923. When the LNER took over, the GCR development stopped, and after a short time the equipment was removed.

three-aspect type was installed on the former Great Central line between Marylebone and Neasden and on the loop line constructed to serve the British Empire Exhibition, to be staged at Wembley in 1924 and actually brought into service in time to deal with the exceptional traffic of the Cup Final, played for the first time at the new Wembley Stadium on April 28, 1923. The signalling provided for a three-minute service at the time of greatest intensity and the single-tracked loop branching from the line to Northolt Junction at Wembley Hill curved round in a clockwise direction past the Exhibition Station to join the line from Harrow-on-the-Hill at Neasden North Junction. By this layout trains arriving from London could de-train or entrain passengers and proceed back to Marylebone without any shunting reversal or light engine movements. The use of the now-familiar red, yellow and green indications, working automatically in most of the signals, created much interest and not a little controversy. Prior to the grouping of the British Railways in January 1923, A F Bound had been Signal Engineer of the Great Central. He was the inventor of the 'Reliostop' system of automatic train control (see Panel). It had been in use between Marylebone and Neasden in mechanical signalling days and it was retained and re-arranged to work with the automatic colour light signalling.

Bound became one of the foremost advocates in Great Britain of multiple aspect colour light signalling. Whereas there were many at the time who, while convinced that there was a big future for three-position signalling, were equally convinced that the signals themselves should be upper quadrant semaphores, as Westinghouse had installed on the Ealing and Shepherd's Bush line and as their competitors had installed on the Chatham side of Victoria. The question had been thrown in to the open forum of the Institution of Railway Signal Engineers in November 1921 when A E Tattersall read a paper on 'Three Position Signalling.' He had a very significant sub-title: 'The necessity for uniformity of aspects and some suggestions relating thereto'. Tattersall had previously been on the Great Northern Railway and at the time of grouping he was made assistant to Bound in the Southern area of the LNER. He had been concerned with the experimental installation of three position upper quadrant signals and his paper was largely devoted to semaphores. The discussion on it extended over three meetings of the Institution and eventually in March 1922 a 'Three-Position Signalling Committee' was set up. That committee sat for not less than two years and eventually came out strongly, though not unanimously, in favour **not** of upper quadrant semaphores but of colour lights. Before discussing the implications of that committee's report however, some interesting developments had taken place in the intervening two years.

So far as the semaphore versus colour-light controversy was concerned, Westinghouse would have been quite happy either way. The company had established and well-proven designs for both and so far as semaphores went they could be all-electric or electro-pneumatic, whichever system a customer might choose. It was interesting that at this very time the largest power signalling contract outside the United Kingdom had been secured – that for the Plaza Constituçion Terminus of the Buenos Aires Great Southern Railway (BAGS) in Argentina. This used the electro-pneumatic system, with three-position upper quadrant semaphore signals. The locking frame had no less than 275 levers, second only in size to that for Glasgow Central installed some 15 years earlier on the Caledonian Railway. Associated with this large installation on the BAGS Railway was a second, at the important junction at Temperley, 19 miles out of Buenos Aires and a station having a very large residential traffic. This again was an electro-pneumatic system, but although big enough to require a locking frame of 179 levers the signals themselves were two position lower quadrant, pneumatically operated.

An important difference was to be noted in all the post-war power frames, whether electric or electro-pneumatic, in that they were equipped with an indication panel behind the levers, providing light-repeater indications of the signals and illuminated stencil indications showing the lie of the points. All these post-war installations were fully track-circuited and furnished with large illuminated track diagrams.

A distinguishing feature between the earlier and the post-war power signalling installations on the main line railways of Great Britain was the elimination of facing point locking bars, which required separate pneumatic cylinders for their actuation. Track circuiting became universal on these large plants and the electro-pneumatic point operating mechanisms had facing point locks incorporated in them. In the large installation of the Buenos Aires Great Southern Railway the number of individual

1928 photograph showing the Plaza Contituçion and Temperley Power Frames for the BAGS under construction (extreme right and centre) and the new 143 lever frame for Cannon Street (left).

The Electropneumatic Power Frame at Temperley on the BAGS.

signal arms was much reduced by the use of route indicators. These were of the 'Moore and Berry' type developed first on the Lancashire & Yorkshire Railway where R G Berry was Signal Engineer.

That type of indicator had been used in a notable post-war installation at Southport. It consisted of a number of large slides, on which figures (denoting platforms) or other characters were painted. They were normally concealed, but when a route was set up the appropriate slide was drawn out and displayed below the signal concerned. It was a device particularly suitable for electro-pneumatic operation, albeit rather large. It was only the first step in a development in route indicators that did not reach finality in Great Britain until the mid-1930s.

In connection with track circuiting the development of impedance bonds must be noted. In the electrification of the Metropolitan and Metropolitan District Railways in London and later on the Liverpool Overhead, the fourth rail system of electric traction was used and with the track circuits confined to the running rails

the conventional form of insulated block joint was all that was necessary – the relays, either Brown's polarised, or the later alternating current two element type – provided the immunity from interference from traction current. But the Central London Railway, the 'Twopenny Tube' (now the Central Line), used the third rail system, with traction return through the running rails and the same system had been adopted for the 'Riverside Electric' of the London & South Western Railway. At the track circuit block joints, impedance bonds were installed connected to each of the running rails. These consisted of a massive copper coil, with a cross section of strip large enough to carry the unbalanced traction return currents, but having an impedance high enough to present virtually an open circuit effect to the small alternating current in the track circuits. It was an interesting job developing the technique of impedance bond design to meet the increasingly severe track circuit conditions.

The disturbances in Ireland prior to the treaty with Great Britain that set up the

The Liverpool Overhead was the first railway to use Colour Light Signals in the UK

Irish Free State took many forms, one of which was damage to and sometimes outright destruction of railway property. The Great Southern & Western Railway (GS&WR) was badly affected, suffering no fewer than 200 'incidents' with signal boxes burnt down and key locations damaged. Furthermore, the generally unsettled conditions made funds for replacement difficult to obtain. The Railway Signal Company, as one of the largest suppliers of token instruments for single line working, was particularly concerned, and Walter S Roberts, the General Manager of the Railway Signal Company, in conjunction with J H Nicholson, Signal Engineer of the GS&WR evolved a method of long-distance operation of points and signals that would obviate the need for rebuilding some of the destroyed signal boxes.

While traffic on some of the branch lines was not particularly heavy, it was essential at that time to keep them open. The Nicholson & Roberts system, as it was known, provided electric power for point

and signal operation by hand generator. In the remote areas where some small interlockings had been destroyed there was no local supply of electricity and to generate it at 100V, only when required, was as ingenious as it was simple. Arrangements were made for the engineering development of this patented system and for its marketing to be undertaken by Westinghouse in London. It provided some interesting small installations.

The first was near Charleville, now called Rathluirc, on the Dublin-Cork mainline. About a mile north of that station a single branch line diverged to the north-west, eventually getting to Limerick. The signal box at the divergence had been known as Limerick Junction, but this must not be confused with the much larger intersection and passenger station 22 miles nearer to Dublin, where the cross-country line from Limerick to Waterford crossed the Dublin – Cork line on the level. At Charleville track circuit control was put in between the station and the junction and for easy operation of the electrically worked points and signals a new design of slide

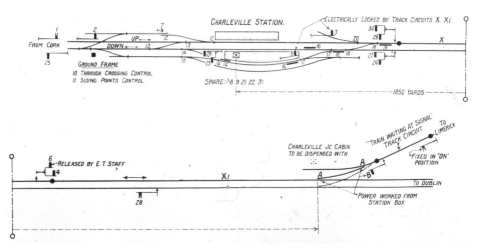

*The track layout of Charleville (above); and the
Hand Generator Operated points (right).*

lever interlocking frame was introduced.
The signalmen had to keep turning the
handle of the hand generator until
indication was received that the function
had responded. Until then, of course, the
stroke of the slide lever could not be
completed. For a simple junction such as
that controlled from Charleville only three
slides were needed; one for the points and
one each for the down and up signals. The
branch or main line signal in each direction
was selected according to the lie of the
points.

At Charleville a single branch joined a
double track main line, but a very
interesting case presented itself at
Banagher Junction, a little to the west of
Clara, on the line from Portarlington to
Athlone. At the time the latter was no more
than a branch, but it now forms part of the
main route from Dublin to Galway. In 1923,
as single line token working was involved
on both routes at Banagher Junction, the
re-modelling was arranged with no signals
at all at the actual junction; the points were
electrically interlocked with the single-line
staff instruments. The normal position of
the points[1] was for the Athlone line, staff
section (see panel) Clara – Ballycumber;
and they were reversed for the Banagher

branch, staff section Clara – Ferbane. While
these pioneer Irish installations were very
small and involved the operation of no
more than three or four functions, the
principle of hand generator operation thus
established came to have a far wider
application – not many years later in Brazil
and then in Great Britain in World War II,
as will be told later.

Contact between Westinghouse in
London and the Union Switch & Signal
Company in Swissvale, had always been
close and cordial, especially since 1915
when the American Company had obtained
a one-third shareholding in the McKenzie,
Holland & Westinghouse Power Signal
Company. The years immediately following
the end of World War I were a time of
intense technological activity in the USA,
particularly towards cab signalling and
automatic train control. The American
railways as a whole had a very bad accident

record. As in Great Britain before the war the need was felt for additional safeguards against the likelihood of drivers and signalmen's error, but in the USA things were taken much further. The Inter-State Commerce Commission (ICC) issued legal orders on some of the busiest lines requiring them to fit either cab signals, or full automatic train control. The Union Switch, like other signal manufacturers, became heavily engaged in the design and development of various systems that would meet the ICC requirements.

Meanwhile in England, although the grouping of the railways and the upheavals in personnel that had followed had tended to retard all but the most urgent needs of signalling, it was the policy of the Westinghouse management to keep in touch with all American developments. Major L H Peter, as engineer in charge of electrical engineering, paid periodic visits to Swissvale to maintain personal contact. One of these visits had an unexpected and astonishingly profitable sequel.

The phenomenon of what is called 'asymmetrical conductivity', or how the conductance of certain metallic substances appeared to vary with the direction of current through them, had been noticed by research workers as far back as 1874; but apparently no sustained attempt had at first been made to put this characteristic

to any practical use. Indeed, as late as 1922, Dr L A Grondahl, research chemist of the Union Switch, discovered the rectifying effect of the junction between a copper oxide film on a copper base. Current would flow one way through such a junction but not the other.

Again no immediate steps were taken to exploit this discovery until Major Peter learned of it. From his pre-war experience in the heavy electrical industry and his knowledge of the trend of affairs in Great Britain at the time, he realised the immense potential advantage of a small, neat, solid-state form of rectification against the established systems of rotary converters, and mercury-arc rectifiers (see Panel). It was quickly arranged for world-wide patent rights to be assigned to Westinghouse in England and by 1925 patents had been filed in most industrialised countries.

In the Engineering Department in London, F G Connor, one of the 1924 graduate recruits from Imperial College, was assigned to the job of developing rectifiers and was soon seconded to the Chippenham Works staff to assist in the first steps in production. Major Peter saw many avenues for the introduction of solid-state rectifiers, far removed from what had hitherto been the traditional lines of business in Westinghouse, with the general application that was rapidly coming of

Staff Sections

One of the earliest and most easily understood methods of allowing trains to run safely in both directions on a single track line was the use of a 'staff', 'token' or 'tablet'. This was a wooden or metal device which was physically passed by the signaller to the train crew, who were not permitted to enter the designated section without it. Upon leaving the protected section, the train crew handed the staff to the signaller at the far end, who could then use it for a train travelling in the opposite direction.

The obvious apparent flaw to this concept was that two trains could not follow one another, as the staff would be at the 'wrong end'. In order to overcome this a number of systems were evolved whereby machines were sited at either end of the 'staff section', and electrically interlocked using simple telegraph techniques. Although flexible enough to allow more than one staff to be issued from one end of the section, these machines still prevented more than one staff being available at any one time.

Rectification

Rectification is basically the conversion of alternating current (ac) (which flows back and forth within a circuit) to direct current (dc) (which only flows in one direction). It has many, many uses in electrical and electronic engineering and these days is usually carried out using semiconductor materials such as silicon.

Transmission of electricity in ac form rather than dc was at the heart of the rivalry between Westinghouse and fellow American inventor and entrepreneur Thomas Edison throughout the latter part of the 19th century. Edison tried to disprove Westinghouse's theories by a series of increasingly unpleasant experiments upon animals, which led to Edison's development of the Electric Chair – and to the verb 'to Westinghouse' meaning to kill by electrocution. However Westinghouse, working together with the brilliant physicist Nikola Tesla, won through by virtue of being right! However whilst ac is ideal for the efficient transmission of electrical energy, direct current is used in most electronic systems.

At the time that this work was carried out the major uses seen for rectification were in systems such as electro-plating plants and electro-static precipitation systems and for the very first consumer and industrial electronic systems. The only way of doing this was to use rotary mechanical machines which were powered by ac, driving dynamos to produce dc.

Although the first application that the Westinghouse company made of the new technology was a dc track circuit system, it was quickly apparent that there was a multitude of other more mundane uses – such as allowing batteries to be charged from ac mains.

The significance of this advance cannot be underestimated – this was the start of the consumer electronics revolution and Westinghouse found itself in the middle of it!

Pages from a 1929 Westinghouse brochure: (left) an Electrical Substation, described thus: 'The set illustrated above was built to special requirements and designed to operate on either of two incoming feeders of a 400-volt 3-phase supply. It has a maximum D.C. output of 6kW and consists of two separate 3kW rectifiers which can be used either singly or in parallel.' (right) 'Some of the radio mains units in which Westinghouse metal rectifiers are now incorporated.'

alternating current in commercial electricity supplies; but the first use, the historic first use of a metal rectifier on any practical work in Great Britain was on the Great Western Railway feeding a dc track circuit from ac mains, just outside Paddington Station. It was brought into service on July 15, 1925. For nine months it remained the only one, but giving entirely satisfactory service it was followed by thirteen more, installed at Plymouth in March 1926, after which it became the standard system of track feed on the Great Western Railway.

At Chippenham manufacture was at first in the 'electric shop' where all the various apparatus for power signalling was assembled. Manufacture of this element, as it developed, was relatively simple. Circular discs, or washers, or rectangular plates could be punched from rolled copper strip and, after cleaning, the blanks were subjected to oxidation and chemical etching.

It is important to record also that at a very early stage ideas for utilisation of metal rectifiers were passing far beyond that of accessories in railway signalling. H G Brown was interested in the early development of radio sets for domestic use and did much to encourage Major Peter and his staff, even though a short circuit in an early battery charger very nearly led to his home being burnt down!

However, the progress of the metal rectifier, or the semiconductor as it is known today, is a fascinating saga of its own and it came to provide one of the largest and most profitable branches of Westinghouse activity at a time when other activities were operating in a low key. The story is told in some detail in a later chapter, but at this stage the reader will appreciate the sense of gratitude felt in the Company to Major Peter for his initiative in turning the discovery and patents of L A Grondahl to such widespread effect.

1 British railway convention defines the directions that a train can run over a set of points as 'normal' and 'reverse'. Although it is not always immediately apparent which direction is which, in general the mainline is the normal direction and a divergent route to a branch or siding is reverse. It is usual for trains to be able to pass over points set in the normal direction at full linespeed, but it is common for speed restrictions to apply across points set in the reverse direction.

Turret lathes in the Machine Shop. This and the pictures on the following page were used in a publication dated May 1928 entitled The Signal Works of the Westinghouse Brake & Saxby Signal Co Ltd at Chippenham Wilts.

Casting lattice signal posts in the foundry

Main electric test area, working on relays

Parts for electropneumatic point layouts laid out for customer inspection

The wood-working shop

7
1924–30 ~ *Seven Years of Signalling Progress*

T HE COMMITTEE on 'Three Position Signalling' set up by the Institution of Railway Signal Engineers in 1922 and which published their report two years later, laid foundations of future signalling practice on which the philosophy of British railways operation is based today and which is the cornerstone of present thinking towards developments that will be needed when train speeds move beyond the 200km/h mark.[1] In recalling how the findings of that historic IRSE committee were first implemented it is interesting also to see the part that members of Westinghouse staff played in arriving at those findings.

The composition of the committee itself was interesting, because it was not by any means representative of the British railways as a whole. Of the nine members two, A F Bound, the Chairman and A E Tattersall were from the Great Central; then there was W J Thorrowgood from the London & South Western and, apart from M G Tweedie, (the Honorary Secretary of the Institution and Secretary to the committee), who held a relatively subordinate position on the Great Western, that was all. The other railway men were W Challis, who was Signalling Assistant to the Chief Engineer of the Metropolitan and W S Every, Signal Engineer of the London Underground. The other three members of the committee were contractors.

Apart from Tweedie's modest contribution from the Great Western, the great railways of the pre-grouping era in Britain, the London & North Western, the Midland, the North Eastern and the Caledonian were not represented. The contractors were H M Proud from Westinghouse and, also from this 'group', T S Lascelles, Engineer of the W R Sykes Interlocking Signal Company. The third contractor was S L Glenn, Engineer of the British Power Railway Signal Company, which had been responsible for installing the three position upper quadrant signals at Victoria on the South Eastern & Chatham Railway referred to in Chapter 5.

All the members of the committee, except Thorrowgood, had experience with upper quadrant semaphore signals, Lascelles particularly in his close studies of contemporary European practice. Thorrowgood had, however, been assistant to A H Johnson on the LSWR, the most outspoken critic of the three position upper quadrant signal. Yet it fell to Thorrowgood to make the first and most spectacular implementation of the committee's findings before many months were out. While in retrospect the composition of that committee might seem a slightly odd one, between them they laid the foundations of modern British signalling practice. There was only one dissident to the report eventually made to the Council of the Institution, S L Glenn. The committee had reached the conclusion that the three-position signal of the future should be colour-light, as Bound had by that time installed on the Great Central section of the LNER between Marylebone, Neasden and the Wembley Exhibition loop. Glenn disagreed and held out strongly in favour of the three-position upper quadrant semaphore.

Even before the grouping of 1923, which brought the London & South Western, the Brighton and the South Eastern & Chatham into the new Southern Railway under the dynamic General Managership of Sir Herbert Walker, there had been proposals for new signalling; and in the records of the Saxby section of the Westinghouse drawing offices there were proposals, dated December 1920, for signal gantries at Charing Cross carrying *not* colour lights, but 3 position electric upper quadrant semaphores, as had recently been commissioned at Victoria. The design of the gantries themselves had clearly been worked out in detail and the electric signals themselves were of the same type as used on the Ealing and Shepherd's Bush line, as referred to in Chapter 6. But these early proposals for Charing Cross evidently fell through, no doubt in view of the pending amalgamation.

With Sir Herbert Walker almost certain to secure the General Managership of the new company, it was likely that London & South Western influences would tend to predominate – particularly in all matters relating to electric traction, of which he was a most ardent advocate. While both the Brighton and the London & South Western had already electrified parts of their London suburban networks, in neither case had these installations been accompanied by resignalling. Both had been in the nature of trial heats of two entirely different systems and Sir Philip Dawson, consulting engineer to the Brighton and architect of the overhead single-phase ac systems, strove might and main to get it adopted as the future Southern Railway standard. Although the immediate decision for the forthcoming electrification of certain of the former SE & C lines went against him, extension on a limited scale of the Brighton single-phase ac system was made later.

Once the amalgamation of the companies was consummated in January 1923, electrification was pushed ahead with great vigour. The extensions to the Brighton system from Norwood Junction and Balham, to Sutton and Coulsdon North, 82 track miles, were opened in April 1925 and the new work on the former Chatham lines from Victoria, Holborn Viaduct and St Pauls to Orpington on the

Southern Railway, Brighton South box, exterior and interior views

dc third rail system of the LSWR was completed in July 1925. There was already a modern system of power signalling at Victoria, but for the City termini colour light signalling was installed. This pioneer installation on the Southern not only applied the principles established by the 'Three-Position Signalling Committee' of the IRSE, but immediately took up its further recommendation for use of a fourth aspect, where the traffic demanded it – the double-yellow – as the preliminary warning.

While the new electric trains, like those of the LSWR, were all fitted with the Westinghouse air brake (although the LSWR was otherwise a 'vacuum' line) it was disappointing to the Company that the first Southern contract for colour-light signals and miniature lever operation went to a competitor. For the second stage however, that involved resignalling at Charing Cross and Cannon Street, the Company was successful and from that time onwards for twenty years the signalling equipment on the Southern was all Westinghouse-made.

It was an activity of which I have the most vivid personal recollections. Throughout that period all signalling work on the Southern came within the domain of the Chief Civil Engineer, A W Szlumper, formerly of the LSWR and Thorrowgood's title was Assistant Engineer, Signals and Telegraphs. So far as Szlumper was concerned it was no nominal responsibility. He was intensely interested in signalling and as long previously as 1892, when London Divisional Engineer he had read a paper before the Institution of Civil Engineers on what was then called the 'Waterloo Signal Station' – in other words the famous 'A' box that spanned the tracks just beyond the platform ends and for which W F Burleigh, then of Stevens & Sons, designed the interlocking.

In 1925 Szlumper personally signed the letter of authority to proceed with manufacture of the signalling equipment for Charing Cross and Cannon Street and I recall the imperious haste in which his letter was couched. Westinghouse were to install the two big locking frames, 107 levers for Charing Cross and 143 levers for Cannon Street; the rest was supply of materials only.

It turned out to be a tremendous race against time, because the two locking frames were required on site in little more than nine months from receipt of order. Pearce did all the locking himself and I do not think that for all his experience he had previously so exacting an assignment. Every possible alternative move into and out of the stations had to be provided for and the resulting locking was intensely thick in the various channels. Furthermore, as the work proceeded on the ground, strong representations were made to us to anticipate the agreed delivery dates and when Szlumper's assistant was told politely but firmly that this was 'not on', he dissolved into rough bullying tactics.

The situation was serious, because this man was one with whom we should probably have to deal for many years after Szlumper's retirement and the almost unprecedented step of H G Brown himself taking over the negotiations was necessary. Then the cordiality of Szlumper himself, in contrast to the attitude of his assistant, and the statesmanship of 'HGB' saved the day, when it was explained that at Chippenham the maximum number of men we could physically get on the work were being employed on those two frames. An interesting feature of the signals themselves was that to save weight on the four-aspect units the cases were made of planished sheet steel, instead of cast iron. To facilitate sighting of the units that were mounted on gantries spanning the tracks the four aspect signals for gantry mounting had the lenses arranged cluster-wise instead of vertically. The two yellows were vertically above each other, with the red to the right and the green to the left.

It will be recalled that in the early months of 1926, when manufacture of the equipment for the Charing Cross and Cannon Street resignalling was at its most intense, there was widespread industrial unrest in the country, leading up to the General Strike that lasted for ten days from May 4. While there was some disruption of activity in the brake shops at King's Cross Works, at Chippenham not a single man failed to report for duty and work continued at full speed throughout the strike. This happy situation at Chippenham robbed me and some others of my London colleagues of the opportunity of volunteering for railway service, because we had to deal with technical queries that arose in the ordinary course of liaison between the Works and the Engineering departments in London. So production of the urgently needed equipment for the Southern Railway went on without the slightest interruption.

Thorrowgood presented two papers to the IRSE, the first outlining the principles on which the four-aspect system had been based and the second describing how it had worked out in practice. A good deal of controversy was aroused chiefly over how to apply the new signalling aspects for junction working. In the immediate approaches to the terminal stations route indicators were used, of a type developed by the W R Sykes Interlocking Signal Company. A number of symbols representing platform numbers or other route designations, were arranged for electrical selection and when required they were swung upwards on to a display ground something like that of a Sykes banner signal.

An earlier version had been in limited use on the London & South Western Railway. The indications provided, however, were not really in keeping with the intensity of light beam from a colour light signal and under Major Peter's direction the

Brighton projection indicator

development of an entirely new type was initiated. This was a fascinating job and involved the projection of stencil indications on to a ground grass screen. The projector units were like miniature slide projectors – 13 of them in all. The spectacle frame on which they were mounted was spherical, so that each one pointed at the screen and had its lens system the same distance away and the designing and the casting in brass of that frame was a truly beautiful piece of work. The letters projected on the screen were 12 inches high and in good conditions provided an excellent indication. This type of route indicator was used in the next installation of colour light signalling on the Southern Railway, the very large interlocking at London Bridge put into service in 1927 and in the resignalling of Victoria and Exchange stations at Manchester, London Midland & Scottish Railway.

The interlocking frame for London Bridge was the largest built since Glasgow Central and had no less than 311 levers.

Because the locking was far more intensely grouped and comprehensive, there had to be *five* tiers of locking troughs,[2] two above and three below floor level, making the total height from the miniature lever quadrant plate to the base of no less than 9 ft 8½ in.

Saxby & Farmer had built many large mechanical interlocking frames in the works at Chippenham, but there had never been one like this, as a spectacle and a piece of precision signal engineering. The lever pitch was 2½ in so that the overall length

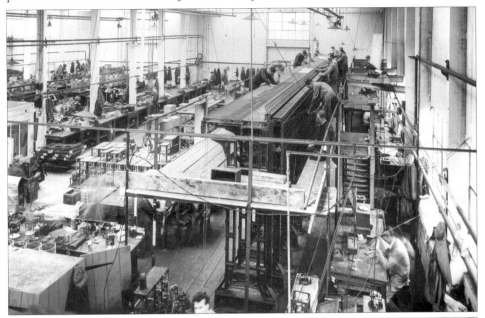

These two photographs show the construction of the 311 lever mechanical interlocking frame for London Bridge, being built in Chippenham in 1927

was nearly 70 ft. It was the aligning and levelling that required such precision in erection, because the lever interlocking was entirely mechanical and the mechanism had to work freely yet provide locking as positively tight as with the most massive of mechanical lever frames. The designing of the locking, which he did personally, was Pearce's masterpiece in signal engineering design. It was, however, for another reason, both the climax and the culmination.

To specify what locking is required on any particular frame is an exercise in philosophy rather than of factual demand. There are no hard and fast laws: the nature of the locking depends upon the traffic pattern, working of course within the basic safety principles for points and signals.

Westinghouse learned this in full measure over the 143-lever power frame at Cannon Street, after it had been in service just over a year. The electric service in and out of that terminus was very intense, but at that time a considerable number of longer distance residential trains came in during the morning suburban peak and left amid the outgoing rush in the early evening. These were then steam worked and involved shunting and light engine movements. In a joint investigation by the operating and signal departments it was found that by making certain alterations to the interlocking an occasional *minute* could be saved at times of the greatest pressure (see Panel). No more than an occasional minute, but it was worth making some considerable changes to the locking. Pearce was away ill at the time the order to do this came in and I was put in as substitute working under the general guidance of A G Kershaw, who, as the former Chief Engineer of Saxby & Farmer, was of course an expert in mechanical locking.

It was a difficult job in itself – far more so in fitting in all the modified bars and dogs in the spaces available, than if one had started with a clean sheet; but when the time came to make the changes on the frame itself the difficulties were many times multiplied. The new pieces were made at Chippenham and it was then estimated that the actual changeover would take a month of nights for a team of four fitters. Each night new pieces would have to be fitted and then these would be removed and the original restored. So the work would continue, night by night, until all the new pieces had been fitted. Then, when the time for the final changeover

Safety versus Operability

Ever since signalling was introduced on the world's railways in order to enhance safety and to pacify a startled population, there has been a conflict between railway safety and efficient operation.

All signalling systems, whether they are mechanical, pneumatic, electric or electronic, are by nature restrictive, enforcing specific rules and sequences of operation on the signaller. Various combinations of operations could actually cause earlier interlockings to 'lock up', requiring a mechanical release of the locking in order to allow train movements to start again, causing delay to traffic.

In the same way, the use of time elements, similar to those described in earlier chapters, ensured safety, but could cause train movements to be delayed. What Nock describes here is the process of optimising interlockings so that train movements, that may not have been anticipated during the design process, could be dealt with more efficiently.

Even today, especially on high density suburban or mass transit railways, much work is necessary in order to find ways of ensuring safety without causing unnecessary delays between trains.

Installing colour light signals on the Great Indian Peninsula Railway

came, all those new pieces would be put in, the result checked by the railway company's inspector and the modified frame put back into traffic.

It was a long drawn out business, because it was only for a few hours in the middle of the night that there were no train movements in the station. But the expense and complexity of the job was a lesson for all time and design work was put in hand soon afterwards on a new type of miniature lever interlocking frame on which the locking would be through electric magnets instead of a mechanical mechanism.

While the sheer size and complexity of London Bridge, with its need of precision erection and the task of altering Cannon Street sounded the death knell of mechanical locking on power frames, two notable overseas installations in the old style must be mentioned, one in India and the other in South Africa. The Great Indian Peninsula Railway (GIPR) was the first in the sub-continent to be extensively equipped with full signalling and interlocking at the stations and it became a stronghold of Saxby & Farmer equipment,

not only at the great Victoria Terminus in Bombay, but throughout the main lines including the exceptional inclines of the Thul and Bhore Ghat.

Some of the mechanical interlocking frames were of the famous Saxby 'rocker and grid' type, but the large frames of 68 and 40 levers at the 'A' and 'B' cabins at Victoria Terminus were of the Saxby '1888' duplex-plunger type. It was these that were replaced by a single electro-pneumatic interlocking frame in 1928. The station was then being very much enlarged and remodelled with complete segregation of mainline and suburban traffic. The new interlocking frame would have been one of Pearce's standard design, with mechanical locking, but the GIPR would not accept the massive teak casing hitherto fitted. It was feared that white ants would eat it. I had the job of working out a design of steel casing. The odd thing was, however, that the white ants of Bombay seemed to be selective in their gastronomical preferences, because when shortly afterwards we received an order for a similar locking frame for the Bombay,

Victoria Terminus, Bombay (GIPR)

Bhore Ghat Reversing, in the 1890s (GIPR)

Baroda and Central India terminus, only a few street blocks away from the 'VT', the BB and CI Railway had no qualms about accepting the standard teak casing!

In conjunction with the colour light signalling the GIPR installed our new projector type route indicators, referred to earlier in connection with the work at London Bridge. In the then-smoky atmospheres of English cities these had a short life. The front glasses became grimed with soot; to give a sharp indication the ground surface of the glass was outermost, but to give one of these glasses a rub with the rag that had any grease on it immediately destroyed the ground surface.

It was far otherwise in the clean air of Bombay and when I went to 'VT' in 1975 I was astonished to see that the projector type route indicators were still in service – nearly 50 years after their first installation – and giving excellent indications in the brilliant sunshine.

Saxby & Farmer as a partnership were well established before railways in the Cape of Good Hope had passed beyond the most primitive stage; so much so that when the Cape Government Railways got to the stage of installing signalling it was the Saxby '1888' duplex-plunger type of locking frame that was adopted and which, in fact, remained standard as long as mechanical frames were being installed. But down at the Cape in 1927 there was a very interesting survival of another Saxby venture. In the early 1890s the firm had become British agents for the Bianchi and Servettaz system of hydraulic point and signal operation and two small interlocking frames of three levers were installed in 1894 at the Tower Bridge in London. They were used for controlling semaphore signals for regulating both the road and river traffic and could strictly be claimed as the first-ever example of power signalling in Great Britain – though not on a railway.

The Bianchi-Servettaz system was by then extensively applied, not only in its native Italy, but also in France and Russia; but the only installation of any size made by Saxby & Farmer was on the Cape Government Railway at Salt River junction, just outside Cape Town, where the important branch line to Wynberg diverged from the main line to the north. This was of such size as to require an interlocking frame of 66 levers. It remained in service even after traffic on the line to Wynberg became so heavy as to require electric traction accompanied by colour light signalling. This was the first stage in the modernisation of the signalling in the Cape Town area generally and the putting in of an all-electric plant at Cape Town station. This had one of Pearce's standard frames, with three-aspect colour light signalling and the projector type of route indicators.

The main home signal thus equipped was a much photographed unit, displayed alongside the tremendous array of semaphore signals, one for each route, that had previously been in service there. Cape Town also saw the introduction of a 'world

These pictures of the interlocking system applied at Tower Bridge are rather out of the chronology of the book, but nevertheless in the chapter in which Nock referred to them. Hydraulic type power locking frames were introduced by Bianchi and Servettaz in Italy in 1886 and applied at Nagari in India, Cape Town, South Africa and in East Anglia by Saxby & Farmer. This apparatus was then adapted by them to the interlocking of the Tower Bridge in London in 1894.

Hydraulic Power Frame, Salt River Station, South Africa

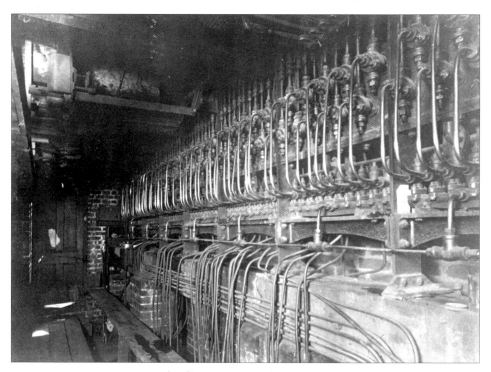

Hydraulic Power Frame pipe connections

Shunt and Subsidiary Signals

Shunt signals *are small signals, usually located at ground level, which give train crew stop / proceed information for low speed shunting moves.*

Subsidiary signals *are also small signals, usually at the same location as a normal signal, which pass additional information to be used by the train crew in conjunction with the main signal. Examples of their use are 'call on' signals, allowing trains to pass a stop signal in specified conditions, such as to have two trains at one platform.*

first' in light signals of a different kind. When the first colour light signals were installed on British railways the shunting and subsidiary signals (see Panel) were small-lens short-range colour lights and they were not very satisfactory. It was on the South African Railways that position light signals were first introduced for this purpose, showing two white lights diagonally for proceed and two white lights horizontally for stop. This type was later adopted as a British standard, with the difference of having one white and one small red horizontally for stop, on a ground shunt. At Salt River Junction the control of the new colour light signals was obtained by means of circuit breakers worked from connections to the locking tappets on the Saxby & Farmer hydraulic frame.

In the meantime, while these important works were being installed in India and South Africa, Pearce was designing the first miniature lever interlocking frame to have no mechanical interlocking. With the general introduction of track circuiting in large power signalling installations since World War I, electro-magnets had been used on power frames for both track circuit and indication locking of the appropriate levers. However, the interlocking between the levers themselves – the central safety feature of the plant – had remained mechanical and there was concern in some quarters that this should be accomplished through electro-magnets. There was thought to be some risk of the magnets being tampered with. Those with experience of some colonial railways knew of cases where certain parts, even of

mechanical locking frames, had been removed, because they hindered the working; and while there might not have been instances in Great Britain of the covers over mechanical locking being 'burgled' it was thought advisable to put the magnets, through which the lever interlocking was accomplished, in individually sealed containers.

The first frame of the new type, designated style 'L' was installed on the Southern Railway at North Kent East Junction in 1929, having 83 levers. Although this was no more than a moderate sized interlocking, the potentialities of this type of frame were quickly realised, in that it was no longer necessary to have all the levers for a single interlocking in one row. This attribute was used to great advantage later in some very large installations on the Southern Railway, when convenience in operating and general supervision was realised by having the 'frame' in two or more sections.

Reviewing the marked progress in railway signalling made during the later 1920s in which Westinghouse had taken a prominent part, it is important to emphasise that at this stage the developments were almost entirely concentrated at large interlockings at city terminal stations and key junctions. Although on the Southern Railway, W J Thorrowgood had postulated the potentialities of four-aspect colour light signalling in dealing with a 'mixed' traffic, this had so far not been put into practice, while the major installations abroad, at Plaza Constituçion, Victoria Terminus

Splitting Signals

Splitting signals are used to pass additional information to the train driver in order for him to modify train speed as required. A typical application is a 'Splitting Distant' signal, which passes information in advance of a junction. Without the splitting signal, the driver would not know which route was set ahead of him and would have to modify his speed to that of the slowest route. With the splitting signal in use, the driver would have plenty of time to determine whether he was taking the main line at full speed, or whether he was going to have to slow to pass into a loop. This is another fine example of enhancing railway operation without affecting the safety of the railway.

Bombay and Cape Town were all in areas of relatively low speed running. But the tools for the future had been forged. One important item of equipment was however still missing and about the form this should eventually take there was much controversy among British signal engineers.

This was the method of route indicating at a junction passed by express passenger trains at speeds of 60mph or more. The practice of using indicators displaying an illuminated letter or figure was not practicable because of the limited sighting range. For the Bombay Baroda and Central India Railway we built some projector type indications showing a 14 inch character instead of the usual 12 inch, but in Great Britain, at first, the colour light equivalent of the semaphore 'splitting' signals (see Panel) at junctions were used. This expedient was criticised on the grounds that one passed a red light, but it had equally strong supporters, as a 'most common-sense' way of signalling a junction. Its most serious defect however was not yet appreciated, while the new colour light signals were being installed in areas of relatively low speed running. The vital relations between train speed, sighting distance of signals and brake power had yet to be fully established.

The ordered progress of colour light signalling development, following so closely on the recommendation of the IRSE

Speed Signalling vs Route Signalling

Even allowing for the most modern, radio based electronic signalling systems, there are really only two types of signalling: Speed Signalling and Route Signalling.

Route Signalling, as used on the majority of UK railways, requires the driver to know 'the route'. That means that he needs to know the location of every signal and the maximum permitted speed everywhere along the line in order to drive safely and efficiently. Signals are not spaced equally and therefore, for example, if a driver passes a caution signal which requires him to be prepared to stop at the next signal, he needs to know where the next signal is. This method allows for very efficient operation of the railway, since all trains are effectively being driven to their optimum. Route signalling simply involves stop / proceed / caution aspects and the passing of no speed information.

However Speed Signalling is used in many parts of the world and whilst potentially less efficient on railways with mixed traffic, it is far less prone to driver error – potentially enhancing safety. Different combinations of signal indications are used to pass information to the train crew as to how fast that train can travel. Aspects are often more complex than on route signalled railways, but a smoother ride and a more regulated service is possible. Far less route knowledge is needed, reducing the workload of the driver, but a more regulated service and therefore a smoother ride is possible.

committee on 'Three Position Signalling' was soon however to receive a severe jolt. In May 1929, A F Bound, who had been Signal engineer of the Great Central Railway since 1906, and who had been Signalling Assistant in the Southern Area of the LNER since January 1923, was appointed to the new office of Chief Signal and Telegraph Engineer of the LMS; and reporting directly to the Vice-President for Works, he had a status equal to the Chief Civil and to the Chief Mechanical Engineers. It was typical of the farsightedness of the high management of the LMS under Sir Josiah Stamp, in recognising the vital part that signalling would have to play in the development of railways in the future.

Bound had been one of the most forward thinkers and exponents in the British signalling world. He had chaired the historic IRSE committee of 1922; he had installed the first multiple-aspect colour light signals in Great Britain and the stage seemed set for extensive progress on the same lines as the LMS. Far from it however! The principles of 'speed signalling' (see Panel) were, and still are of course, widely practised in North America and in Australia and Bound apparently became so enamoured of a system diametrically opposed to the usual British ideas as to plan a number of new installations, to the consternation of a majority of British railwaymen; but by 1930, when the resignalling scheme for which we had obtained the contract at St Enoch station, Glasgow, began to be turned upside down, the economic situation of the country as a whole had already taken a downwards dive, with repercussions in many diverse directions.

---

1 When Nock wrote this in the 1980s, train speeds much beyond 125mph or 200km/h were rare. Since then European and Japanese railways have made train travel at greater than 300km/h commonplace on many main lines. However 200km/h remains the highest speed generally accepted as practical for fixed lineside signalling. 2 Two tiers would be more normal at the time.

8

The Great Slump ~ Rectifiers to the Rescue ~ A Notable Brake Development

AT A MEETING of the Westinghouse Board, in London, on February 17, 1930, some very important new appointments were made. That remarkable American, John Wills Cloud, was still in the Chair and H G Brown moved up to be Deputy Chairman. Captain Peter became Managing Director, an appointment that was to prove of immense value and significance in the difficult years to come, while W H Powell, hitherto General Business Manager, became General Manager; to him thereafter the chief executive officers reported. Following the death of Richard Payne, J Griffith Hall was confirmed as his successor as Secretary.

The effect of Powell's appointment was soon felt from end to end of the Company. Two senior executives, H J Winter (Brake Engineer) and W A Pearce were relieved of their responsibilities and appointed as consultants only; Donald F Brown, son of the Deputy Chairman became Brake Engineer, while the drawing office at King's Cross, hitherto operated as three separate sections, was put under the unified control of A G Kershaw. Major L H Peter was appointed Chief Electrical Engineer and H M Proud Chief Commercial Engineer, though actually the latter title applied only to signalling. The Leeds office, which had

remained from the days when McKenzie & Holland had such extensive business under the North Eastern Railway, was closed.

A year later Cloud resigned his position as Chairman of the Board and was succeeded by Lord Southborough, but for a time he remained a director. Cloud's resignation brought some personal memories to me. He had been extremely active in English companies since his appointment as Vice-President and Managing Director of the Westinghouse Brake Company in 1899. He was not only a very shrewd and successful business manager, but was himself a prolific inventor and long before the English company entered the field he had a number of patents connected with the *vacuum* brake. In the late 1920s his scientific theories were tending to get 'way out' – to use a modern colloquialism. He used to sit in the Board Room and Head Office and write pamphlets and books of the most abstruse character. Then one day Major Peter came up to the drawing office and told Pearce that the Chairman wanted to borrow 'a draughtsman with some electrical knowledge' and could he spare me for a week or two. Pearce of course, had known Cloud of old and I shall never forget that irascible old face of his creased up into a most mischievous grin. It was as if to say 'I know what you're in for'! Anyhow, an hour or so later A S Hackwood, the Patent Agent of the Company, ushered me into 'the Presence'.

In the 30 years he had been resident in England Cloud had not lost one vestige of his American speech and idiom and he asked me at once if I knew anything about the precession of the equinoxes.[1]

I think I surprised him a little by answering that I did, because I had a brief encounter with the subject at Imperial College in the little astronomy we had to learn in connection with surveying. After a moment he looked at me and said: 'Yer do – waal, I've an idea . . .' and he went on to explain that he thought the phenomenon of precessional couples could be used to form a new type of electrical motor and rapidly sketching out his ideas instructed me to get a model made to try out the theory.

I was completely out of my depth on the latter, but from the Chairman of the Board, orders were orders. When I got back to the office and told Pearce he said, 'Oh yes, another perpetual motion machine!', laughed and arranged to transfer my current work elsewhere for a time. When, in due course, I took the drawings to the London Works Manager, the tough little Billy Woodhouse, he was not amused. There were many special pieces that had to be bought out and I had to do this. When eventually the model was finished Cloud was delighted with it; but it didn't work. He was terribly disappointed and then shrugging his shoulders said 'Waal, thanks for your help. Take one of my books. Nobody can understand it ...!', and he handed me a copy of 'Castles in the Ether', which he had published in the previous year, 1928. It is still on my library shelves and looking at it again today I am not surprised that I also could not understand it. I can understand it even less today!

Reverting now to the hard facts of 1930–1, my own recollections of this period of upheaval – for upheaval it was – are most vivid. At the end of 1929 my own period as a trainee had come to an end and it had been decided that I should stay in the power signal drawing office. Under Pearce I became a designer and involved in some interesting work I began to know the 'old man' much more intimately and to appreciate his outstanding skill. He was as irascible as ever and drove one near to distraction at times with his persistent cross-questioning on the rights and wrongs of a particular project. But despite this I was very sorry when I learned that he was to retire and still more when I came to realise that, to use a biblical quotation: 'A new king had arisen over Egypt who knew not Joseph.' It was however not only within the firm, but without, that the next few years were disturbing – to say the least of it!

Just at the time when economic conditions were making signalling contracts few and far between the competition was becoming more intense than ever before. We now had three strong competitors in the field: there were our old rivals the British Power Railway Signal Company; then there was a new combination, with German and British interests allied; the Siemens and General Electric Railway Signal Company and finally the General Railway Signal Company, a subsidiary of Metropolitan Vickers, formed to market the products of the GRS of America, which previously had a working alliance with the BPRS. The last mentioned, subsidised for a time from the personal wealth of an influential director, snatched nearly all the few signalling contracts that were awarded by British railways at that time, by the simple process of quoting at less than cost price. It was something of an anomaly that certain contracts that involved novelties in British signal practice were executed by a firm that inevitably went bankrupt and disappeared from the scene well before the decade was out.

Within Westinghouse things became very quiet, particularly on the brake side. In power signalling, through Major Peter's influence, we received authority to make drawings of anglicised versions of recent Union Switch developments, against possible future orders. Some of these involved a good deal of work. The more junior members of the three sections of the drawing office were pooled, in order to spread the work around; but there was not enough, even with this expedient, to keep them all occupied and in the autumn of 1931 redundancies were inevitable. It was the same with the Signal Estimating Department and with the outside constructional staff. In the works at Chippenham things were at a very low ebb, with a considerable proportion of the workforce laid off. At the same time however an appointment of much significance for the future had been made.

Following the great amalgamation of 1920, with the need to coordinate production and maintain close liaison with head office in London, a central progress department had been set up in Chippenham under Herbert A Cruse, with R A Henson as his assistant. This proved very successful and in 1930, foreshadowing further developments that the Board then had in mind, Cruse was appointed Assistant Works Manager. It was considered that important economies in production costs could be made if the entire manufacturing activities of the company were to be concentrated at Chippenham, where there was plenty of space for expansion, rather than by modernising the rather cramped, 50-year old premises at King's Cross. But while all this forward planning was in mind, immediate business slumped still more heavily and in 1932 staff salaries from the highest to the lowest grades were cut uniformly by 10 per cent.

It was then that one of the major diversifications of the previous decade came to the rescue, if no more than partially. Thanks to the energetic development of the rectifier activity by Major Peter into fields far removed from railway signalling the business was flourishing and a large demand quickly developed for battery chargers and for battery eliminators in the early radio sets being developed at that time. A manufacturing facility had been set up at Chippenham under the technical guidance of two young electrical engineer graduates, R H Cubitt and R G Sell, but although production of elements was simple there were many puzzling incidentals. It was easy enough for circular discs, washers or rectangular plates to be punched or guillotined from rolled copper strip. After cleaning, the blanks were subjected to two stages of oxidation and chemical etching. They were then completed by deposition of an electrode on the cuprous oxide, of aquadag[2] or a metallic sprayed layer of zinc or a vacuum deposited layer of gold.

The puzzling feature in the early days was the quality of the copper. This was found to depend on oxygen content and trace metallic impurities characteristic of the mines from whence the ore came. The best copper came from the Chuquicamata Mine in Chile where this ore was near the surface in the form of relatively pure sulphate. Refining consisted of dissolving the ore in water and extracting the copper by a simple electrolytic process. This copper was the most pure high conductivity copper available. Impurities either in the copper or accidentally introduced during rectifier manufacture resulted in poor or unstable rectifiers. The quality of Chilean copper deteriorated as demand increased and deeper deposits had to be mined; but it was still the best available.

In desperate efforts to try to eliminate possible sources of contamination during manufacture it was decided to eliminate impurities picked up from the sea or from the local foundry by Westerly winds. Tackling this in a dedicated and scientific fashion, R H Cubitt decided to erect a weather vane. It had long been felt that the problem of obtaining good rectifiers was one of being able to detect either desirable or undesirable impurities. However the most sensitive optical spectographic methods could not detect these impurities. While the metallurgical problems gave many anxious times to the engineers concerned with production and no less of course to Major Peter, whose overall responsibility the whole activity was, the business as a whole flourished exceedingly. The difficulties with copper led to other metals being considered.

Even before the end of the nineteenth century the rectification effect in selenium had been demonstrated and in the 1930s the scope and equipment of the London Laboratory, of which S A Stevens was the first research engineer, was greatly expanded. It was to prove an investment of outstanding value to the Company, as will be told in a later chapter of this book.

A very important development in braking began in the late 1920s. In the USA at that time most attention was being devoted to the control of heavy freight trains, the length and gross-tonnage of which was ever on the increase. The tests on the Virginian Railway in 1921 with coal trains loaded to 16,000 tons stand today as a classic episode in the development of the air brake. But in Great Britain the situation was quite different. While most railwaymen of the day would have agreed that the continuous braking of freight trains would be very desirable it was then far beyond the realms of practical politics and indeed of finance. On the other hand a critical situation was discerned as imminent in the working of intense suburban and inter-urban traffic.

It was appreciated that the air brake was superior to the vacuum in such duties and as previously mentioned the London & South Western Railway, although a vacuum brake line, had chosen Westinghouse when its first electrical multiple-unit trains were obtained for the 'Riverside Electrification'. At the same time there was no question but that greater skill was needed in using the air brake. If, in approaching a station or a signal at danger, the initial application had been too heavy and there was a probability of stopping short, the brakes had to be completely released and then re-applied to a lesser degree. In application also, with the standard No 4 brake valve, the operating handle required to be put into the lap position to hold the degree of braking that had been made.[3] There was also the risk, after a heavy application and subsequent release, that there had been insufficient time for the auxiliary reservoirs to be charged before a second application was needed. The braking would then not be fully effective and an overrun or even a buffer-stop collision might result.

In these intense duties one needed the simplicity of a straight-air brake, in which the degree of application or release corresponded to the position of the handle of the driver's brake valve; but such ordinarily was inadmissible because it lacked the automatic feature in the event of a breakaway.[4] The conception then developed of a straight air brake, electrically controlled, that could be superimposed upon the standard automatic air brake. The first British trial of such an arrangement was made on the Southern Railway in 1927. That railway had inherited from its constituent, the London Brighton & South Coast, the celebrated 'elevated electric', so called *not* because it ran on tracks elevated from the highway as some of the city electric lines in the USA, but because it had an overhead electric supply, at 6,600V, single phase ac. The electrified network of the Brighton Railway penetrated only a short distance beyond the South London suburbs and in Southern Railway days, the old three-car trains were known generally as the 'Crystal Palace' units. It was one of these, hitherto fitted with the standard automatic air brake, that was chosen for a trial of electro-pneumatic braking.

The electro-pneumatic system consisted of a straight air brake fed from a continuous main reservoir pipe, air from which was admitted to the brake cylinder on each coach through an application magnet valve. Pressure was retained in the cylinder or released from it by a holding magnet valve. The driver's brake valve, of American design, incorporated electrical contacts which, in accordance with the handle position, energised or de-energised appropriate line wires running throughout the train to which the magnet valves on each coach were connected. This arrangement had a flexibility and simultaneous action that was absent in the standard automatic air brake, in that graduations in both application and release could be made and there was complete synchronisation of all braking adjustments throughout the train, instead of the sequential operation inherent in a system that relied upon the propagation of pressure waves down the train pipe from the driver's brake valve.

The Westinghouse quick-acting triple valve had certainly made the rate of propagation very rapid; but application of the brakes was not simultaneous. It was of course essential – indeed mandatory – to retain the automatic brake and more over to change over to its use in the event of failure of the electrical supply.

This requirement was met by the incorporation of an interlock magnet valve in the driver's brake valve. In the event of any interruption in the electrical supply this immediately vented the train pipe of the ordinary automatic brake and produced a brake application. The electrical supply on the Brighton 'elevated' electric trains came from the overhead supply line in which, of course, there were many short gaps at junctions and in the approaches to large terminal stations like Victoria and London Bridge. Brief interruptions in the traction supply were of no consequence in running the train, but with the EP brake the interlock magnet immediately detected them and slammed on the Westinghouse automatic brake, whether the driver wanted to or not! This made the brake virtually unmanageable and with many such incidents progress was delayed and the train so equipped became very unpopular with everyone concerned. Furthermore, the drivers heartily disliked the American type No 20 brake valve. They considered it quite inferior in performance to the standard No 4, with which men of the Brighton Railway – for some 50 years a Westinghouse line – were thoroughly familiar. So the experiment on the Southern came to an end and the use of the EP brake was not revived there for another 20 years.

In the meantime W S Graff-Baker, Assistant Chief Mechanical Engineer of the Metropolitan District and of the London Electric Railway since 1922, was making it his business to keep in touch with all current developments that affected the running of an intense train service. He visited the USA and was a close friend of Captain Peter, with whom he frequently discussed braking problems. He obviously became aware of the troubles experienced in the trials of electro-pneumatic braking on the Southern, but the advantages were too great for the principle to be laid to one side. The difficulty with interruptions in the electrical supply was overcome by provision of a 50 volt dc supply from batteries on the train, but a more significant improvement from the personnel viewpoint was the introduction of a new type of driver's brake valve, known as the No 21, which gave

These pictures from an early 1940 handbook, Interlocked Electro-Pneumatic Brake Equipment, *show the complexity of the EP system. The equipment is shown exposed (left) and with its cover in place (right)*

electro-pneumatic control of the train by exactly the same handle-movements as those with which the drivers were familiar on the standard Westinghouse No 4.

The trials, on the District line, on what was officially designated the 'F' stock in 1928, were as great a success as those on the Southern were a failure and equipping of more trains went ahead rapidly. When the District and the London Electric Railways were merged with the Metropolitan in the London Passenger Transport Board, set up in 1933, Graff-Baker continued as Assistant Mechanical Engineer of the enlarged concern and two years later he succeeded W A Agnew as Chief Mechanical Engineer (Railways).

Although it is taking things a little out of strict chronological sequence the strong and

continuous development of the EP brake on London Transport can be described at this stage, because it forms a natural continuation in the story, from the trials and initial equipping of trains after 1928. The really big advance in braking practice on a 'rapid transit' type of service came in 1937. It could not be ascribed to any one person individually, but was a team job, the successful accomplishment of which was due principally to four Westinghouse men: A W Simmonds, Brake Engineer; Kenneth H Leech, Chief Draughtsman and N G Cadman, Test Engineer in London; and C S (Bill) Williams, Executive Engineer (Brakes) at Chippenham, to which the complete manufacture of brakes had been transferred in 1932. The novel features of the new EP brake were threefold: a brake valve on which normal applications were made by moving the handle to 'full service' position and leaving it there, no movement back to a 'lap' position being required to hold the degree of application made; the use of a retardation controller; and thirdly a combined cylinder and slack adjuster for fitting on the bogie – one per brake block. This latter eliminated all brake rigging on the cars and was a very big advance.

The principles involved in this new conception of braking for 'rapid transit' passenger stock were sophisticated in themselves, but their accomplishment included some of the most advanced mechanical design yet incorporated in any Westinghouse product. Although there had been some considerable tidying up in the arrangement of the various components in the first application of EP braking, the brake equipment on locomotives and trains had traditionally been a series of bits and pieces, hung on where convenient. The new equipment was vastly superior, both in appearance and in its grouping for easy access and maintenance on the trains. This was to some extent brought about by the need to accommodate it on 'tube' stock, on which space was at a premium; but the neat and compact grouping of the major functions into combined units made a truly elegant solution. The Brake Controller, for example, one of which was mounted at each driving position in the train, included the driver's brake valve, equalising discharge valve, reducing valve, interlock valve and a duplex pressure gauge, registering main reservoir and brake pipe pressures. The combined brake cylinder and slack adjuster was an ingenious unit which automatically took up the slack inherently developing in any brake applying device on account of brake block wear.

Most comprehensive of all was the unit modestly called the 'EP Brake Unit', which was an assembly of no fewer than twelve individual valves and electrical switches all mounted on a single pipe bracket. The overriding fundamental advantage of this arrangement is that no pipe connections were needed between a large number of pneumatic functions. All the connections were made by cored passages inside the cast iron pipe bracket. The unit incorporated not only the EP functions, such as the application valve, interlock switch and rectifier, but also the triple valve for the ordinary application of the brake. The pipe bracket itself, with its intricate air passages, was a masterpiece of design and no less a masterpiece of foundry work in its production at Chippenham.

1 A slow backward motion of the equinoctial points on the ecliptic, caused by the greater attraction of the sun and moon on the excess of matter at the equator, such that the times at which the sun crosses the equator come at shorter times than they would otherwise do (!)
2 Aquadag is the registered trademark of a dispersion of extremely fine, pure graphite in a water carrier that dries to form an adherent film on virtually all surfaces - including glass and flexible materials. It is frequently used in making Cathode Ray Tubes.
3 The 'Lap Position' is simply that position, in which a partial brake application can be maintained once made. It is still a term used today.
4 When E C Sharpe checked Nock's manuscript he indicated that this is not true since it does not take account of Electropneumatic brake developments in the USA, and trials on the District Line from 1915, at which point such a system was available in the UK.

9
Evolution Despite the Slump ~
Notable Advances in Signalling

LL ENGINEERING DEPARTMENTS of the Company recorded many striking achievements in the difficult years between 1930 and 1938, Brakes, Signals and Rectifiers each making many interesting and highly important new developments. To take these in strict chronological order would however tend to make a rather disjointed story and so I have separated them out by products in this and the following chapters.

Towards the close of Chapter 7 I emphasised that the many developments in apparatus design in signalling had been applied in the areas of suburban or terminal station concentrations, where speeds were relatively low and that the immense potentialities of multiple aspect signalling had scarcely, as yet, been glimpsed. While contracts for some of the novelties in signalling practice eluded us at first, the Southern Railway was becoming as exclusive a Westinghouse preserve as the former North Eastern Railway had been for McKenzie & Holland in pre-grouping days. So, when the first of Sir Herbert Walker's great projects for main line electrification came to be implemented, that of the Brighton line, it proved a notable opportunity to show what continuous colour light signalling could do in the

handling of a heavy and fast main line traffic. By 1931, some 293 route miles had been electrified in this way.

The first of the new work covered the 36 miles between Coulsdon and Brighton. The former station then marked the furthest point out of London for purely suburban services and the general scheme of the new signalling embodied three-aspect colour lights, four aspects being used in only a few cases where it was not possible to obtain full braking distance between successive signal locations. A point of much interest was that, except at Brighton terminus, the interlocking frames were all mechanical. The line was track circuited throughout and to provide all the safeguards of full power operation the frames were fully equipped with electric lever locks and circuit controllers. At certain junctions existing apparatus of Saxby make was adapted by the Southern Railway staff to the new purpose, but elsewhere new mechanical interlocking frames of the Saxby & Farmer 1924 pattern were built at Chippenham and fitted with the necessary electrical equipment. It was an interesting example of the integration of mechanical and power signalling apparatus in a thoroughly modern concept. The new power frame at Brighton was of the new

The 225 lever Style L frame installed at Brighton on the Southern Railway

all-electric 'L' type, with 225 levers, for operating convenience in the cabin arranged in three sections – the outer ones being inclined to the centre one.

The capacity of the re-equipped line for handling heavy traffic could not have had a more striking demonstration than on the evening of Whit Monday, 1933, as reported thus in *The Railway Gazette*:

> In the course of the homeward rush from the seaside on Monday evening last, there were several achievements on the part of the Southern Railway calling for attention. At Brighton a special control tower was installed and brought into use about 4pm, its object being to direct passengers to the various platforms and trains. Between 5pm and 10pm no fewer than 107 trains left Brighton Central Station, carrying 75,000 passengers. On the average, therefore, a train departed every three minutes – or slightly less – throughout the five hour

period and each train carried on average just over 700 passengers – 15,000 an hour. The great bulk of this traffic was for London or beyond and had to be carried over the main line, which has only the one track as far as Balcombe Tunnel box – 19 miles – and in addition to the trains from Brighton there were those from Worthing and Hove also passing over almost the whole of this distance. More noteworthy still is the fact that from Keymer Junction to Balcombe Tunnel there were also the Hastings, Bexhill, Eastbourne and Seaford trains to be accommodated by the single up road in addition to those from Brighton and Worthing. Actually, between Keymer Junction and Haywards Heath the up trains moving over this road were:
> - Between 7 and 8pm, 13 trains
> - Between 8 and 9pm, 16
> - Between 9 and 10pm, 18
> - And between 10 and 11pm, 14 trains

The greatest density being one every 3.3 minutes throughout the hour. Only by the employment of automatic colour-light signalling and of very heavy electric trains for the most part, could this traffic be moved within so short a period.

It must be emphasised of course that not *all* the credit for this remarkable feat of mass-passenger transportation must be given to signalling. The new express multiple-unit trains were fitted with Westinghouse brakes which, with multiple aspect colour light signals, permitted the safe working of such traffic at such close headway.

While much satisfaction could be felt within Westinghouse at being associated with so notable a development in our cooperation with the Southern Railway, it was disappointing not to be 'in' on the inauguration of multiple aspect colour light signalling on the East Coast main line, between York and Northallerton. The widening of this heavily used 30-mile stretch, together with the installation of the new signalling, was one of the works undertaken by the British railways, with Government subsidy, for the relief of unemployment. At that time A E Tattersall was Signal Engineer of the North Eastern Area of the LNER and into that installation he crowded a number of signalling novelties, such as control from a thumb-switch panel, at Thirsk; route switching, combined with the use of searchlight type signals (See Panel). The British Power Railway Signalling Company got the contract, but in an incredibly short time it was obsolete. There can have been little or no liaison between the senior officers of the engineering departments of the LNER.

Front and side views of a searchlight signal

Searchlight Signals

Searchlight Signals are signals in which instead of having a different lamp unit for each colour, or aspect, a single light is lit and a filter is placed in front of the lamp. The coloured filter is changed by means of an electro-mechanical device. The beam is focused using a parabolic mirror and visibility is possible over a much longer range than for a multiple lens signal.

'W' Curve

In order to design a safe signalling layout, the Signal Engineer has to know what distance a train needs in order to stop from a given linespeed. The 'W' curve is a graph which defines stopping distances from a series of linespeeds for a given 'standard' train. Trains which do not have the braking performance of this standard train are not permitted to run at the full linespeed.

The line was virtually level throughout with a slightly rising tendency in the northbound direction and the signal spacing on the up line was as little as 1,200 yds on some of the fastest stretches, as approaching Thirsk, and between Alne and Tollerton. Maximum speeds were then generally between 75 and 80mph. The signal spacing was almost exactly in accordance with the 'W' curve standardised many years later by British Railways for locomotive hauled trains and between York and Northallerton it placed a theoretical maximum on the speed that could be run.

Carrying the story of this particular stretch of line two years further forward, to 1935, there came the introduction of the Silver Jubilee train, a lightweight streamlined flyer, capable of running at 100mph on level track. Like the ordinary Anglo-Scottish express trains running over the route it was at first fitted with the standard vacuum brake, except that its retardation characteristics were a great deal worse. On the 'Pacific' engines of the LNER the bogie wheels and the radial trailing trucks were not braked and on the Silver Jubilee the ratio of engine and tender weight to the total trailing load was much higher: 168 to 235 tons on the Silver Jubilee against 154 to 520 tons on the Flying Scotsman. The higher proportion of unbraked to total weight in the case of the Silver Jubilee meant that it could not be stopped in accordance with the 'W' curve, and in fact it had to be limited to a maximum speed of 70mph between York and Northallerton – ironically the section with the most modern signalling on the entire route between London and Newcastle. On the mechanically signalled sections elsewhere safe running up to the official maximum limit of 90mph – often actually exceeded – was made possible by special instruction that two block sections ahead were to be clear before 'line clear' could be given to that train. This was an operating instruction. There were no positive interlocks to ensure it.

It was also on the York – Northallerton section that the problem of long range sighting of junction signals came to a head and was resolved. There were a number of locations where crossover roads providing for movements from main to relief lines were installed; and at these, in addition to junctions such as Sessay Wood and Thirsk, splitting colour light signals were at first used. The signals themselves were of the searchlight type and in the configuration leading up to a turnout the signal for the diverging route would be about 2ft below that for the main route and about 2ft on the diverging side. The diagonal distance between the two lines would be a little less than 3ft.

This section of the LNER main line is exceptionally straight and in clear weather signals could be sighted from a long distance ahead. Although the beam from the signals was very concentrated there was inevitably some spread and several times, when riding on the footplate at night the proximity of a red and green light in such a configuration and the spread of the beams, led to complete intermingling and with optical mix of red and green one saw, at maximum sighting range, a single very bright white light. At this time Tattersall was already trying out the first position light junction indicator, consisting of a series of red neon tubes extending upwards and diagonally from the top of the main signal unit. At first he had a tube pointing vertically to indicate the straight road ahead, and this also mixed beautifully with the green of a clear signal aspect and produced a haze of white light at maximum sighting range.

One of the largest contracts Westinghouse obtained in the 'relief of unemployment' period was for the re-signalling of Cardiff General station, Great Western Railway. This had two large all-electric interlockings of the 'L' type, but the colour light signalling was of a type unique to the GWR. From its very inception, right back in 1835, that old Company had earned a reputation for doing things differently from everyone else and in adopting colour light signalling they did not, at last, take up 3-position semaphores, as had been so confidently forecast some 20 years earlier, nor the normal form of three-aspect colour light signalling.

In the new work at Cardiff, as in the equally important installations at Paddington and Bristol made by one of our competitors, the aspects displayed to the driver were the same as in semaphore signalling at night. Thus for example, instead of replacing the traditional home and distant semaphores and their slotting with a single three aspect signal, they used two new signals of the searchlight type one above the other, to give green over green for clear, green over yellow for caution, and red over yellow for stop. It was remarkable indeed that in those early years of the 1930s the four main line railways of Great Britain were installing four different forms of colour light signalling, thus:

• GWR: Searchlight signals reproducing the night indications of the former semaphore signals.
• Southern: Multi-aspect colour light signals, 3 or 4 aspect according to traffic.
• LMS: Speed signal aspects of the American type.
• LNER: Multi-aspect, but using searchlight type signals instead of the multi-lens type being standardised on the Southern.

The first installation of speed signalling, in the true American style, was at Mirfield, on the main west to east line of the former Lancashire and Yorkshire Railway, where it was intersected by the one-time highly competitive Manchester – Leeds line of the former London & North Western Railway. Its introduction could be traced to A F Bound's visit to the USA in 1931, not very long after his appointment as Chief Signal and Telegraph Engineer on the LMS. The contract for this work went to the British Power Railway Signalling Company. Quite apart from any disappointment that may have been felt at Westinghouse at losing this very interesting job it was nevertheless a venture that caused all British signal and operating men to think hard. For it was not merely a change in signal aspects; it was a radical change in the basic philosophy of British operating. It was all very well to argue that it was used all over America. That was not the point. At Mirfield a driver approaching any one of the diverging junctions was not told where he was going, but instead how fast he should run – high, medium or low speed. The fact that the normal maximum speed of trains passing through Mirfield without stopping was not very high made the situation less critical than it might have been otherwise; but from a driver's point of view it was certainly a milestone of the first magnitude in British operating history.

I remember the many angles from which it was discussed among us younger engineers at Westinghouse. Big things had been expected from the LMS following Bound's appointment and with Government finance being made available we talked about how speed signalling might be applied to the really big main line junctions like Rugby, Crewe and Preston; but to our growing surprise considerably less seemed to be happening on the LMS than elsewhere, once Glasgow (St Enoch) was finished and Mirfield was put into commission. One sensed that such radical changes were not entirely welcomed by other officers concerned with the running of the trains and the Government's funds made available for signalling were spent in directions other than major rebuilding of large interlockings, as was taking place on the other main line railways of Great Britain.

In the meantime signalling activity in Westinghouse remained at a very low ebb. Looking hopefully to the future Major Peter had initiated detailed studies of the Union Switch & Signal Company's coded remote control system of operation having the trade name of Centralised Traffic Control (CTC). American-made coding and storage units were obtained and a small specimen installation set up at Chippenham. The likelihood of business on the home railways was not very great; because although there were many single-tracked routes, particularly in Scotland, where CTC could have greatly improved traffic operation, these lines were already fully signalled and equipped with single-line token apparatus. The savings in operation and staffing would not have justified the cost of installing and maintaining CTC. The prospects for this very attractive system seemed much better on some of the overseas railways with which we had close associations.

Another field of potential activity lay in marshalling yards. In the course of his visits to the USA Major Peter had studied current American practice and brought back

CTC

Centralised Traffic Control was a major step forward in efficient train control. The system was introduced in the USA during the 1920s and provided a means of speeding up train movements on single-track routes, by giving the dispatcher (signaller) a direct means of sending orders to trains without needing to deal with telegraph or telephone messages or paper systems. Before CTC it was necessary to communicate with the train crew by talking to operators at intermediate stations who passed information on to them. CTC used two line wires to pass information in a coded and sequential form, not unlike the old-fashioned telephone exchanges, directly across distances of up to 100 miles.

With CTC it was possible for operators to set routes at interlockings a great distance away from their operational base. This was of particular importance to 'long thin' railways such as those in North America.

Approaches to Glasgow St Enoch. Platform departure and arrival signals (above and opposite page).

drawings and operational data relating to the Union Switch electro-pneumatic form of wagon retarder, or rail brake as it became known in Great Britain. Gravity operated marshalling yards had already been installed in this country, notably at Wath on the Great Central Railway and at Feltham on the London & South Western; but none of these had employed the American technique of retarding wagons running from the hump by power operated devices. The Union 'Model 28' electro-pneumatic retarder was closely studied in London and a number of preliminary drawings made; but for the large new concentration yard built by the LNER at Whitemoor, near March, Cambridgeshire, a very different form of retarder was chosen.

On that railway the retarders were the responsibility of the Chief Mechanical Engineer, H N Gresley (later Sir Nigel Gresley). He considered the Union model 28 was too complicated and installed instead the German Frölich type, with electro-hydraulic control. To add to the discomfiture of British manufacturers the apparatus for point operation was also supplied by a German firm – AEG.

In the meantime for some time previously it had been known at Westinghouse about a rail brake of a totally different kind, which was based upon the retarding effect produced by the eddy currents set up in a metal disc rotating in a magnetic field. This effect, as applied to railway wagons, had first been demonstrated at the Transport Exhibition at Munich in 1925; but much experimental work had to be done before an 'eddy current rail brake' could be applied to the actual job of retarding wagons in a marshalling yard. This was eventually done in November 1928 at Magdeburg with success. An interest in this form of brake was immediately acquired by Westinghouse and because the braking effect was obtained far more from the eddy current action rather than from friction between brake beam and wheel the operating mechanism was extremely simple.

No time was lost in acquainting Mr Gresley with its details, because it was known that a second new yard was to be constructed at Whitemoor for dealing with northbound traffic. When the time came we secured the contract, not only for the rail brakes but for the automatic point setting. In the lean year of 1932 it was like manna from Heaven. It involved a large amount of drawing office work and I had men from the brake and the mechanical signalling section, in addition to the regulars from the old Power Company, working on the numerous detail parts that were required.

Hump Yards

Hump Yards are marshalling yards equipped with, as the name suggests, a 'hump'. Trains are loose shunted (i.e. the wagons are not all connected to one another) slowly over the hump. Upon passing over the hump the wagons run under gravity and the control system selects the correct siding to route the wagon to. As the first wagon, or 'cut' of wagons, rolls towards its final destination, the next is pushed over the hump by the shunting locomotive.

Unsurprisingly, this was a risky affair in the early days and much damage was done to staff and vehicles by over-enthusiastic shunting or inattentive working practices. In order to make Hump Yards more effective, mechanical devices – retarders – were invented to regulate the speed of vehicles passing over them, so that the entire operation was much more controlled.

Even today many large marshalling yards work on this basis, but at the time described here, Westinghouse were world-leaders in this cutting edge technology.

A wagon passes over the Eddy Current wheel brake in this photograph from WB&S publicity material of the time.

So far as the eddy current brake was concerned however the operating department of the LNER threw an almighty spanner into the works. At that time there was in circulation a number of wagons with the Mansell type of wheel, which had bolts projecting beyond the face of the tyres. The beams of the eddy current brake, by the very nature of the magnetic interaction that created the retarding effect, extended higher above rail level than those of the Frölich and would have fouled the bolts on the Mansell wheels. A request was made that as these wagons were relatively few they might be segregated and not put through the rail brakes; but the operating department was adamant. There was nothing for it therefore but to cut the upper part of the beams back sufficiently to clear.

This of course would have greatly lessened the effectiveness of the braking.

In a demonstration at Chippenham in March 1931 for railway officers and the technical press, a brake 50 ft long was used and it was shown that a loaded 20 ton wagon entering the brake at 15½ mph could be stopped *dead* in 49ft. In tendering for the special conditions stipulated for Whitemoor northbound yard the length of the brakes with the cut-away beams was increased by 70ft and the maximum excitation current increased by 50%. This it was considered would compensate for the cutting away of the beams. Gresley was satisfied and we got the order; but in the heaviest working conditions the modified eddy current brake did not prove so effective as the Frölich. It was a pity about

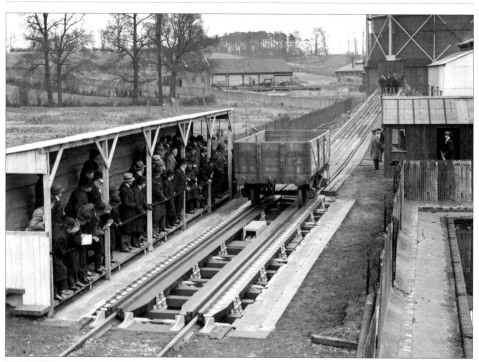

March 1931 Retarder tests at Chippenham. The railway officers and technical press gather in a makeshift shelter waiting for the 20 ton wagon to be pushed down the hill towards them. Not a hard hat or safety barrier in sight and no clear indication of what would have stopped the wagon if the retarder hadn't.

that cutting away requirement, because basically we had a far better brake with a much smoother action.

That same lean year of 1932 saw also the commissioning of the first English-built installation of Centralised Traffic Control, surprisingly enough on the Metropolitan Railway. One of the works undertaken for relief of unemployment was the construction of a double-tracked branch line from Wembley Park to Stanmore, a distance of just over four miles. Stanmore was then little more than a deeply rural settlement in high wooded country and served by no more than a single tracked branch of the former London & North Western Railway, from Harrow and Wealdstone station. The service there was provided by a steam push-and-pull auto-train and there were no through services to London. It was adequate for the community then residing at Stanmore. The Metropolitan Railway, with that business acumen for which it was famed, saw the prospect of an excellent residential traffic from estates built in completely virgin country between Wembley Park and Stanmore and from the outset provision was to be made for fast and frequent electric services into Central London. All this seems quite unlike the remote terrains in North America where the Union Switch & Signal Company had installed CTC; but control of the new branch of the Metropolitan Railway from a CTC panel in the existing power signal box at Wembley Park seemed a most attractive proposition.

There was however, a stronger reason than might outwardly be apparent for the Metropolitan Railway to adopt a signalling technique that had hitherto been entirely American in its origin and nearly so in its application. Since 1925 the Superintendent of Signals and Telegraphs had been Major R F Morkill, born in Canada and from 1910 in the service of the Union

Switch & Signal Company. Before his war service in 1914-18, in which he had commanded the Railway Signal and Interlocking Company of the Royal Engineers, he had been Signal and Electrical Engineer of the Grand Trunk Railway in Canada. From his earlier association with the Union Switch he was always keenly interested in Westinghouse activities and the use of CTC on the Stanmore branch was an imaginative stroke. Actually its very success led to its early demise. From serving a tract of open country with three intermediate stations originally in little more than green fields, it became a fully built-up dormitory area and the line needed much more elaborate facilities to handle the very heavy traffic that developed. It must be one of the very few instances on the world's railways where CTC has led to so phenomenal an increase in passenger traffic.

For the record, a few details of the Wembley Park – Stanmore installation are worth recalling. The junction of the line at Wembley Park formed part of the all-electric interlocking at the latter station, but beyond the junction the signalling was automatic up to the immediate approach to the terminus at Stanmore. Three aspect colour light signals were used with electric train stops. At the terminus itself provision had to be made for the handling of goods as well as passenger traffic and while the station consisted of no more than two terminal roads on each side of an island platform, with a scissors crossover layout, connections were provided for access to goods sidings. All these connections were controlled from the CTC panel in Wembley Park signal box. Two forms of CTC were then being marketed by the US&S in the USA and for Stanmore what was known as the circuit code system was chosen, requiring no more than three line wires. In view of the prevalence today of highly sophisticated electronic methods of remote control, the relatively simple, semi-mechanical methods of setting up the control and indication codes may be recalled. By present day exponents of the art of remote control it is sometimes jokingly called 'Steam CTC'.

Below the two rows of thumb switches, which were in turn below the illuminated diagram on the control panel, were two rows of push buttons. These were known as start buttons, one each for the point and signal switches above them. When it was desired to change the position of any points or the aspect of a signal, the corresponding thumb switch was set and the start button pressed and then released. That initiated the setting up of a code, through the agency of a chain of electro-magnetic relays of a type similar to those used in automatic telephone switching, but rather larger and more robustly suitable for use in railway signalling. For a control code to be transmitted took approximately 2½ seconds, with another 2½ seconds for the indication code to be transmitted back to the panel, confirming that the remote function had responded correctly to the control set up by the panel operator. It was, of course, the time taken in the transmission of the codes that limited the fields in which 'Steam CTC' could be used.

All in all however the 1930s proved a time of notable development in signalling, even though some of the new apparatus and principles were not immediately remunerative. Projects on a much larger scale came several years later, when the fortunes of the Company had already taken a dramatic upward turn by the securing of the great contract for braking equipment for the entire stock of freight vehicles of the Polish State Railways.

10

The Air Brake in Europe and Asia ~ The Great Polish Contract ~ China

T H E S T O R Y has now to be taken back to 1928 when Clyde C Farmer, Director of Engineering of the Westinghouse Air Brake Company, was in Paris investigating conditions on the European Railways and the possibilities of introducing a modified form of the air brake, including graduated release, for freight trains. T J Aldridge, then on the staff of Major Peter, had just completed a twelve month tour of European railways as a result of being awarded one of the two Robert Blair Fellowships granted annually to university graduates with practical engineering training. On completion of his tour, it was thought that the information he had gathered and the contacts that he had made would be useful to Mr Farmer and he was sent over to Paris to assist in the development of a graduated release valve for European railways. When this development was completed, he went to Italy for two years as Brake Engineer of the Italian Westinghouse Company; but it was on his return to England in 1931 that the fruits of his earlier tour and the contacts and friendships he made in the course of it began to ripen. He was appointed Continental Engineer at a very interesting and critical time.

There were well-established Westinghouse companies in France, Germany and Russia as well as in Italy, each with its own recognised sphere of activity, but the field was particularly wide open in Poland and the Baltic States of Lithuania, Latvia and Estonia. In each of these the situation politically, economically and especially as far as communications were concerned was in a state of rapid evolution following the re-establishment of Poland as an independent sovereign state after the end of World War I and the granting of independence to the other three. The first years after the war had been anxious, tumultuous and involving a war between Poland and Lithuania and the situation generally had been very confused. So far as railways were concerned, the position was quite chaotic.

Until 1914 Poland as a country had not existed for more than a hundred years. It had been partitioned between Prussia, Austria and Russia and when the time had come for railways to be built each of those countries had constructed only what they needed for their own convenience without any regard for communication between cities in the three divisions of the country. Furthermore the owning Powers had built to their own standards and gauges – Germany and Austria to 4ft 8½ in and Russia to 5ft 0in. This latter was not really of much consequence, because at the end of World War I the whole network had been so devastated as to be virtually unusable. On the main line eastwards from Warsaw, for example, no fewer than 2,500 bridges and 539 out of 910 stations had been completely destroyed.

The Peace Treaties at the end of the war allocated 4,762 locomotives, 10,379 passenger carriages and 111,092 goods wagons to Poland; but while this was naturally appreciated the difficulties of rehabilitation were more of personnel than of equipment. Under the three separate 'colonial' types of administration, very few Poles had been allowed to hold positions of responsibility and with the newly-created Polish Ministry of Railways given no more than 48 hours notice to take over the railways (!) the situation was not exactly easy. In the forging of what was virtually a new State, giving it cohesion, unity and a coordinated corporate life, a first-class railway system was a basic necessity; and if the existing lines had been rebuilt that was just what they did not constitute.

The network had to be planned and built anew with much additional mileage. There had to be a unified gauge and standard practices in operation and equipment. The Ministry, set up after the armistice of 1918, was naturally some time in completing the groundwork of its task of rehabilitation. In March 1927, Polish industry was placed under the control of the State but the railways were given an autonomous and commercial administration of their own. In September 1930 the Minister of Communications, as the General Manager of the Polish State Railways, appointed a committee of management to act in his name.

By that time traffic had increased considerably. Many new 'link' lines had been built and important new business was being developed from the industrial regions of Silesia, northward to the new port of Gdynia at the seaward end of the Polish Corridor. Before the war the railways in the German zone were extensively equipped with the Westinghouse brake, as were also the 5 ft gauge lines operated on Russian principles, but the two lines running to the south and leading to Vienna and Prague were among those under Austrian influence and using a form of vacuum braking. Clearly the air brake would be standardised for the future; but the nature of the terrain and the traffic made it necessary to consider more advanced techniques than the standard Westinghouse equipment. The working of very heavy freight trains over steep gradients and equally the desirability of making fast running over the more level stretches, began to influence proposals for a complete re-equipment of the entire freight stock of the Polish State Railways (PKP). When this intention became known, there was naturally intense competitive interest in a project that would involve some 100,000 wagons, but before negotiations opened in earnest there came some exploratory trials on freight trains in Romania. This was already a Westinghouse area, but the need was for improved equipment in dealing with very heavy trains. Jack Aldridge, assisted by C F B Shattock and A J Ruane, went out and ran some trials, but these did not lead to any contracts.

Negotiations with the Polish State Railways began in 1932, conducted at top-management level by Captain Peter and technically in Poland by Jack Aldridge, A W Simmons and A J Ruane, Sales Engineer. The unprecedented magnitude of the job, worth in round figures about £5 million, made the financial arrangements and guarantees as vital as the engineering details and in this Captain Peter played an outstandingly skilful part. As negotiations proceeded so the competition increased. It was a new Battle of the Brakes on an international scale and for far higher stakes than any previously wagered. German interests were very deeply involved and they strove might and main to undermine our position, in the same way as Westinghouse and vacuum interest fought over the British railway position in the 1880s. The mastery in all matters of braking technology shown by Aldridge and Simmons deeply impressed the Polish engineers and gradually built up the complete confidence they came to place in Westinghouse.

Many years later when I was writing a biographical note about Captain Peter for the Railway Gazette at the time of his retirement, he recalled with a relish many episodes in what he called 'My private war with Germany'. He triumphed and the gratitude of the Company at the securing of such a contract could not have been better expressed than in the words of the Chairman, Lord Southborough, at the Annual General Meeting in 1935, thus:

It was in January 1934 that the press made the first announcement that we had signed a preliminary contract with the Polish State Railways in connection with the equipping of 29,000 wagons with air brakes and of 73,000 wagons with the continuous piping and couplings. The negotiations which had been carried on in Warsaw by Captain B H Peter, our Managing Director, and which resulted in the signing of that preliminary contract, were continued in London. A delegation of Polish Government officials, headed by Mr Julian Piasecki, the Vice-Minister of Communications, and Mr Adam Koc, the Vice-Minister of Finance, came to London. The result of these continued negotiations was that a final contract was signed between the Polish State Railways and our Company on April 24th, 1934, which was subsequently ratified and at the end of June 1934 passed into operation.

The work is being divided between England and Poland and satisfactory sub-contracts with Polish manufacturers of the highest standing have been made. A very happy relationship between ourselves and those with whom we are working there has been established.

The English portion of the work has provided and will continue to provide, employment for many additional men at our works in Chippenham and there can be no question that the contract is of great importance to our company. We have also made sub-contracts in this country, under which large quantities of raw materials will be delivered over a term of years and this has provided work for those employed in other industries.

We desire to pay a tribute to Mr Piaseck and to Mr Koc for the patient and courteous manner in which they conducted the negotiations with us. These gentlemen were thoroughly conversant with what was required for their railways and we were in the happy position of being able to supply the requirements in all respects. They conducted the negotiations in the most able manner and with great dispatch considering the magnitude of the contract and the many difficult problems which had to be faced and solved.

If I may say so, our experience of the conduct of the negotiations and of the subsequent business arrangements in Poland, has given us great satisfaction. We feel that we have entered into really friendly relations with the most important statesmen and officials in the country and that we may look forward to close cooperation and smooth working to bring this great railway development to a highly successful conclusion. Poland is making rapid progress, and Captain Peter and our officials out there have the greatest confidence in and respect of the country and its people.

As relative to the negotiations, I should also like to acknowledge with pleasure the valuable assistance rendered to us by the Export Credits Guarantee Department, in connection with the negotiating and financing of the contract. It was of paramount importance to us to have the advice and practical assistance of our Government.

When parting from the Polish contract for today, I must tell you how deeply indebted the Company is to Captain Peter, the Managing Director, for his able handling of the negotiations with our friends in Poland. He was of the greatest possible assistance to us politically and technically and I venture to believe that he was also able to do much to promote the interests of the Polish State Railways. Then, again, since the signing of the contract, Captain Peter has been constantly on the Continent watching the development of the business and we shall largely depend upon him for his support during the coming years. He has our grateful thanks.

Before coming to the technical details of the equipment, it is good to record also that on the signing of the contract in April 1934, staff salaries throughout the Company, which had been cut by 10% were restored to their former levels and we entered upon a period of abounding prosperity.

The equipment of the freight stock on the Polish State Railways was in two forms as indicated in the Chairman's speech. The first and by far the most important part was the complete equipment of 29,837 wagons, while the second was that of providing through piping and couplings for rather more than double that number of wagons. The vital necessity for all this equipment was that it should conform to all of 33 conditions laid down by the International Union of Railways (UIC) and be approved by that body as suitable for international traffic on the Continent of Europe. The

The sheer size of the Polish contract becomes apparent in this view.

Cylinder bodies being machined for the 9" x 8" brake cylinder supplied under the Polish Contract.

The Polish Contract again, showing the brake cylinder assembly shops at Chippenham. The casting dates on the bodies can be read as October 1934.

triple valves, inherently the heart and soul of the Westinghouse brake, were of the Lu.Vi type which, though it could be described as a development of the long-established 'Westinghouse Improved Triple Valve', had additional selective functions, namely:

- Empty and load
- Passenger and freight
- Plain and mountain.

In the first instance, when a wagon was not loaded or had a partial load so that the gross weight was not less than a predetermined figure (marked on a plate on each side of the wagon) a handle on the plate was placed in the empty position which so disposed the leverage of the brake rigging that a certain reduced degree of brake force was obtained, thus avoiding skidding of the wheels. When the wagon was loaded so that the gross weight was in excess of the prescribed figure, the handle was placed in the load position to give a higher value of brake force.

The distinction between 'passenger' and 'freight' operating was necessary to provide when wagons were included in passenger trains or when a train of freight wagons was run to passenger train schedules. This was provided for by having a changeover cock on the triple valve which had two operative positions. It stood normally in the 'freight' position giving the relatively slow times of application and release of the brakes required by the UIC regulations. When the wagon was marshalled in a passenger train the position of the cock was changed accordingly and by changing the passages in the triple valve gave the quicker rates of application and release required by the UIC in such service.

The 'Plain-Mountain' changeover cock, also mounted on the bulb of the triple valve, stood normally in the 'plain' position. When, however, the wagon was required to work over a route including long and severe gradients and the cock handle was moved over the 'mountain' position the exhaust of brake cylinder air was slowed down.

The type of changeover gear adopted was then relatively new in Europe. After the establishment of the UIC in 1926 the French Westinghouse Company had developed a scheme for 'empty-load' operation using two cylinders, one being used for an empty wagon and the second brought into operation when loaded; but just before the time we obtained the Polish contract, the Swedish firm of SAB Bromsregulator, of Malmö, brought out their empty-load changeover box with an ingenious and very compact design of automatic slack adjustor in the brake tie rod and arrangements were made to include this Swedish equipment in the apparatus supplied to the Polish State Railways. The SAB Brake Regulator was particularly attractive in that it had a double-action, working automatically in both directions. It increased brake shoe clearances that were too small and decreased those that were too large.

The securing of a contract of such magnitude in the face of intense international competition was an outstanding achievement in itself, quite apart from the beneficial way it affected every single member of the Company's staff and the prosperity it brought to the Borough of Chippenham. But traditionally it had always been the Westinghouse way to consolidate the good business relations evident at the moment of signing a contract by the most efficient and cordial personal service during the execution. With the Polish contract it was naturally essential to have a strong team resident in Warsaw, and the assignment was of such importance that Donald Brown himself, Chief Brake Engineer, headed that team. He had with him two men of wide experience and exceptional ability in S E W (George) Stokes, and C B E Cresswell. Of Stokes, one of the greatest characters I have ever met, it could be said that he was born into signalling. His father I W Stokes, originally on the Great Western, went out to Bombay in 1903 to become the first Signal Engineer of the Great Indian Peninsula Railway, and his eldest son, 'George' as we always knew him, joined Westinghouse as a pupil in Chippenham in 1921. How, through outdoor experience in London, Liverpool and the Argentine he rose to become resident engineer for the big Cardiff installation of colour light signals on his father's old railway, would almost fill a book of its own. In the course of this Westinghouse had no finer ambassador. His selection as '2 i/c' to Donald Brown in Poland was felicitous beyond measure.

Ted Cresswell first became acquainted with Westinghouse products on the Southern Railway, which he joined in 1923 when the first dc electric trains were being built for the 'Chatham' line electrification between Victoria and Orpington. For several years he was at that country-end of the electric service, maintaining the Westinghouse brake equipment on the trains. In the course of that work, by his ability and charming personality, he became a marked man, so much so that when the Polish contract was secured Westinghouse approached the Southern Railway and asked if they would release him. We wanted him in Poland. So he joined Westinghouse, to become another ambassador of rare quality. How he, with George Stokes and his wife escaped from Poland at the beginning of the war is an adventure referred to in a later chapter.

Switching the story of Westinghouse exports from Eastern Europe to China, in the early 1930s the British locomotive building industry secured some important orders for locomotives of designs that had previously been supplied from America and for which American drawings were actually furnished to the British contractors. These included powerful units of the 2-8-2 mixed traffic and 4-6-2 passenger types built by Nasmyth Wilson & Company of Manchester and by the North British Locomotive Company in Glasgow. These were specified as having the 6ET Westinghouse brake equipment with the large cross-compound type of air compressors. Both of these designs were for no more than moderate-sized locomotives compared to the giant 4-8-4s, twenty-four of which were built in the Vulcan Foundry Limited in 1934-35. There was nothing American about the design of these latter, which were wholly British; but of course the 6ET brake equipment was becoming standard on the Chinese railway and the new Vulcan locomotives were so equipped. The Chinese market was then being carefully developed by the company though, unhappily, the political and military activities that eventuated brought this promising business to an end.

The 6ET brake equipment was an important development of the standard automatic air brake that included independent control of the engine and tender brakes.[1] In the driver's cab there are two brake valves. Of these the 'H6' controls the automatic brake throughout the train, operating the brakes on the engine and tender through the medium of the 6E distributing valve and the brakes on each vehicle through the triple valves in the ordinary way. But with the H6 it is possible to release the train brakes while still holding the engine and tender brakes applied. The engine and tender brakes could then be partially or completely released as required. This was a valuable and much appreciated feature as it greatly simplified the handling of long trains. More accurate stops could be made and with the train brakes released and the slack in the couplings closed up, it was also a great help in restarting a heavy train.

The independent control of the engine and tender brakes was effected through a separate brake valve known as the S6. This provided a 'straight air' control and its operating handle would be in the 'running' position at all times when the engine, tender and train brakes were being operated simultaneously. The S6 valve would not be touched in such conditions. But with the brake applied throughout, that on the engine and tender could be wholly or partially released by moving the S6 handle to the release position. The necessary pneumatic interlocking and coordinating of these operations was effected through the 6E distributing valve on the locomotive. Similarly if the train brakes were released and the handle of the H6 valve was in the 'running' position, a simple 'straight air' control could be applied to the engine and tender brakes.

Just at the time of writing this chapter, I learned that the Chinese Minster of Railways had signed an order sending one of the giant Vulcan 4-8-4 locomotives to the National Railway Museum at York as a mark of Sino-British friendship. But he

The Chinese Locomotive. This photograph has been provided by, and reproduced with the kind permission of the National Railway Museum, York

Chinese Locomotive

The Chinese Government Railways Class KF7 number 607 was indeed donated to the NRM at York – and is still there. The locomotive was built in 1935, with a 4-8-4 configuration. The locomotive was withdrawn from service in 1981 and transferred to the National Railway Museum on 25th March 1983, some two years after Nock wrote this section. The loco is currently on static display within the Great Hall of the Museum.

added the interesting proviso that as all of them were still in full use, it might be a little time before one could be released (see Panel). It is indeed a testimony to British design and workmanship that locomotives and their equipment built 45 years ago should have so survived the vicissitudes of war, civil war and general upheaval as to be so useful today that one of them could not be immediately released to implement this remarkable gesture of goodwill. When one of these huge engines does arrive, it will be good to have an example of the 6ET brake equipment and huge cross-compound air compressor on show at York.

1 When E C Sharpe commented on Nock's manuscript he commented 'Really Ossie, all out of timescale'.

11

Exciting Years Before World War II

THE FIVE YEARS leading up to the outbreak of the Second World War proved a formative period for British railway engineering and operating practice. It was a time that brought a closer appreciation on the main line railways of the intricate relation between speed, signalling layout and brake power. Although the work that was done at that time did not bring a great deal of business in to the Company it linked the activities of the major branches of Westinghouse activity. From the very inception of electric traction on the London Underground Railways the fundamental relations evolved, and their representation had formed the cornerstone of operating practice. Up to that point the same intensity of working had not occurred on the main line railways, and it was not until the somewhat anomalous situation on the LNER over the running of the high-speed Silver Jubilee Express between York and Northallerton had arisen, that the importance of the problem struck home.

This critical situation affected the Signal and Brake departments of Westinghouse in apparently quite unconnected ways, though an onlooker from outside could see clearly enough that they were directly linked. The signalling between York and Northallerton had been designed as a compromise to provide maximum line capacity for trains the running speeds of which ranged from about 50 to 75mph. To maximise utilisation of the line the majority of these trains, both passenger and fast freight, were very heavy and as such had the most favourable characteristics for the performance of the standard vacuum brake.

As explained in an earlier chapter however the make-up of the high-speed Silver Jubilee train was exactly the reverse, and as its success foreshadowed the introduction of other similar trains, the step was taken of converting the three-aspect colour light signalling on that critical section to four aspect. It was fortunate in a way that the searchlight had been used for this installation because the conversion could be made very simply – physically at any rate – by mounting a single unit, capable of showing a yellow light, above the existing searchlight signals. This immediately solved the braking problem between York and Northallerton, because the braking distance from the first warning – now the 'double yellow' – to the red, was doubled. The Silver Jubilee, and the beautiful Coronation train of 1937 could henceforth run at their maximum line speed over this section.

So far as the signalling of these high speed trains was concerned however the modifications between York and Northallerton were a mere 'drop in the

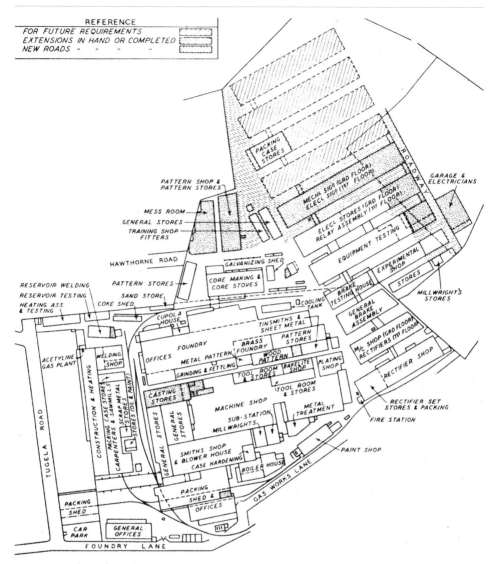

On June 11th, 1938, Modern Transport *published an article entitled 'Railway Equipment Manufacture. A Famous British Enterprise. Growth of Westinghouse Works at Chippenham.' From that article we reproduce the plan of the works in Chippenham as they were at that time, when some 2,700 staff were employed on site, with 300 more at York Way.*

ocean'! The rest of the East Coast Main Line, 392.7 miles between King's Cross and Edinburgh, was mechanically signalled, and the operating instructions involved the practice of 'double-blocking'. Although the safety record in working these trains was, as yet, immaculate the feeling was always there that one day a signalman might make an error and give one of these trains

inadequate warning. Better brakes were needed. After his appointment as Chief Mechanical Engineer of the LMS, W A Stanier had introduced the Great Western type of direct admission valve, which gave an improved performance of the ordinary vacuum brake. The Great Western Railway benefitted in any case by using a higher degree of vacuum than any of the other companies by using a cross-head pump to maintain the vacuum instead of the ejector. But on the LNER Sir Nigel Gresley confided to Captain Peter that he did not like the direct admission valve and was looking for something better. L J LeClair, and the specialist vacuum brake designer A G Brackenbury got to work, and by the end of 1935 the new Quick Service Application (QSA) valve was sufficiently developed to be fitted to a King's Cross articulated suburban train for trials.

With the QSA valve, when making a brake application, a reduction of the vacuum in the train pipe made in the usual manner caused the quick service valve on each vehicle to effect a further local reduction in the brake pipe, thus increasing the speed of propagation throughout the brake pipe to an extent not otherwise possible. As each quick-service valve opened and let air locally in to the brake pipe, a separate stream of air was admitted at the same time into the brake cylinder. That stream of air bore a definite proportion to the volume admitted to the brake pipe through the ejector, or driver's brake valve, and to this volume let into the brake pipe by the quick service valve. Thus, at all times the amount of air admitted into the brake pipe and the cylinder was under the direct control of the driver, and did not depend on the uncertain factors of volume reservoirs with leakage chokes, as embodied in earlier forms of vacuum rapid-acting valves. With the QSA valve a service brake application was obtained at the rear of the train in about one-third of the time required with the standard vacuum brake.

The effect in actual running was to make the vacuum, with QSA valves, approximately equal in retardation capacity to the standard air brake. Tests on the LNER showed that from a speed of 90mph the stopping distance from an emergency application was reduced from 4,750 ft with the standard vacuum brake to 4,300 ft – a useful saving of 450 ft. It was not enough to provide safe working up to 90mph with the signal spacing of the three-aspect installation between York and Northallerton, and four aspects were essential.

Signalling in the North Eastern Area of the LNER was one of the principal points of interest in British operating practice in the later 1930s, because of the rapid development of relay interlocking. As in the case of four-aspect colour light signalling on the Southern, Westinghouse lost the first contract, the epoch-marking installation at Thirsk; but after that all new work in the North Eastern Area came our way for many years afterwards. It was a notable time in the Engineering department at York Way, King's Cross. In the mid-1920s the Signal Estimating department was in the charge of Mostyn R Gardner, a quiet man whose modest demeanour belied his abilities. He had been with the Ministry of Transport, and was an expert in electrical supply systems, particularly in the design and operation of sub-systems. He then went out to Brazil to commission some installations of hand generator interlockings, out in the back of beyond, where his ability to improvise, and 'make-do' with none but the most primitive appliances sent the local appreciation of Westinghouse sky-high. In the meantime, his assistant in the Signal Estimating department, Charles F D Venning, had taken over, of whom I can write as a much appreciated colleague, and as a close friend. He was a highly skilled circuit designer, whose talents were used to the great advantage of Westinghouse during that exciting period when the art of relay interlocking was being developed.

When the time came for Leeds 'New' station to be resignalled it was felt that the system of route switching that A E Tattersall of the LNER had pioneered at Thirsk was not suitable for the track layout at a busy

Relay Interlocking

The concept of Relay Interlocking is not fully described in Nock's manuscript. Relays are electro-mechanical switches – a small current applied to a coil causes a mechanical switch to move, allowing a greater current to pass through contacts of the switch. This is directly analogous to transistor technology, and the use of many, many relays combined together is directly analogous to the many hundreds of thousands of transistors in a modern microprocessor. Relay Interlockings therefore provide the same functionality as mechanical lever frames, preventing unsafe movements of points or the display of incorrect signal aspects, but all electrically. Much more complex systems could be designed using relays rather than mechanical frames, and the system was far easier to modify and could control much larger areas.

city station, where there were engine movements, apart from through running. The motive power was entirely steam. So, although the principle of relay interlocking (see Panel) was retained the functions were all individually operated from separate thumb switches on the control panel. In retrospect it was rather a 'messy' job. One of the characteristics to which the signalmen took some time to get accustomed was that if they attempted to operate a function that was locked, and turned the appropriate thumb-switch, it was necessary to restore the switch to its original position when the function did not respond. Otherwise that function would operate once the locking was freed – often at an inconvenient moment. It was to provide simplicity of working, within the continuing desire of the LNER to have route switching, that Charles Venning designed his notable One Control Switch system of route relay interlocking.

It was first used in the resignalling of Hull Paragon station in 1937 – 8, a third generation Westinghouse job. At the turn of the century it was a typical McKenzie & Holland mechanical installation, with tremendous arrays of semaphore arms covering every conceivable route. Then came the change to electro-pneumatic operation in 1908 by the 'Power Company'. Much of the ground gear was still in excellent condition in the 1930s and was used in the new route relay interlocking.

The Publicity department at King's Cross, then under Bert Hichisson, seized upon the initial letters of the description One Control Switch, and neatly turned it into the familiar OCS, known by every railwayman in pre-nationalisation days as signifying 'On Company's Service', and advertised it accordingly; but the young men of the Signal Estimating department had a more homely appellation for it: 'Old Charlie's System'. The second OCS panel box was at Northallerton, brought into service on the very day war was declared in September 1939, and it had already been specified for the enormous installation at York, the completion of which was however much delayed by the war.

In the meantime events in signalling must be traced back to 1935, on the Southern, when it was the turn of the Western Section, the former London & South Western Railway, to begin receiving the benefit of major resignalling works. As with all previous schemes on the Southern the actual installation was done by the railway forces, but Westinghouse were the suppliers in a big way of the necessary equipment, including a large all-electric interlocking frame of 309 levers at Waterloo with the two outer sections each of 75 levers at right-angles to the central one which had 159 levers. The approach lines were resignalled as far out as Hampton Court Junction, 13¼ miles, and the section from Clapham Junction westward saw the implementation on an intensive scale of the multiple aspect signal philosophy postulated by W J Thorrowgood in his historic paper before the IRSE in 1926. Although the section is quadruple track throughout, provision had to be made on both fast and slow lines for intensive electric suburban service, while on the main lines express passenger trains from Bournemouth and the West of England regularly ran at speeds up to 70mph. To meet the former requirement the four-aspect colour light signals were, in places, spaced at no more than 615 yds apart, with suburban trains using the double-yellow as their 'all clear'. This, according to the modern 'W' curve of British Railways gave adequate service braking distance from a speed of

The old semaphore signals at Hull Paragon, replaced under the resignalling scheme.

New Searchlight Signals and Route indicators at Hull Paragon.

The complexity of the resignalling at Hull Paragon is apparent when looking at this track plan, included in the Westinghouse brochure 'Route Relay Interlocking and resignalling at Paragon Station, Hull, L & NE Railway'.

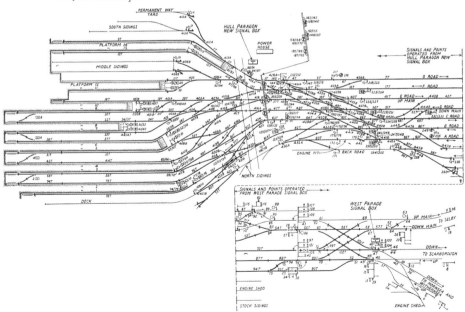

May 1939, and the Drawing Office is working hard on a South African Interlocking Project. Jeppe scheme plan is on the wall.

a 7 by 7 square with positions for up to 49 lamps lighted selectively to form letters or figures indicating routes or platforms. The third innovation, so far as the Southern and Westinghouse were concerned, was the use of disc-type banner signals, solenoid operated, for shunt and subsidiary purposes. To avoid the use of miniature coloured lights on these discs, at night they were floodlit from a special external unit.

The installation staff of the Southern Railway working to standard circuits and standard equipment, had by that time become so familiar with the various techniques that major 'openings' were taken completely as a matter of course. I well remember the weekend of June 27-8 1936, on which the outermost section of the Waterloo job, to Hampton Court Junction, was brought into service, not because I was personally involved in the signalling, but because I was riding up from Portsmouth on the footplate of one of the non-stop expresses, then steam hauled.

At 11.00am on the Sunday morning one might perhaps have expected some slight technical 'hang-overs' from the night of changeover; but no. Running on time we entered the newly finished colour light area at 77mph and ran with clear signals to Clapham Junction. It was only on the final section where there had *not* been any changeover work in the night that there was some slight delay. The new plant at Waterloo itself was brought into service on 18 October 1936, replacing the famous 'A' box which had spanned the tracks since May 1892.

60mph. The Southern electric trains at that time were using the ordinary standard Westinghouse air brake. For the express passenger steam hauled trains there was ample service braking distance from the 'double-yellow' to the 'red', from an initial speed of 70mph. These trains were then fitted with the standard vacuum brake.

While the main signal aspects followed the principle of multiple aspect signalling established in the Southern since 1925, there were three changes so far as the auxiliaries were concerned. At main line junctions, approached and passed by many trains at full speed, the 'splitting signal' was abandoned for ever, and in its place was installed the position light junction indicator, as first used experimentally in the form of red neon tubes by the LNER at Thirsk, but on the Southern as a row of three white lights. No junction indication at all was displayed for a train taking the straight road. Except that five white lights are now used, this form of junction indicator is now standard on British Railways.

In the approaches to the terminal points, and other areas of slow running where the projector type of route indicator had previously been used, an entirely new type was installed, the so-called 'Theatre-sign', or multiple lamp type, consisting of

Signal boxes at Waterloo are famed for their longevity, for while the mechanical frame of 1892, for which W F Burleigh designed the interlocking, lasted for 44 years, its successor, the 309-lever all electric style 'L' is still in service today, 45 years after its commissioning.[1]

While these notable developments on the British home railways were in progress a sustained attempt was made to market the double-wire system of mechanical operation abroad, but with no more than limited success. In the countries of the British colonial empire installations were made, such as Nigeria, the Gold Coast (now Ghana) and in Palestine;[2] but one of the most interesting was the equipment of a series of stations on the Iraqi State Railways. From India, business in single line token instruments of the Neale type, both of the ball token and tablet varieties,

Original caption says: 'For safe operation on Single line sections of rail roads use is made of the Neale's Tablet Instrument produced by WB&S Co. Some of the components produced from Bakelite materials are shown in the foreground.'

remained brisk and it involved us on the design staff in London with many variations of the age-old problem of getting a quart into a pint pot, as extra safety features were specified by some of the Indian railways to meet their particular operating conditions. The existence of a pair of instruments, fully wired up, in the demonstration room adjacent to the drawing office was invaluable on giving some ideas as to where we might tuck in extra contacts and such like. At home, with the collapse of the British Power Railway Signal Company, and our own business expanding, several of their men joined our design staff, one, B C di Marco, to attain very high office (Commercial Director) in later years.

The London laboratory of the Rectifier department, with staff and equipment so assiduously built up by Major Peter, was on the brink of a major breakthrough in the field of selenium rectifiers in 1937. After the first demonstration of the rectification effect of selenium, as far back as 1877, a long period elapsed before the process was taken up again, at first by a researcher named Presser, in Germany in 1927. The British patents relating to his work were closely studied, and active development began in London, by Dr A L Williams and L E Thompson, who later became Group Managing Director of Westinghouse. By 1939 Thompson, in collaboration with A Jenkins had established the selenium process in a manner that integrated a highly scientific operation with relatively simple production methods. The efficiency of this rectifier, given the trade name 'Westalite', was far in advance of our competitors. This was due to appreciation of the role of controlled impurities of the required type and quantity in the selenium layer, in the chemically treated surface layer, and in the tin-cadmium-thallium contacting electrode. Mass production methods were fully exploited by preparing large areas of strip of the finished product, and finally punching, or guillotining to any required size. The Company was thus well placed to deal with mass production of large Government orders for rectifiers received during the war years.

In 1935 there had occurred an event that would have stirred the shades of Saxby, Easterbrook, the partners in McKenzie & Holland, and other fighters over patents in the pioneer days. The General Railway Signal Company issued a writ against Westinghouse claiming damages for infringement of patent by reason of the CTC installation at Stanmore, Metropolitan Railway, referred to in Chapter 8 of this book. It was a surprising action, because the Stanmore CTC followed precisely the practice already well established by the Union Switch & Signal Company in the USA; and there that company was in a state of competitive and amicable coexistence with the GRS. The two companies shared the market in CTC installations, and no case of patent infringement had arisen between the two. Certainly, in November 1927, the American GRS had obtained Letters Patent in Great Britain for '. . . improvements relating to Signalling and Power Operated Switch Systems for Railways', and the British GRS Company had become the registered legal owner of this patent. The action, in the British High Court of Justice, was clearly an attempt to stifle any pretensions Westinghouse might have had to further CTC installations in the United Kingdom, and the plaintiff's case was couched in fairly general terms. It proved to be a case of great length and complexity, fought for no less than 38 full days in the Chancery Division of the High Court, before Mr Justice Morton. Mr Lionel F Heald KC led for the plaintiffs, while Westinghouse briefed no less celebrated a barrister than Sir Stafford Cripps.

The hearing took place at the end of 1938. At that time our Secretary, J Griffith

Hall, himself a barrister, used frequently to take a light lunch at the Georgian Tea Room on King's Cross station that I also used to frequent, and he told me of many interesting asides on the proceedings. One was of the marvellous grasp that Sir Stafford Cripps acquired of the intricacies of circuit design, and of the finer points of signalling – so much so at times as to mildly embarrass some of our top men! A great deal was thought to hinge upon the prior art, up to August 6 1925, when the American GRS had applied for a patent in Great Britain, eventually accepted, as previously mentioned, in November 1927.

In this respect Westinghouse, with a far longer history of invention and achievement was in a strong position, and the question had arisen, as stated by Mr Justice Morton in his summing up, and eventually judgement:

> Was the patent in suit, in the original form, invalid upon all or any of the grounds stated in the Pleadings and particulars? These grounds are:
> a) That this alleged invention, the subject of the patent was not new on 6 August 1925, but had been disclosed in the United Kingdom in certain publications and by certain prior users,
> b) That the said alleged invention was obvious and did not involve any inventive step having regard to (1) general common knowledge in the art of controlling railway signals and points on 6 August 1925, and (2) the public knowledge existing on that date in relation to the said art, and disclosed in the said publications and alleged prior users, and plans and descriptions relating thereto.

In his cross-examination Sir Stafford Cripps tied the plaintiff's witnesses into some rare knots, and his final speech made this remarkable statement, after having called no witnesses:

> The plaintiff's witnesses have been most generous in the admissions they have made,

and I cannot see that there are any other facts that are required for the proof of the defendant's case.

Although the outcome was a triumph for Westinghouse, with Mr Justice Morton holding, on February 1 1939, that the claims in the plaintiff company's specification were so ambiguous and obscure that they did not specifically or clearly define the nature and scope of the monopoly claimed and that no infringement had been established, the case had created immense interest, and the report on it occupied 2½ closely printed pages in *The Railway Gazette* of February 17 1939. There were in addition certain points of patent law that arose, of much interest to the legal profession, also discussed editorially in *The Railway Gazette* of the same date.

While the year 1938 had seen the culmination of the involvement of the Signal side of Westinghouse in this momentous patent action, the Brake department became almost incidentally concerned in another historic railway event. On the LNER, trials were proceeding with the QSA valve with coaching stock of the high speed streamlined trains. Until the end of 1937 these, which of necessity had to be conducted on Sundays when the line

was relatively clear, could not have been conveniently arranged from London. There was only one Silver Jubilee set, and this was in Newcastle from Friday night until Monday morning. With the introduction of the Coronation service there were two train sets, one each remaining in London and Edinburgh respectively over the weekend. The tests were usually made from King's Cross to Peterborough and back, and a normal schedule of stops was:

Knebworth (communication cord)
from 60mph
    Langford Bridge
from 90mph
    St Neots
from 70mph
    Connington (down)
from 90mph
    Connington (up)
from 60mph
    Offord
from 80mph
    Tempsford
from 70mph
    Cambridge Junction (Hitchin)
from 60mph

The streamlined 'Pacific' engines of Class 'A4' were used, and the graphic record of

Believed to be the Dynamometer car used on the Mallard run

Mallard Run

It is not clear why Nock doesn't name the locomotive involved in this astounding feat – an unbroken record. LNER A4 Pacific 4468 'Mallard' of 1938 is one of the most famous steam locomotives that was ever built. Mallard was named by her designer, Sir Nigel Gresley, when he thought of the name whilst feeding ducks at Salisbury Hall! When first built the loco cost £8,500, and the radical streamlining of her and her sister locomotives was seen as iconic of the modern age of the 1930s. Withdrawn from service in 1963, Mallard is maintained in superb condition and displayed at the National Railway Museum in York.

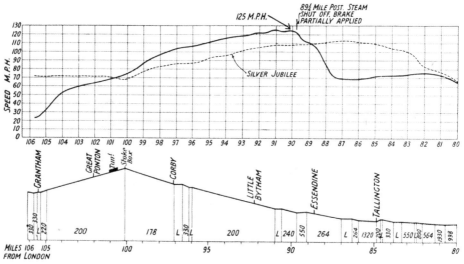

From the Westinghouse Review of April 1949, this is the official dynamometer chart recording the speed and braking – both world records.

each stop made by the Westinghouse test staff working under N G Cadman. On all these tests L J LeClair, as Sales Engineer, maintained top level liaison with the senior railway staff present, while of course A G Brackenbury, the designer of the QSA valve was always there. There were many incidental jobs to be done and a number of us, not directly connected with vacuum brake design, were roped in from time to time. In the course of this work arrangements were made for a test on Sunday July 3 1938.

The party duly turned up at King's Cross, and found to their surprise two unusual things about the train: firstly, it included the Darlington dynamometer car, and secondly

the engine was a strange one to them, with a crew speaking in strong Yorkshire accents, instead of the familiar Cockneys from King's Cross 'top shed'. Comments on these points were passed off lightly, until they started away, and then it was revealed that brake trials that day were merely a cloak for the real purpose of the journey, which was nothing less than to break the world record for railway speed! How the streamlined 'Pacific' engine was pressed to attain the tremendous, for those days, maximum speed of 126mph on the descent from Stoke summit towards Peterborough is now a matter of history; but another matter of history concerning the science of braking is not so well known. (See Panel).

Mallard with the dynamometer car coupled immediately behind the tender

The crew of Mallard on her record breaking run, Fireman Bray, Driver Duddington and Inspector S Jenkins

After the speed record had been attained steam was shut off and brakes applied at a speed of 124mph – a world record for braking on a steam train, at over 2 miles a minute. The dynamometer car chart showed that within 3½ seconds of shutting off steam the full effects of braking were well in maximum action. Deceleration was smooth and even. Indeed in the saloon next to the dynamometer car tea had been served, and only faint ripples registered the change in speed. Although as a result of this series of trials, and ones made subsequent to this record run, Sir Nigel Gresley decided that QSA valves should be fitted to all the high speed trains of the LNER, the completion of the job was interrupted by the war, and in actual fact the success of the QSA proved both the culmination and the swan-song of vacuum brake equipment for high speed operation.

1 Waterloo signal box with its Westinghouse style 'L' Power Lever Frame was commissioned on October 18 1936, as the final part of the resignalling project to modernise the main lines to Hampton Court Junction from Waterloo. Four aspect coloured light signalling was provided except at Waterloo station where there were some two and three aspect signals provided. The signalbox lever frame remained in use for 48 years until its operation was taken over by a new NX Panel on February 5 1984 in the same signalbox. Waterloo box was closed October 30 1990 and the entrance–exit panel moved to a temporary box (to allow construction of Waterloo International station). The signal box was demolished to make way for the Waterloo Eurostar terminal. The panel/ temp box finally closed when control of Waterloo station passed to the Wimbledon Signal Centre on April 21 1991.

2 Clearly the geography of this area has changed considerably since Nock wrote this chapter, but to avoid confusion the 1980s terminology has been left unaltered.

12
World War II ~ A Time of Epochal Changes

THE OUTBREAK OF WAR had immediate and serious effects from end to end of the Company's activities. For some time previously staff in London and Chippenham had been training, in their own time, in Air Raid Precautions (ARP), while arrangements were contemplated for the transfer to Chippenham of the sales, publicity and all engineering staff as a temporary wartime measure. In Government circles it had been expected that the Declaration of War on Nazi Germany would be followed, possibly within hours, by severe air raids; but while by moving to Chippenham it was hoped that the dislocation of design and other essential engineering work would be minimised, acquisition of the premises to accommodate the London staff had only just been concluded and removal could not take place immediately. Much temporary ARP work was done at York Way by volunteers from many departments of the Company, and as a trained warden (under Hertfordshire County Council) I was charged by Griffith Hall to supervise this work. Much of it was done in breathless haste, but fortunately the expected air raids did not come, and having prepared sandbagged shelters, and such precautions as we could against poison gas, we turned to the far bigger upheaval of moving to Chippenham.

For the great majority of the London staff and their families, it was a shattering experience amid the hazards and uncertainties of war to leave the environment and personal associations of a lifetime and go out virtually into the unknown. It was generally appreciated that the move had been arranged by the Company as much with personal welfare in mind as to maintain continuity of essential work, but the individual difficulties that arose, together with the total absence of any enemy attacks on London, tended to make some members of staff feel that the whole operation had been unnecessary. Nearly a year was to pass, indeed, before the justification of this act of Management foresight was to be read in letters of fire! For Chippenham too, though in a different way, the upheaval was no less profound. Many Westinghouse families who had spare rooms gave accommodation to evacuated Londoners; unfinished new houses were hurriedly completed and shared in many cases by two families. There was a general spirit of making do, not helped however by the conditions of total blackout at night. That early period, before the Nazi onslaught of May 1940, is sometimes referred to as the 'Phoney War'; but for some of us in Westinghouse there was nothing phoney about it. One needed to mention one word only – Poland!

The great contract for equipping the Polish State Railways wagon stock with air brakes was nearly but not quite finished when war came in September 1939. It had been sufficiently advanced for Donald Brown to return home earlier in the year leaving the intrepid S E W (George) Stokes as engineer in charge, and with him Ted Cresswell. The war had begun with Warsaw itself being struck as with a thunderbolt. At first Stokes and his wife, and equally Ted Cresswell, intended to stick it out, doing all they could to help their friends in the Polish State Railways; but very soon they realised they were in danger of being cut off by the advancing Germans. All communications had been destroyed, the Polish Government and the British Consulate and Embassy had left Warsaw and the city was being ceaselessly bombed.

How the three of them escaped, to slip stealthily through the forest that divided Poland from Lithuania in a nightmare journey of three weeks by car, train, but mostly on foot, through the narrowing corridor between advancing Germans from the west and Russians from the east, was an adventure that makes some of the escapades of 'James Bond 007' read like a mere game of 'cops and robbers'. For those who would read the full story of this incredible episode in the lives of two Westinghouse men, and a Westinghouse wife who was badly wounded in the process, see Blackwood's Magazine for 1940. An excerpt of this magnificent article is included as Appendix 2.

Reporting more prosaically upon the effects of war on the Polish brake contract, at the Annual General Meeting of the Company in February 1940 Lord Southborough recalled:

That the final month of the Company's financial year synchronised with a hiatus in all normal business relations. All work on the Polish contract halted. The Polish Government had told the Company that promissory notes due for payment after October 1939 could not be met. The contract had run exceptionally smoothly and up to October the Polish Government had promptly met all payments. In view of the new situation it had been considered necessary to make substantial provision in the accounts against eventualities in connection with the contract.

It is sad to think that a great work on which so much diligence, technical skill and hard effort had been lavished should have been blasted to destruction in this way, and what was left of it used for a very different purpose from that originally intended.

Another Westinghouse job that had loomed large in the 1930s, the little Stanmore CTC installation, had a more peaceful ending in the early months of the war. It is strange to recall that this plant, over which the long drawn-out lawsuit was fought between 1935 and 1939 was even then in the process of being replaced. Following the establishment of the London Passenger Transport Board in 1933, immediate consideration was given to the development of the Metropolitan Line, and to the provision of direct running connections between the extension line and the Bakerloo Tube. As part of this enterprise the track layout at Wembley Park was completely remodelled, and connection to the Stanmore Line made by burrowing, rather than a surface junction. The whole of the signalling was replaced with standard interlocking frames, equipment and circuitry of Underground rather than Metropolitan type.

Reverting once again to personal matters; that poignant autumn of 1939 saw the severance of another long standing Westinghouse connection, because on November 6 my old chief in the Power Signal Section of the Drawing Office,

GB 82 56 b
Nur für den **Dienstgebrauch**
Bild Nr. F. 867 b/40-038 (Lfl. 3)
Aufnahme vom 18. 9. 40

Chippenham
Maschinenfabrik
„Westinghouse Brake & Signal Co. Ltd."
Länge (westl. Greenw.): 2° 06' 33"   Breite: 51° 27' 53"
Mißweisung: − 11° 12' (Mitte 1941)   Zielhöhe über NN 61 m
Maßstab etwa 1 : 9 100

Genst. 5. Abt.   August 1941
Karte 1 : 100 000
GB/E 32

August 1941. This photograph taken by the Luftwaffe clearly identified Chippenham as a 'machine factory' belonging to the Westinghouse Brake & Signal Co Ltd. Fortunately whilst the London office suffered during the blitz, the Chippenham site was to escape lightly.

Walter Allan Pearce, died at the age of 76. An editorial note in the *The Railway Gazette* paid an eloquent tribute to him:

... signal engineering loses one who played a prominent part in the story of the development which has wrought such a change in ideas and methods since the end of the last century, and left a deep impression thereon. Brought into contact with the designers of some of the earlier really practical power-signal apparatus in the United States, where he spent some time in the early nineties, Mr Pearce was later associated with the introduction of the electro-pneumatic system into Great Britain at Bishopsgate, Great Eastern Railway, where an American type frame was installed during 1898 . . . [*The Railway Gazette* concluded:] 'Of a very retiring disposition, Mr Pearce mixed little in engineering assemblies, and his rare gifts were consequently not nearly so widely known as they deserved to be. Many of his designs are still firm favourites, and their excellent performance, years after he produced them, is a lasting tribute to the judgment and technical skill which commanded the admiration of all who were privileged to know him.

Turning now to matters directly connected with the propagation of the war effort, there is first of all the very important practice of braking for road vehicles. From its rather shaky start in the 1920s, the business had been gradually built up commercially under Tom Barty, Sales Engineer, who had originally come to Westinghouse, before the amalgamation, from the Caledonian Railway, primarily to foster the business in steam heating. On the design and technical development H M Hoather, who had come to the Brake Drawing Office from Imperial College, joined A W Simmons to specialise in road brake work, and maintain technical liaison with the manufacturers in the road haulage industry. Primarily the air brake on a road vehicle is analogous to a 'straight air' brake on a train, in that the operation of the driver's brake valve admits air directly from the reservoir to the brake cylinders. The brake valve however required to be of a type that would be operated by a foot pedal.

On petrol or diesel driven vehicles, the compressor, providing the necessary air, was driven from some part of the engine or gear box, and so could not conveniently be stopped when the required pressure was reached on the reservoir. The equipment therefore included an unloader valve, which when pressure had reached its predetermined maximum value sealed off the reservoir, and opened the compressor delivery pipe to atmosphere. On a trolley bus the control was different in that the compressor was driven by a separate electric motor, which could be stopped when required. The reservoir had connected to it a governor unit, mounted on the floor plate of the driver's compartment, which broke the electric circuit to the compressor motor when the pressure in the reservoir reached the required maximum figure, and restarted the motor when the pressure fell to a lower limit.

To the knowledgeable outside, the Westinghouse brake was associated with the 'chug-chug' of the steam operated air pump, so familiar as once to be mentioned in one of Ian Hay's popular novels. A very different type had been developed for electric trains, and for a road vehicle, a still smaller design was evolved. Kenneth H Leech, Chief Draughtsman of the Brake department, an enthusiast for any form of engine, steam and internal-combustion alike, was a specialist and supreme expert in compressor design, and under his direction a range of really beautiful machines produced. For they *were* small. They had to be and externally looked like internal combustion engines. Although it was developed to a considerable extent in after years, the range was already well tried and ready for quantity production by the outbreak of war, when the services of Leech himself were commandeered for a very special assignment.

When an air brake was fitted to a trailer, air was usually supplied to a separate reservoir on the trailer from the reservoir on the towing vehicle; but there were several varieties of trailer brake, according to the requirements of the particular service. As the war developed, a very large number of brake sets for road vehicles was built at Chippenham and saw active service in many war zones.

From the Westinghouse Review *of March 1953, this photograph shows the Guard of Honour presented by the Westinghouse Home Guard detachment for Her Majesty Queen Mary when she visited the works.*

Signalling work began to take different forms. At Crewe, one of the 'key' junctions of the national railway network, the replacement of the old London & North Western type power interlocking frame, by the modern Westinghouse 'L' type, was pushed vigorously ahead, and the LMS ordered further style 'L' frames to be held in readiness for replacement of any others that might be destroyed in air raids. During the 'phoney' period some work was done on the large contracts we had received from the LNER for resignalling at York and in the Southern Area eastward from Stratford to Gidea Park; but on both of these work was soon suspended. At an early stage in the war work was done to improve junction layouts on routes leading to the Channel Ports, when supply to the British Expeditionary Force (BEF) in France was still a consideration.

An unusual job of this kind was the putting in of an additional connection between the Great Western and the Southern Railway at Reading East. Normally this would have been done, very simply, by the GWR's own forces, but they were up to the hilt in other work. We had no patterns or tools for making the distinctive GWR signal fittings, and were told to supply the nearest we had. I well remember the chase through our old pattern stores to find the nearest likenesses. The best we could do were American style pinnacles and Great Central spectacle castings!

Then came the dramatic and terrible May of 1940 when the Low Countries were overrun and the BEF encircled and driven back towards the sea, soon to be evacuated in that incredible operation at Dunkirk. But even before the brief campaign had brought our army to such a desperate position, the acute danger from parachute detachments dropped behind the front line had been shown and the call to form Local Defence Volunteer Groups at home had gone forth. At Chippenham, Major C S (Bill) Williams formed a detachment, and later he commanded 'E' company of the Wiltshire Home Guard, fifty percent of whose total strength came from Westinghouse.

Air raid precautions were strengthened, including the construction of roof posts for 'spotters', a body of skilled aircraft identification enthusiasts later to form the nucleus of the Royal Observer Corps. Bill Williams, I may add, had seen five years service in World War I first with the Royal Naval Division at Gallipoli, and then in the Portuguese Army.

The Wiltshire Home Guard and the Westinghouse ARP services at Chippenham were not called upon for any active service, although there were 'incidents' not far away; but it was far otherwise in London, fortunately without any casualties. For in October 1940, when the German Luftwaffe, defeated in the Battle of Britain, turned to heavy bombing of civilian targets at night, the buildings at York Way suffered severe damage. The top storey of the South Block, where the sales and general administrative offices had been before evacuation to Chippenham, was severely damaged, while the eastern end of the North Block, where the Rectifier Drawing Office and the Brake Demonstration Room had been, was completely demolished. The detonation by high explosive also took a slice off the signal end of the drawing office; but although a large number of documents were destroyed – some indeed that would have been very helpful to the writer of this book – the vital drawings of rectifier and signalling apparatus were safely ensconced at Chippenham.

The stories of rapid repair of air raid damage on the railways of Great Britain during the night blitz are legendary, and Westinghouse men were proud to help in providing equipment for replacement at literally a minute's notice. After Christmas 1940, we returned to work on Boxing Day, which that year was on a Tuesday. We had not long been in the office when Major Peter telephoned from London saying that just before Christmas a High Explosive bomb had landed on the Southern Railway just outside Victoria Station; it had lifted one of the signal gantries clean off the mountings and hurled it into a street some hundred yards away. The gantry itself had been an old one dating back to the Sykes

installation of 1908, but later equipped with colour light signals. A new gantry to carry the appropriate signals was wanted – quickly! The works could not wait for finished drawings. As the design was worked out we telephoned sizes of steelwork required, so that the requisite material was ready, cut to size as soon as the drawings were finished, only an hour or so later and were taken across to the shops to show them how to put together the pieces they had cut.

While the iron signal shop, as we then knew it, fabricated the main structure we finished drawings of such details as support brackets for signals, ladders, handrails and such like, and the complete job left the works on the morning of December 30th, just four days almost to the hour after we received the first request.

The iron signal shop, under its quite unflappable foreman Albert Puddle, was called upon for some unusual jobs in the war years. Bear in mind that his team was used to the ironmongery connected with lattice signal posts and the paraphernalia of semaphore signalling. Westinghouse then received from the Admiralty a contract for rangefinder windscreens for destroyers, on which the 3-man or 5-man crews operating the rangefinders were in a completely exposed position. It was not a

An example of the rather less common products produced by the company during wartime. This 1944 photograph shows a Westric charger specifically sold for use with electric fence equipment.

question of providing armoured protection. They were purely windshields, of the lightest possible construction. There was no possibility of using lapped joints, the fabrication at all joints was to consist of 1/16th in thick sheet steel edge-welded. Puddle and his men rose to the occasion magnificently and the Admiralty were delighted and ordered many of them.

So far as the Admiralty was concerned however it was the job to which Kenneth Leech was specially assigned that surpassed all, in its complexity, in the ingenious basic conception, and in the marvellous workmanship put into it. This was the searchlight sight. With the smaller and faster ships of the Royal Navy, like destroyers, an abiding problem had been to keep the searchlights trained on the target once it had been located – no easy task on a bucking and rolling vessel in a heavy sea; and even before the war began the Admiralty had worked out preliminary designs for a gyroscopic device that would enable the beam from a searchlight to be kept on the target no matter how the ship rolled and pitched.

Preliminary arrangements for us to manufacture this ingenious apparatus were concluded some months before the war, with Leech, while continuing with his normal brake work, having the necessary technical liaison with the Admiralty engineers. At the outbreak of war it became, with certain other Admiralty contracts, his sole occupation. When the first of the searchlight sights was ready one or two of us from the other disciplines were privileged to see it and it was, without question, the most remarkable piece of mechanical engineering ever produced in the Chippenham works.

Rectifier production was at a very high level during the war. While Dr Williams and L E Thompson worked steadily on with the basic research in selenium that was to yield such rich rewards later, the Engineering department under Donald Ashby was busy designing a multitude of new sets for all the service departments as well as in the equipment of factories heavily engaged in war production. Work in the Signal section of the Drawing Office tended to move in fits and starts at that time and we were frequently called upon to help the Rectifier section cope with its constantly heavy loading. In the works it seemed as though most of the female population of the entire neighbourhood had been mobilised to assist in rectifier production. The assembly of the units was light work, well suited to deft fingering. The foreman of the Rectifier Shop was Rowley Angell, and somewhat inevitably his large, cheery, indefatigable work-force became known as 'Rowley's Angels'.

The activity in colliery decking plants which had originated with electro-pneumatic control as described in Chapter 5 had continued, albeit in no more than a relatively modest way during the 1930s. When Donald Brown had succeeded H J Winter as Brake Engineer, the colliery engineering was transferred to the Mechanical Signalling section of the Drawing Office under A G Kershaw. He eliminated the electric control and made the interlocking all pneumatic. In due course the engineering of it came under my wing, but its relatively small extent can be judged from my being able to deal with enquiries, prepare schemes, and supervise the making of such drawings as were needed in addition to all my ordinary design work in signalling – and during the later part of the 1930s we were very busy!

On the various sites Fred Rayner was able to supervise and commission all the various installations and his work, not only as a first rate engineer but as a liaison officer, was invaluable in maintaining the prestige of Westinghouse in the coalfields. I remember going up to Sheffield to join him and our northern agent for some

Queen Mary visited the factory in 1942, and these rare photographs (above and overleaf) show Her Majesty inspecting the factory – a rather incongruous figure surrounded by the dirt and bustle of the heavy metalwork that was involved in those days.

delicate negotiations at a pretty grim time in the war, with a colliery manager who wanted a plant put in 'the day before yesterday' as we used to say. Knowing the extent to which Chippenham was loaded I could not promise a very early delivery of

From Westinghouse Review *of May 1952, and illustrating an article on the ladies of the Veteran Employees' Association (Chippenham Branch), this photograph also shows the unmis-takable figure of HM Queen Mary. The caption read: 'In 1942 HM Queen Mary visited the Works, and four of our lady veterans were presented to her, along with other long-serving ladies from various departments. In the front row are Miss Marjorie Escott (first from left), Miss N O'Riordan (third from left), Mrs M Hughes (third from right) and Mrs I Hill (second from right).'*

the material. The colliery manager stormed, our agent kept smiling, but old Rayner said little. Over lunch the manager drew me aside and said: 'Is Rayner going to boss the job for you?' I nodded. We received the official order within a fortnight.

In readiness for the re-entry of Allied Forces onto the Continent of Europe, a large number of British railway coaches were equipped to make ambulance trains, and as they were to be used on the Continent, they were equipped with the

Westinghouse air brake, to be hauled as required by French or other European locomotives. Some of these trains were set aside for home use and the locomotives for these were taken from the Great Eastern section of the LNER on which the powerful and efficient 'B12/3' class 4-6-0s were Westinghouse fitted. These ambulance trains were manned by volunteer crews who lived with them. They were based on various strategic points in the country, and stood ready to go anywhere. The class 'B12/3' locomotives being Westinghouse fitted were a fortunate choice because on account of relatively low axle loading they had a very high route availability. The only thing was that some adjustments of brake gear were necessary to synchronise the working of the new equipment from Chippenham on the coaches with the old equipment on the locomotives to avoid snatches when braking.

Towards the end of the war, under Major Peter's direction, every bit of time that could be spared from immediate tasks was devoted to projects for post-war development. In signalling a close study was made of coded track circuits (see Panel 1) and in June 1944 at the height of the flying bomb attacks R M McGregor and J P Coley read a paper to the IRSE in London on the subject – an occasion punctuated by near and distant crashes as these missiles landed on London. At one time it had been questioned as to whether this meeting should be postponed, but the intrepid Major R F Morkill, President of the Institution would not hear of it. As he remarked at the time: 'Just when we've got Hitler on the run we're not going to let him upset British arrangements!'

It was nevertheless a courageous thing to do, in the prevailing circumstances, seeing that if one of the erratically landing flying bombs had pitched upon the Institution of Electrical Engineers[1] during the meeting, the casualty list could have been grievously heavy. But the meeting was well attended and all was well.

Just a month earlier, before the flying bomb attack had started, another important paper looking to future development had

Coded Track Circuits

In the earlier description of Track Circuits, a very simple arrangement of connecting a power supply to one end of a track circuit, and a relay to the other end, in order to determine whether a train was in the section, was described. Coded Track circuits are a development of the same principle. Instead of putting direct current or a simple alternating current into the track circuit, a complex waveform or coding is used. In its simplest form this can be bursts of ac, separated by a period of no voltage being applied. More complex, modern, systems use Frequency Modulation techniques (switching between two frequencies at a given rate) to carry out the same function. By placing an aerial above the rail, the coding of the track circuit can be detected by train-carried equipment, and information decoded onboard. This means that it is possible to send information similar to that passed by semaphore signals directly to the train driver. This is not only clearer for the driver to interpret, but also more efficient, since information can be sent to trains continuously, not just when passing a signal.

There are further advantages of using Coded Track Circuits. The first is that electrical trains can generate a lot of interference which may cause a normal track circuit to malfunction. However the chances of trains producing a complex coded waveform are very remote. In addition it is possible to 'tune' coded track circuits, so that insulated rail joints are no longer required, making maintenance of the track easier, and the ride smoother.

been presented to the Institution of Locomotive Engineers: 'Brake Equipment and Braking Tests of Southern Railway CC Locomotive'. In this paper A W Simmons was joint author with Lionel Lynes, Technical Assistant (Carriages and Wagons) of the Chief Mechanical Engineer's Department of the Southern Railway. *The Railway Gazette* commented:

> In this first account of the highly specialised equipment that was developed by the Westinghouse Brake and Signal Company Limited to provide a complete braking installation capable of dealing with every kind of service demand – on a locomotive intended, it should be noted, to operate every kind of traffic from express vacuum fitted trains to unbraked, loose-coupled goods vehicles – no attempt was made to gloss over the fact that the resulting system was necessarily intricate. Further complications arose through the decision both to use a deadman's handle type of control (so as to make the locomotive suitable for operation by one man) and also to provide for possible emergency applications of the brakes by the passenger emergency communication apparatus on the train.

It should be added that the CC electric locomotive, carried on two six-wheeled bogies and weighing nearly 100 tons, was not provided with regenerative or rheostatic braking. Thus it depended for its brakes entirely on the two Westinghouse systems (straight air and automatic air). The straight air brake was intended for use when running light, when hauling unbraked trains, when shunting, and to set in combination with the vacuum brake on passenger stock. The automatic air brake was the reserve brake for application by the deadman's handle, or in case the driver

should have found the straight air brake non-effective. The apparatus may have been intricate, but it was necessarily so in trying to cope with the incredibly diverse and complicated conditions of running, in which a mixed traffic electric locomotive was required to work.

It was perhaps no more than a coincidence that on the very same page of *The Railway Gazette* in which editorial comment was made on the Simmons – Lynes paper, there was a printed letter from a correspondent under the heading 'Continuous Brakes for Goods Trains'. After emphasising some of the difficulties of wartime operation, this writer concluded:

> Until public opinion forces the companies to realise that they must as a national obligation, deal similarly with the braking of goods trains, progressive improvements in passenger and freight services alike will be hindered, because of the excessive track occupation due to the slow speed of the latter. Unbraked goods trains should now be considered as an utter anachronism to be consigned as soon as circumstances permit to the limbo of oil lamps, foot warmers, and other tokens of the past.

Staff standing on the remains of the Kings Cross North Block following its destruction in 1940

---

1 The IRSE held its meeting at the IEE's London base from 1908 to 2006. This is at Savoy Place, on the Victoria embankment, adjacent to the Savoy Hotel.

Westinghouse at War

Whilst researching various elements of the book, the editors found a collection of censored wartime articles related to the Company's activities during the war. This was released for publication on 12th April 1945, having been 'blue-pencilled' by the Ministry of Information Technical Censorship Department. Now fully declassified, we can reproduce not only the article, but also the censor's objections!

The War Production Record of Westinghouse Brake & Signal Co Ltd

Towards the end of 1943, it was realised that the large majority of the Westinghouse Brake & Signal Co's employees, whose War work had been a long and strenuous period of monotonous repetition on small parts, had little idea of the ultimate purpose or importance of their efforts. The Company thereupon decided to stage a private exhibition of their War products then passing through the factory, with the view to creating for these workpeople a new interest in their work, despite the fact that output was actually increasing at the time.

    It proved a decided success in its primary object and, in addition, was visited by Members of the Services, the Ministries and Production Committees, etc.

    The exhibition was held in the Company's spacious Works Canteen. In the foreground of the accompanying illustration will be seen a display of Metal Rectifiers, well known to readers of "The Electrical Review", and indeed to all those in the Electrical Industry. It was not possible in the exhibition, nor is it possible in this limited space, to cover the many and varied purposes for which Westinghouse Metal Rectifiers had been and are still

being used on War service. They have found their place in every theatre of war – on aerodromes, in every type of aircraft, in tanks, in signalling and telecommunication, as well as in every branch of War Industry itself.

    They vary in output from a few microwatts to many kilowatts, and full details would make a too lengthy list, but the Company's output may perhaps be best summarised in the following terms. The number of rectifier elements produced, up

A wartime exhibition of the work being carried out during the Second World War showed the wide variety of production being carried out by the Westinghouse staff.

to the beginning of 1945, reached the amazing figure of 115,000,000 while completed sets amounted to 76,500. In these sets were included transformers and chokes, also made in the same factory, to a total of over 120,000, in the manufacture of which was used 1,625 tons of electrical steel sheets for the various shapes and laminations, while the weight used of copper wire of various gauges and coverings was over 500 tons.

This does not, of course, complete the war production story, as metal rectifiers form only one branch of the Company's output of electrical plant. For instance to the Admiralty went amongst other items 134 sets of Searchlight Control Gear; 220 sets of Gyro Compass Gear; 2,080 Junction Boxes and 156,000 Cable Glands for degaussing equipment on merchant ships; 6,200 Contact Stacks for anti-submarine apparatus; 300 Sector Lights for aircraft carriers; 480 Solenoids for fire control gear; to the Air Ministry 85,000 Voltage Regulators; to the Ministry of Supply 5,700 3" Magslip Transmitters, etc., etc.

Figures of production of non-electrical equipment were also impressive with 31,800 Mechanism Plates, 37,800 Soluble Plug Devices and 20,000 sets of parts for sinkers of mines, 7,000 Gun Sights of different types, and apparatus in large quantities for frigates, corvettes, mine sweepers and landing craft, and for depth charge equipment, etc., for the Admiralty; for the Air Ministry 2,966 Live Line Pumps, 1,559 Tailwheel Shock Absorbers for "Lancasters" bombers, 2,955 Undercarriage Jacks and 450 Tailwheel Shock Absorbers for "Blenheims" bombers, 5,100 Fairing Door Jacks for "Typhoons" fighters and 1,100 Bomb Door Jacks for "Bothas" bombers, with large quantities of various precision parts for Rolls-Royce "Merlin", "Vulture" and "Peregrine" engines; to the Ministry of Supply, for the Army went 1,021 2-pdr Anti-tank Guncarriages, 9,605 Variflow Pumps, 10,100 Handles and Valve Boxes for tanks, 1,250,000 Bodies and Tails for anti-tank grenades, 85,000 3" Mortar Bomb Cases, large numbers of parts for various types of guns, 14,137 Air Compressors, 7,138 Combined Reservoir and Governor Units, 4,310 Charging Valve Units, 9,696 Foot Control Valves and 3,028 Boosters for brakes for F.W.D. and heavy armoured vehicles, 6,350 Emergency Relay Valves for tank transporters; and to the Ministry of Supply for railway service 493 Air Brake Sets for ambulance trains, 1,240 sets of Brake Equipment for Austerity locomotives, 4,500 Vacuum Brake Sets for tank wagons, war flats and bogie well wagons, and railway signalling equipment of various types in large quantities.

The foregoing, while by no means complete, provides a good indication of the scope and volume. The large variety was made possible by the nature of the Company's pre-war business, which called for the manufacture of compressed air and vacuum brakes, mechanical, electrical and electro-pneumatic signalling for railways, air brakes for road vehicles, metal rectifiers and other electrical equipment, etc., to meet the varying needs of users in all parts of the World.

[Interestingly another one of the documents conveyed similar information, but added:]

Although still engaged on the production of war material in large quantities, it is now possible to give some thought towards the time when the factory, which has throughout not only been kept up to date, but augmented by more and better plant, will be able to devote its full and greatly improved resources to the fulfilment of the large and world-wide demands for its normal products.

13
Post-War ~ The First Eventful Years

A T T H E E N D of the preceding chapter reference was made to some of the engineering developments towards post-war reconstruction that were in hand, and in January 1945 there came the first group of organisational changes made in the engineering departments of the Company. At the end of 1944, A G Kershaw who had been Chief Mechanical Engineer since 1935 retired, and a first re-organisation of the Chief Engineer's department, under Major Peter, took place. K H Leech whose work on wartime Admiralty contracts was finished was appointed Design Engineer, in charge of all the sections of the Drawing Office; the Electrical and Brake Engineering departments remained unchanged for a time, but an appointment of much significance for the future was that of Leslie E Thompson to be Assistant to the Chief Engineer. In the previous year H A Cruse, General Works Manager, had been appointed to the Board of Directors, and in 1945, E J Fouracre, Sales Manager, and Donald F Brown, Assistant to the Managing Director were also made Directors. This inclusion of no less than three senior executive officers, in addition to the Managing Director, on the Board, was something of a change for Westinghouse. Until then only W H Powell, the General Manager, had been a director, while holding executive office from 1935 until his retirement in 1942.

For the engineering and sales staff, evacuated from the London offices since 1939, intense activity towards the building up of new business went on against the background of looking forward to a return to their normal environment, albeit an environment changed from what had been left behind six years earlier. The damage inflicted on the premises at York Way, cleared up temporarily during the war, was in process of permanent repair, and consolidation, and early in 1946 Donald Brown, acting for the Managing Director, visited Chippenham, and advised all staff concerned to start making arrangements for their personal move back to London, stressing that it was desirable for each family to settle its own affairs as quickly as possible so that when the time came for the office moves the men could give all their attention to the Company's side of the removal. The matter also loomed up, very significantly, of the expansion of the staff. Obviously this had to be done in London, and for a time it became one of my own duties to interview and recruit draughtsmen for all three disciplines, and begin the building up of a nucleus in a temporary office at York Way.

At the same time, by the way in which requirements were building up at Chippenham, some of us began to wonder where the increased staff would be eventually accommodated in London. Nevertheless orders were orders. My own family removal was effected in the early autumn of 1946, and each Monday morning, after a weekend in my new home, I went to York Way to interview prospective draughtsmen. Many other London families made their way back during the autumn and the glacial winter of 1946-7, only to find how much things had changed since the outbreak of war; but to them all London was 'home' and that was what mattered principally. Then in the spring of 1947 Donald Brown came to Chippenham to announce that the Board had decided that the Engineering departments, Electrical, Brake and Rectifier alike – together with all the Drawing Offices, would *not* be returning to London. To the great majority of the staff the news was a bombshell, but to all it was deeply disquieting as seeming to represent a breach of faith on the part of the high management, who had on several occasions during the war assured the London staff that they would move back as soon as possible afterwards.

A few days later Major Peter, addressing a mass meeting of his staff at Chippenham, revealed that his brother, absent abroad at the time, had not been present at the Board meeting when the decision was taken. Captain Peter was naturally very upset to think that opportunity had been taken in his absence to revoke a promise that he had made, not once but several times, and he resigned from the Managing Directorship shortly afterwards. In a gesture of appeasement the Board appointed him Deputy Chairman; but he took little further interest, and retired altogether a few months later. Thus was lost, at the early age of 60 years, the services of a man whose technical ability, business acumen, leadership and charming personality had rendered incalculable benefits to the Company.

For a few days after the announcement feelings ran high in the Engineering departments at Hathaways Building. Even when it became clear that Major Peter was entirely sympathetic, there was nothing that could be done to erase the feeling of being so badly let down. The situation was so different from any previous happening in the relations between Westinghouse and its staff. One or two engineers resigned forthwith, but gradually a calmer atmosphere took over. Donald Brown was appointed to succeed Captain Peter as Managing Director, while some of the older ones amongst us fell to wondering how the *volte-face* had been contrived. It is frequently said that work is one of the most effective antidotes to worry. We had certainly enough on the books in 1947, together with the unpalatable prospect, for some of us, of a second household removal, back, if not to 'square one' then to somewhere not many miles away. There is reason to believe that most members of the Board were deeply disturbed at the depth of resentment aroused by their suddenly announced change of plan; but at the rate the Engineering departments were growing, the decision proved ultimately to have been the only practicable one, though that was apparently not the main reason for making it in 1947.[1]

It was followed, less than two months later, by some important changes in organisation, which were prompted by the expanding nature of the business. Innovation and development being all important at such a time, Major Peter was relieved of his previous responsibilities as Chief Engineer to take up the new post of Chief Development Engineer, covering all branches of the Company's activities. L E Thompson was appointed Chief Electrical Engineer; N G Cadman, Chief Brake Engineer, while K H Leech retained his previous responsibilities in charge of all design activities in Chippenham, but now, like the other chief engineers reporting direct to the Managing Director, had his title changed to *Chief Design Engineer*. A W Simmons went to London to take up the new post of Brake Development Engineer. Under L E Thompson, the Signal and Rectifier sections of the Electrical Engineering department were respectively under D G Shipp and D Ashby.

If the upheavals in the Westinghouse Engineering departments had been considerable in 1946-7 they were microscopic compared to those about to be experienced by some of our principal customers. The British General Election of 1945, by which Winston Churchill, to quote his own words, 'was dismissed by the British Electorate' and the rest of the world was stunned into disbelief, made inevitable the nationalisation of the coal mines and the railways. The result of the election caused a severe recession in confidence in the future of Great Britain, and led to the withdrawal of international financial backing

The front cover of Westinghouse Review, *January 1949, shows the wall of bicycles coming towards the camera as thousands of employees leave the site at the end of the working*

at a time when it would have been invaluable for post-war reconstruction schemes. In Europe one saw the ironic spectacle, to British eyes, of countries whose property and equipment had been wrecked to a far greater extent than anything experienced here making far more rapid recoveries to normality. A sad feature for Westinghouse men was the virtual sealing off by the 'Iron Curtain' of a large area of Eastern Europe, where we had enjoyed first class business and made a great number of friends. Poland, Lithuania and Romania from now onwards might have been on another planet!

Railway reconstruction in Western Europe brought one very interesting and important job, on the Netherlands State

Railways, on which the new electric trains were fitted with the Westinghouse high-speed air brake. It proved an extremely valuable example of the growing, closely integrated relationship between signalling and brake power. First however, to the high speed brake itself; this was based on the fundamental characteristic that the co-efficient of friction between brake blocks and wheels deteriorated as the speed increased. Theoretically therefore, as the speed increased a higher brake force could be applied without risk of skidding the wheels.

In the new Westinghouse high speed brake there was a centrifugal switch in the electric contacts which were arranged to close at a pre-determined running speed,

Class of Train	Type of Brake	Initial Speed(mph)	Emergency Stopping Distance
Heavy Express Passenger	Vacuum with QSA valve or Standard Air Brake	75	2,800 ft
Partially Fitted Goods	Standard on about half the vehicles	55	2,770 ft
High-speed Passenger	Westinghouse High-Speed Brake	90	2,850 ft
Unbraked loose-coupled Goods	Straight air on loco; Hand brake on van	28	2,170 ft (full service stop)

and through an electromagnet to cause increased air pressure to be applied in the brake cylinders. On the new Dutch trains the higher pressure was cut in at 37mph, while during the period of retardation it was cut out at 28mph. This high speed brake worked extremely well, and running tests gave some interesting results that I was able to quote in a paper I had the honour to read before a joint meeting of the Institutions of Locomotive and Railway Signal Engineers in October, 1949.

In much earlier work in connection with installation of multi-aspect colour light signals one became constantly aware of the varying service braking distances of different classes of train. The four-aspect colour light signal provided a useful compromise, by permitting the slower classes of traffic to use the double-yellow as their clear signal while the QSA valve went some way towards providing a better brake for the fastest trains. But the improvement made by the new Westinghouse high-speed brake was remarkable, and in that paper I was able to quote some comparative figures, for emergency stops, on level track (see table),

The correspondence in stopping distance between the first three was remarkable, indicating that each could be run on a section equipped with three-aspect colour light signals spaced 1,200 yds apart, as on the York / Northallerton section of the LNER, before the introduction of the streamlined high speed trains – as indeed

the first two categories of train regularly were. The last example is quoted as showing the appalling limitations, and waste of line capacity represented by the old-fashioned loose coupled goods trains.

The nationalisation of the railways of Great Britain, as from January 1 1948 naturally led to a great deal of speculation within the supply industries and everywhere else for that matter as to what future engineering policies would result from the new appointments made to the central staff of the Railway Executive, and from the subsequent and consequential changes in the six Regions. While the underlying reason for nationalisation had been almost entirely one of political doctrine the experienced and dedicated railwaymen who had the job of carrying it out knew, from the tasks they had undertaken during the war, and which were fresh enough in memory, that there were advantages in nationwide coordination. The same applied to engineering practice and equipment.

The question on everyone's lips was: which practices of the former privately owned railways would be chosen as future standards? One thing was certain however; the state of financial stringency in which the Labour Government had found itself precluded any large scale investment in new equipment, and when R A Riddles, the Member of the Railway Executive responsible for mechanical and electrical engineering, announced that they were

Health and Safety

The workplace in the 1940s was a very different place to that we expect today. With a great deal of 'metal-bashing' and foundry work going on, the potential for injury was high. The Medical Department Report for January 1 to December 31 1948 was reproduced in the Westinghouse Review for April 1949, and makes fascinating – if quite alarming - reading.

ACCIDENTS AT WORK	Total for 1948
Eye Injuries	1,515
Fractures	23
Sprains and Strains	254
Bruises and Abrasions	2,697
Lacerated, Incised, Contused Wounds of Head, Body and Legs	75
Lacerated, Incised, Contused Wounds of Hands and Arms	1,730
Burns and Scalds	401
Other Injuries	925
Industrial Diseases	21
TOTAL	7,640

WELFARE	Total for 1948
Skin Diseases	102
Boils and Carbuncles	284
Respiratory Diseases (Colds etc.)	2,596
Sundry (Boils, Dental, Advice etc.)	4,586
Lesions not attributable to work	1,667
Redressings	21,297
Preliminary Examinations – Female	180
Preliminary Examinations – Male	753
Number of Cases necessitating following up	5
Cases seen by MO Special Appointment	1,055
New Employees seen by MO	481
Apprentices seen by MO	147
COMBINED TOTAL	40,793

An average of 3.3 accidents occurred in the factory for every 100,000 hours worked.

Accidents resulted in a loss of 536 hours for every 100,000 hours of working. This is approximately 0.5%.

The sepsis rate, that is the total number of works accidents divided by the number of septic cases which involved a loss of time, expressed as a percentage, was 0.22%. Workmens's Compensation was claimed in 162 cases.

going to invest in the form of motive power that gave the highest tractive power per pound sterling of prime cost, in other words, steam, there was general disappointment in the supply industry.

The technical staff of the Railway Executive, in all disciplines, spent a great deal of time collating details of existing practices in the four main line railways of the 'Grouping' era, to enable comparisons to be made and guides to future policy assessed. Not all disciplines were able to indulge in the spectacular, though largely abortive, method of running competitive trials, as was done with steam locomotives in the summer of 1948. Signalling, for example, was examined entirely on paper, and, as with all other engineering activities, the mere composition of the new central staff, quite apart from any policies they might frame, was a matter of severe contention among men on Regions that were not directly represented at the Centre. At first however, their duties were little more than those of collecting information. The Regions had much arrears of work to make up, including, especially in the case of the former LNER, some very large installations of colour light signalling, work on which had been suspended during the war. The question of automatic train control also arose, with the Great Western, almost on the eve of nationalisation, staging a spectacular and widely publicised demonstration of the development of their own system to work with four-aspect colour light signals – a practice that was looked upon with the greatest disfavour elsewhere in Great Britain!

There was much talk about the ethics and practicalities of continuous brakes on freight trains, and opportunity was taken to re-assess the comparative positions of vacuum and air brakes. It seemed to many far-sighted men on British Railways' staff that the time had come for a very serious reconsideration of the air brake as a future standard. All prejudices apart, its advantages from a technical and operating point of view were so obvious. While it was generally agreed that the cost of making a change at that particular time put the whole thing completely out of question,

there was every reason for making a new assessment of all the facts. In this Westinghouse was glad enough to assist. Of course commercially, so long as the decision was eventually taken to equip all freight vehicles with continuous automatic brakes, it did not matter which was chosen, because the Company could supply either. We were however to suffer some heart-rending experiences before the matter was finally resolved.

While the situation on British Railways was getting deeper and deeper into the melting pot, Brake Engineering, the Drawing Office and the Works designed and built their biggest ever compressed air cylinders. They were ordered by Head, Wrightson and Company of Thornaby-on-Tees for some huge 'dump' cars they were building for the Steel Company of Wales. These cylinders were not for operating the brakes, but for supplying power for the dumping action. They were required to have a stroke of no less than 4 ft and exert a force of 27 tons. A cylinder 24 in diameter was needed working at a pressure of 135lb per sq in. But such a giant could not have

Assembly and test of Telescopic Dump Cylinders. In the Chippenham Museum archive this photograph is captioned 'Mr P Wooten and Mr H Baker, Fitters, are assembling while Mr J Allen, Foreman Brake Test Department, and Mr F Tyler carry out air-tightness tests.

And here are the telescopic dump valves in use, this being the front cover of the November 1949
Westinghouse Review.

been accommodated on the cars if made in a conventional way, and it was designed to operate telescopically with one cylinder working inside the other. When air was applied first the inner cylinder was raised, and then the long stroke was completed by moving the piston of the inner cylinder. Use of the telescopic principle meant that when fully closed the cylinder was not much more than half the length of a conventional cylinder for such a total stroke, and it could be accommodated comfortably on the dump cars.

Reference has been made in earlier chapters of this book to the basic research on rectifiers constantly in progress in the London Laboratory, and it is now time to describe two major fields in which the fruits of that research were being put to practical use. First of these was the huge Faraday power plant at the administrative headquarters of the General Post Office long distance communications (see Panel). One of the problems of long distance

transmission at that time was the progressive weakening of the level of conversation with distance, and it was overcome by boosting, at intervals, by repeater stations. One of those was to be located in the Faraday Building, in the City of London, on which so many lines converged. This work was completed in 1951.

It was then one of the largest repeater stations in the world, and it provided the first instance of the use of large rectifiers in the power supply of such stations. The very large demand for a power supply had outstripped the capacity of the existing plant, and space available ruled out any extension of the rotary converter installation already in use. Metal rectifiers offered the best solution to a difficult problem, and Westinghouse got the job of designing and building not only the very large rectifiers needed but also the control equipment. It was a tremendous feather in the cap of the Rectifier department.

Faraday Building

Situated in Queen Victoria Street, EC4, the Faraday Building was also known as the 'Citadel'. In the 1930s and 1940s, this building was the very centre of Britain's telephone network, connected to nearly every other system worldwide.

In use by the General Post Office (GPO) since 1902, the building became the central switching point for all of London – making it a prime target during the war. In the 1940s the north east part of the building was turned into a fortress-like structure.

The building was in use as a major switching centre until the advent of digital technology in the 1980s. However it is still owned by British Telecom.

These two pictures come from Westinghouse Faraday Review *of April 1951, which carried this view of the front of the Faraday Building on the front cover, and a detailed four page article within.*

THE
FARADAY
POWER PLANT
by A. V. HICHISSON

Captioned by Westinghouse Review *as follows: 'The Control Desk being assembled by Mr H Burgess (kneeling) and Mr H Tidy (on right). Mr W Fowles the Foreman is facing the camera. The 16 feet long suite of cubicles containing the AC and DC Voltage Control and Alarm Units can be seen behind the desk.'*

In the Faraday Building power was received from one of two alternative ac supply mains, and, through suitable switch and control gear, rectified by Westinghouse rectifiers to direct current suitable for filament and High Tension power supply to the multitude of amplifier valves. They had also to maintain voltage of two enormous standby batteries (occupying a floor area of 4,000 sq ft!) which were floated across the respective loads, always ready to take up the loads should there be a temporary interruption in both ac mains supplies. The Westinghouse contribution to the installation was a massive one, consisting not only of eight large rectifier equipments but also of the very comprehensive control equipment. The console, from which one operating engineer could exercise primary control over the whole installation, was a splendid piece of modern electrical engineering, looking at first glance like some of the control consoles we were then building for the new signal panel interlockings on British Railways.

The rectifiers themselves were of the oil-cooled type, of special design. In this installation the oil did not set up its own circulation, as was more usually the case in the standard Westinghouse sets for electro-plating work, but was circulated by a pump system, which drew the oil through the tanks, circulated it to another part of the building, cooled it, and then returned it to the banks. In view of the vital communication in other parts of the

The Plastics Department of Westinghouse came into being in 1929 under the direction of Mr C S Williams. Plastics were extensively used across the businesses, and this photograph taken at the 1949 Westinghouse Exhibition at Chippenham shows just a part of the huge range of parts that were moulded and pressed.

Faraday building, each rectifier was isolated in its own fireproof cubicle, with fireproof doors, and each cubicle was equipped with a spray fire extinguisher system which was guaranteed to dowse any fire within 5 seconds. From this it will be well appreciated that 'Faraday', the largest rectifier plant yet undertaken by Westinghouse, involved a great variety of engineering expertise, electrical and mechanical and ranging far beyond the fundamental principles of rectifying an ac supply.

In these days, when there is hardly a household in the land that does not have its own television set it is interesting to recall how Westinghouse rectifiers were introduced in the very early development of the 'box'. In January 1950, when our one-time staff magazine *Westinghouse Review*

had been going for a year, A H B Walker, Joint Chief (with S A Stevens) of the London Laboratory, contributed a fascinating article entitled, 'Metal Rectifiers and Television'. He began thus:

> Interest in television is growing rapidly at present, and with the opening of the new transmitter of the Midland Area at Sutton Coldfield an even more rapid increase in the number of fortunate 'viewers' is certain. Metal rectifiers are playing an important part in the development of television. . .

and he went on to describe the great difference in power supply needed as compared to that of an ordinary radio set, and the tremendous saving in bulk, weight and cost possible by using metal rectifiers instead of mains transformers, or rectifier-

This photograph from the January 1950 Westinghouse Reivew illustrated the article on the Viewmaster television. The original caption read: 'The Viewmaster chassis seen from the power unit side. The 14A.86 and 36EHT.100 rectifiers are visible, but the other three metal rectifiers are mounted beneath the chassis.'

valves. Reading Walker's article again today, after a lapse of just 30 years, one is reminded of how much more prevalent then, than now, was the radio or television amateur, and at the Radiolympia exhibition in the late autumn of 1948, Westinghouse exhibited the 'Viewmaster'. It was designed for the amateur to build at home, and

needed no previous experience providing he could use a soldering iron.

Walker continued:

The Viewmaster incorporates five metal rectifiers (eliminating four valves) but this is not altogether surprising since Westinghouse had something to do with the design! Since its introduction, only two months ago at Radiolympia, some 2,000 kits of rectifiers, i.e. 10,000 units, have been ordered, which at any rate shows that the 'spare time' constructor is still very active and that it is well worth while to try and keep him Westinghouse-minded.

As a concluding footnote he added:

Those at Chippenham who are impatient to install television sets may be wondering whether the 'Viewmaster' would work at Chippenham. It is not really designed for such long-range reception, but at the time of writing no one knows how strong or constant a signal the Birmingham transmitter will produce in Wiltshire. If the signal strength proves to be reasonable and a good, high directional aerial can be used, then the 'Viewmaster' will probably operate satisfactorily in Chippenham if aided by an aerial pre-amplifier.'

From the Westinghouse Review *of March 1950, this wonderful view shows the Westinghouse Road Brake Test Bus.*

The brakes on some of the new buses are, I think, just a shade—

fiercer than before—

but then, if it comes to that—

so are their clutches.

Westinghouse Review was the result of the wish often expressed, for some newspaper or magazine in which current affairs could be recorded – not an official publication inspired and edited by the Management but rather something written and run by Westinghouse folk themselves. In 1948 the Management had given its approval to the launching of such an enterprise, and an Editorial Committee under the chairmanship of Dr A L Williams and drawn from all sections and grades was formed. Presumably because of my past sins in the literary field I was invited to join the Editorial Committee, and after Williams left the service of the Company in 1951 I became its Chairman, until a lean period in the Company's business in 1956 led to its being closed down. During the 6 ¼ years of its existence it was a pleasant little addendum to my ordinary duties as Chief Draughtsman of the Company.

Before concluding these notes on the immediate post-war years there was the memorable association when Westinghouse, or at any rate the effects of its products, appeared in 'Punch'. After the war, in collaboration with AEC (Associated Equipment Company), the builders of London's buses, we developed an improved design of brake and clutch valve. The result was caught by 'Fougasse' in his own inimitable style.

1 Intriguing though this is, Nock does not explain what the main reason actually was!

Westinghouse Review

Between January 1949 and March 1956, the Westinghouse Review was published, always with the involvement of O S Nock, to provide the burgeoning workforce with information on the work that they were carrying out.

In the first edition it was written:

'In the past years a desire has often been expressed for some newspaper or magazine in which Westinghouse affairs might be recorded – not an official publication inspired and

edited by the Management but rather something written and run by Westinghouse folk themselves.

That long-cherished desire has now been fulfilled. A representative Editorial Committee, drawn from all sections and grades of the Company, has been at work for some months, and we now have pleasure in presenting the first number of 'Westinghouse Review'.

The magazine represented the entire Westinghouse organisation, not only Kings Cross and Chippenham, but also McKenzie and Holland and Westinghouse in Australia, Saxby and Farmer in India, and the European companies with which Westinghouse was still associated.

The first edition was sold for 3d, rising to 4d in September 1951, with a circulation of 3,050 copies in 1949, with 2,725 being sold when the antepenultimate edition was published in 1956.

The magazine was substantial with editions averaging over twenty closely typed pages of three columns and extensive photography. Articles covered projects, products and specific parts of the company, for example the Works Laboratory, or the Foundry, combined with photographs of Weddings, Sports Days, Produce Shows and so on.

There was a great deal of the history of the company covered in the magazines, and throughout this book, the editors have been able to cross-refer much of Nock's source material using articles within the Westinghouse Review.

A complete set of these magazines is held at the Chippenham Museum and Heritage Centre

14
Subsidiary Companies ~ Overseas and Home

THE NINETEENTH CENTURY pioneers of the great industry of railway brakes and signals were imperialists to the last degree. George Westinghouse Jr set out systematically to build a great worldwide empire centred upon Pittsburgh, Pennsylvania, and so equally in England, but on a more limited scale, did John Saxby, his great rival in Worcester, and those staunch upholders of the vacuum brake, Gresham and Craven. McKenzie & Holland were first off the mark, with William Griffiths, one of the partners, going to Australia in 1878 to organise the firm's display at the International Exhibition held in Sydney in 1879 and 1880. The exhibit won a 'First Award of Merit', but apparently Saxby was also there – in Australia at any rate – because an early publication of the firm claims a 'Gold Medal' at Melbourne in 1880. As things eventuated however Saxby made no significant headway in Australia. It was McKenzie & Holland who captured the entire market, and that of New Zealand, leaving India to Saxby & Farmer. In 1884 Sidney P Wood, one of the partners in McKenzie & Holland, went to Australia to set up manufacturing facilities in Melbourne, at what became known as the Semaphore Iron Works, and two years later the Brisbane factory, the Toombul Iron Interlocking Works, began operations. In

the meantime Saxby & Farmer had opened an office in Bombay, while about the same time James Gresham sent his youngest son, Sam, to India, to advocate the adoption of the vacuum brake as a standard in that country.

The chronology of overseas company incorporation subsequently was:

- 1905, Saxby & Farmer (India) Ltd., in England
- 1907, Westinghouse Brake Company of Australasia Limited, in New South Wales
- 1923, McKenzie & Holland (Australia) Proprietary Ltd., in Australia (State of Victoria)
- 1952, Westinghouse Brake & Signal Company (Australia) Ltd, incorporated to acquire all capital of McKenzie & Holland (Australia) Pty Ltd and the Westinghouse Brake Company of Australasia Pty Ltd.

In 1954 Gresham & Craven joined the Westinghouse Group, becoming a wholly owned subsidiary. Until then G & C, in association with the Vacuum Brake Company, had been a strong competitor. The visit of Sam Gresham to India, and the brake trials run there in 1888 were very successful, and in 1889 the Director General of Railways issued an official despatch confirming the adoption of the vacuum brake as standard for all India. Following this Burma, Ceylon, Malaya and

Siam[1] also adopted the vacuum brake, as did most railways in Africa and South America. So far as the British Empire was concerned, Westinghouse in London and its subsidiaries had only Australia and New Zealand using the air brake.

In India, whatever the Westinghouse companies may have lost to Gresham & Craven on the brake side they certainly made up for it in signalling, through Saxby & Farmer (India) Ltd. At first however the set up was a little unusual. In 1892, following the success of the India brake trials, Gresham & Craven formed a new company, Heatly & Gresham Ltd, to deal with the Indian business, and set up a depot at Entally, Calcutta. Saxby & Farmer at that time had no connection with the Westinghouse Brake Company and thus were unconcerned with the air versus vacuum rivalry on brakes. In view of this they at once fastened on to this enterprise, and arranged for Heatly & Gresham to act

as their agents. In 1893 they sent a young man of 22 years of age, W G Wheatley, to act as their resident representative in Calcutta. He became the very personification of British Signalling in India, in a career in that country lasting for 43 years, during which time he arranged for the purchase of Heatly & Gresham's factory at Entally, the setting up of the independent company, albeit registered in London, and the manufacture of a large amount of mechanical signalling equipment locally.

In 1923 it was decided to register Saxby & Farmer in Calcutta, as an Indian company, and Wheatley became the first Managing Director. As power signalling interests increased 'S & F' became something of a prestige posting for young engineers from Major Peter's staff in London, and T J Hornblower, C M Hall and B F Goodchild, successively, went out to build up technical strength, each in turn to

This wonderful view of Saxby & Farmer India comes from the December 1949 edition of Westinghouse Review.

become Managing Director of the Indian Company.

Wheatley was a great character. On each of his visits to England he would come up to the Drawing Office to see what we had in hand for India. He was one of those men whose immaculate appearance caused other men to turn and look at him. With his snow-white hair, ruddy complexion, and usually a carnation in his buttonhole, he positively generated goodwill as he spoke with pride and affection of what our one-time colleagues were doing in India. It was no surprise to learn that in India also he never varied his superb turnout, which, even in the hottest weather, could well have been an example to weaker individuals who might more easily have wilted under the Indian sun. He was a magnificent ambassador of Westinghouse in the greatest days of the British Raj in India.

It was under his direction that in 1930 the works at Entally was remodelled to enable it to undertake manufacture of complete vacuum brake equipments and at the same time he was fortunate enough to secure the service of Percy J Cruse from Chippenham as Works Manager. It was somewhat ironic that Entally, once the property of Heatly & Gresham Ltd, should have become a formidable competitor in the Indian market of their English principals, Gresham & Craven (Private) India Ltd, and a new factory was equipped at Gobra, Calcutta to manufacture brake cylinders and other brake equipment. Two years previously however Percy Cruse had returned to England, and he was appointed special officer in charge of the progress of the Polish brake contract through the Chippenham works. In 1936 Wheatley retired as Managing Director and was succeeded by T J Hornblower.

The political disturbances in the country that preceded the outbreak of the second world war, and the granting of independence afterwards, had a very serious effect on the business of S & F. The general trend was at first to purchase railway equipment from other than British sources, or those with close British affiliations. In 1953, however, when the centenary of the first railway in India was celebrated, Westinghouse at home joined S & F in putting on a brave show at the Centenary Exhibition staged in New Delhi in March of that year. A V Hichisson, the Publicity Manager, went out from London to assist in the design and preparation of our stand on which many varieties of brake and signalling equipment were displayed, including several items not then used in India. But all in all it was a declining and depressed market, and the operational losses of the company increased year by year. The end came, so far as direct responsibility was concerned, in 1969, when 51% of the share capital was sold to the Government of West Bengal for 1 rupee.

The story of the Australian companies is one of varying but generally successful fortunes. In signalling in particular the local management from the very outset took the greatest care to gear operations to suit Australian rather than British railway philosophy. It was realised that the general trend on all the railways of the Commonwealth was to incline towards American principles. By the mid-1920s in power signalling one found ample evidence of their predilection in the use of 3-position upper quadrant semaphore signals. Despite this rivalry from across the Pacific Ocean, McKenzie & Holland (Australia) Proprietary Ltd managed to secure orders for the greater part of all the signalling material needed for the electrification of both Melbourne and Sydney suburban railway networks. It is noteworthy that two major items of equipment that became standard in the English parent company were first used in Australia, and subsequently adapted to British use. These were the Style 'M' electric point machine and the Style 'F' electric train stop.

The Australian examples of the former were a direct copy of the Union Switch design which differed primarily from W A Pearce's Style 'C' in having the facing point lock and detector incorporated in the machine. The Australians took the American design exactly as it was, with a single detector rod coupled to both switch blades. British practice, however, required that each switch should be independently detected, so before the Style 'M' could be marketed at home the design had to be modified to provide a second detector bar, and appropriate contacts. It was however not until we received some new contracts for the Metropolitan Railway that English conditions required an electric train stop of better performance than Pearce's adaptation of his standard signal machine; and then the Australian Style 'F', while giving excellent performance, was too large for the somewhat constrained conditions in the London Underground tunnels, and a general redesign had to be made to secure a rather more compact ensemble. The principles however were pure Australian.

McKenzie & Holland (Australia) Pty Ltd also looked after New Zealand, and taking the situation up to the end of the Second World War some interesting developments had taken place on the Government railways. Again the signalling principles tended to incline towards American rather than British practice when power signalling was first introduced, with 'speed' and not geographical aspects at junctions. A considerable amount of single-line automatic signalling was installed, with colour light signals and power operated points; but the major break-through towards really modern systems came just before and during the war, with the installation of CTC on the North Island main-line.

The first section, from Wellington to Paekakariki was completed in 1938, and the second, in the mountainous central section of the line between Te Kuiti and Okajukura, a few years later. These plants, forming the first stage of the projected CTC throughout the 340 miles from Wellington to Frankton Junction, were engineered and the CTC equipment built in England, though McKenzie & Holland exercised a watching brief locally, and manufactured much of the standard signalling equipment required.

As in India, so in Australia Westinghouse was fortunate in its leadership of the signalling activity. For more than 30 years the management of McKenzie & Holland was in the hands of J B Jacobson, who by his personality and business ability established the closest and most cordial relations with railway managements in the six different areas of Australia and in New Zealand. In Australia, on four out of the five state systems, and on the Commonwealth line across the Nullarbor Plain, the signal engineers reported to the Chief Civil Engineer. It was only in New South Wales that the signal engineer was a chief officer reporting directly to the top management. Then there was J C ('Cam') Dickens, who succeeded Jacobson as Managing Director while another 'Aussie' very well known in England, and always so welcome in gatherings of the IRSE, was Fred Stewart, Signal Engineer of McKenzie & Holland.

The Brisbane works of McKenzie & Holland opened in 1886. Largely at the request of the Queensland Government Railways, the plant was set up to manufacture both signalling and also permanent way equipment. Latterly there was concentration on track work, although at one time much mechanical signalling apparatus was made, not only for Queensland, but for the Commonwealth Railways – far away from any of the industrial centres of Australia – and also for New Zealand, and for the State Railways of Tasmania. The works also became a

New Zealand Mainline System, showing the Direct Line Pyramid Section (left); the Test Panel Units and Relays (above); the Control Machine and Units (below); and the Cabinets (bottom). The original caption to the latter read: 'This Centralised Traffic Control Machine at present under construction at the works of WB&S Co is intended for service in New Zealand. It will provide centralised control of all the railway signals over a 40 mile section of single track, thus eliminating way side signal boxes. Bakelite materials are extensively employed in its construction.'

Fred Stewart of McKenzie & Holland, Australia. Dated 1955. When this photo appeared in West-inghouse Review of June 1955, it was captioned 'A recent visitor to York Way and Chippenham was Mr Fred Stewart, Signal Engineer of McKenzie & Holland (Australasia) Pty Ltd of Melbourne. Mr Stewart also acts as Australian correspondent for Westinghouse Review.'

supplier of steel and iron castings, also of forgings to the mining and general engineering industries throughout Queensland, and to some of the other states of Australia. In Queensland, track equipment was supplied to the many narrow gauge railways serving the sugar cane industry. Although it is carrying the story of Toombul Iron Interlocking Works, now known as Northgate, forwards many years, the heavy pre-occupation of the plant with equipment for permanent way led, in 1972, to its being made the centre of a new subsidiary company, Westinghouse Track & Engineering (Pty) Ltd, taking over the activities of the Queensland branch of McKenzie & Holland (Australia) Pty Ltd. (See Panel).

Since the formation of the Westinghouse Brake Company of Australasia Ltd in New South Wales in 1907, and its subsequent registering as a proprietary company in 1937 under the modified name Westinghouse Brake (Australia) Pty Ltd, business had flourished. With the standardisation of the air brake

New Points and Crossings Shop, Brisbane circa 1957

Westinghouse in Australia

The roots of Westinghouse in Australia go back to the Sydney International Exhibition of 1879-1880 which attracted McKenzie & Holland of Worcester to send exhibits for display. These were reported as having been commented on by the judges to the effect that "this arrangement of interlocking etc has the merit of great efficiency combined with moderate cost". The exhibit won "First Degree of Merit". Shortly afterwards McKenzie & Holland sent a full time representative to Australia, Mr W. Liley. He was soon successful in securing the provision of an interlocking for Campbelltown Junction on the New South Wales Railway. In the meantime Saxby & Farmer had exhibited at the Melbourne International Exhibition in 1880, winning an award, but were either not successful in or did not pursue further business in the country.

Further work for McK&H led to the establishment of the "Semaphore Iron Works" at Spottiswoode (Spotswood) near Melbourne, Victoria in 1884. Then, in 1888, the Queensland Government invited the company to open a works in Brisbane. This was built at Northgate on the northern extremity of the then Brisbane railway network, opening in 1890, whereupon the company entered into a three year contract for the supply of signalling equipment to Queensland Railways. The Northgate factory traded as The Toombul Iron Interlocking Works. Both the Northgate and Spotswood factories were enlarged during the early part of the twentieth century with mechanical signalling apparatus being augmented with the production of electro-pneumatic signalling equipment. As well as copying English designs and importing some English products, the Australian plants diversified into their own designs for the local market. Equipment was made for all the Australian State Railways and for New Zealand Railways. In 1929 the Spotswood plant commenced manufacture of Westinghouse copper oxide metal rectifiers.

The company structure in Australia developed and diversified to include general iron and steel founding, general fabrication, machining and assembly plus the manufacture of permanent way track parts. Some of the non-railway Northgate products included horse-drawn graders, rock crushing plants, and marine and industrial diesel engines. Of note was the design and manufacture of a steel girder bridge installed on the Beaudesert railway in Queensland, the manufacture and supply of all the rivets used in the construction of the Storey Bridge in Brisbane and the painter's gantry for the Sydney Harbour Bridge.

Meanwhile, the London based Westinghouse Brake Co. had established a local representative, William Nesbit, prior to 1907. Nesbit was instrumental in forming the Westinghouse Brake Co. of Australasia Ltd in 1907. All material continued to be imported from England until business demanded the establishment of a small factory at Concord West outside Sydney to manufacture air brake equipment. The 1914-18 World War created difficulty in obtaining supplies from England thereby accelerating expansion of the Concord facilities. In March 1937 formation of a proprietary company changed the name to Westinghouse Brake (Australasia) Pty Ltd.

Following the amalgamation of the major signalling players in the UK under the Westinghouse banner it was decided to give McKenzie & Holland in Australia full local control of its affairs. To this end, a new company McKenzie & Holland (Aust) Pty Ltd was registered in Victoria with its head office at Spotswood and Northgate as a branch. Later, in 1960, McKenzie & Holland (NZ) Ltd was formed in Wellington, New Zealand, to manufacture Westinghouse rectifiers.

Power signalling schemes were provided by McK&H for Brisbane, Melbourne and Sydney at various times. During the Second World War the Brake Co made depth-charge throwers, brake equipment for aircraft and parts for the 25-pounder gun.

In 1951, Westinghouse in the UK decided to establish a holding company in Australia to manage and report the trading for the separate Westinghouse and McK&H operations. This was named Westinghouse Brake & Signal Co (Australia) Pty Ltd. In 1970 the manufacture and distribution of road vehicle brake equipment was separated from Westinghouse Brake (Australasia) Pty Ltd into a new subsidiary known as Westinghouse Road Brake Co Pty Ltd, with premises at nearby Regents Park. Then on May 22 1972 the signalling company changed its name to Westinghouse McKenzie Holland Pty Ltd to give recognition to the parent company in the UK. A further name change occurred on October 1 1973 encompassing all the companies in Australia when the company became the Westinghouse Brake & Signal Company (Aust) Pty Ltd with each operation becoming a division within this company.

The Brisbane Foundry in 1957.

in Australia and New Zealand they were working in what was virtually a captive market. To meet the conditions of passenger train operation little development of apparatus was needed. Train speeds were generally much lower than those of Europe, though in New South Wales on both the North and West main lines freight train loads were very much on the increase. Severe gradients were encountered in the crossing of the Blue Mountains – 1 in 33 – and on the North Line the descent to the crossing of the Hawkesbury River, if not so long, was equally steep. The New South Wales Railways introduced some huge new freight locomotives, first of the 4-8-2 type (Class 57), built by Clyde Engineering, and then of the Beyer-Garratt articulated type, capable of hauling loads of 1,500 tons over these heavy gradients; but these lengthy trains had also to be controlled going *downhill*, and that is where it was up to Westinghouse!

These huge freight locomotives were fitted with the No 6ET brake equipment, as described in Chapter 10, and as fitted to locomotives on the Chinese National Railways. They had also the driver's straight air brake valve to provide 'straight air' control of the brakes on the engine and tender, and on the train.

This control, being extremely accurate and flexible is particularly suitable for gradients such as those in the Blue Mountains and on the Cowan Bank, descending to the Hawkesbury River. The locomotive brakes could be graduated both in application and release, thus enabling the driver to maintain a uniform speed in descent, while all the time having the safety features of the automatic brake constantly available in case of emergency.

An interesting point regarding these freight locomotives distinguished the Garratts from the Australian '57' and '58' class 4-8-2s: the latter were built by the Clyde Engineering Company, Sydney and railway shops respectively, and naturally had Australian made brake equipment. The English-built Garratts were also required to have the Australian 6ET brake equipment, and this, together with the large cross-compound steam driven compressors, were also built in Australia and fitted to the locomotives when they arrived from England.

At home, apart from the ever-welcome visits to York Way and Chippenham of senior officers of the Australian Companies, we had a longer contact with Australia in the years just after the end of the Second World War. In 1944, just before his appointment as Assistant to the Managing Director, Donald Brown was sent to Australia by Captain Peter to make a survey of the general position and the possibilities of future business. One result of this visit was that soon after the end of the war, one of the staff at Concord West, Fred English – very Australian despite his name! – came to Chippenham and for a time worked as assistant to 'Bill' Williams as a production engineer on the brake side. I, for one, shall not forget his dynamic personality!

I was then Chief Draughtsman of the Brake department and was many times glad of the enterprise and dash of 'Digger' English in getting awkward manufacturing projects under way. He returned to Australia to become Production Control Superintendent at Concord West.

Leaving the Indian and Australian enterprises for the time being, reference must now be made to the acquisition of two important British subsidiaries. Until 1953 Gresham & Craven Ltd, with the sales side of most of their business handled by the Vacuum Brake Company, had been a strong competitor. The company was very much a family concern, with Neville Gresham, grandson of the founder, as Managing Director. His brother, Harry, was London representative and shares in the company were held entirely by members of the family. In 1953 however the death of two other brothers, and the death duties arising therefrom, made it clear that any other deaths in the family would require the sale of the business in order to pay the duties, and it was felt desirable to sell out before this eventuality arose. An approach was made to Westinghouse, and the chance of eliminating a competitor seemed too good to lose. Unfortunately the implications of certain parts of the business tie-up between Gresham & Craven and the Vacuum Brake

Company were too lightly passed over, and the latter, asserting its rights, claimed complete sets of drawings of all equipment, and promptly entered into an alliance with Laycocks of Sheffield for supply of vacuum cylinders, valves and all else.

So far as Westinghouse was concerned, although one competitor had been eliminated at the expense, unwittingly, of creating another, the overall gain was a substantial one, in that the long experience, business goodwill and technical strength of Gresham & Craven was now added to that of Westinghouse at a time when a very critical period in railway brake history was approaching. Following the nationalisation of British Railways and the decision to adopt the vacuum brake as standard, investigations began into the stand-ardisation of individual items of equipment. In 1949, for example, vacuum brake ejector trials were held at Swindon, and out of eight types tested the Gresham & Craven SSJ type was recommended for standardisation. In 1952 the Gresham & Craven quick release vacuum brake system was adopted for a number of diesel rail car sets built by AEC of Southall for Irish Railways.

In 1954, the year after Gresham & Craven Ltd and Gresham & Craven of India Private Ltd became wholly-owned subsidiaries of Westinghouse, a new augmented vacuum brake system for large diesel and electric locomotives was developed. This system used 25 in of vacuum above the pistons on the locomotive only during brake applications by providing a direct link to the exhausters when the latter were isolated from the main brake pipe. The system was first fitted to 60 locomotives of the Co-Co type for Ireland, and afterwards to large main line diesel electric locomotives for Malaya, Sudan and India. A new series of bogie mounted horizontal vacuum brake cylinders was developed for this system.

There is an amusing story to be told about the introduction of the new locomotives in Malaya, the first diesel main line units in that country. Although basically a standard English Electric design, very close attention was given by the Chief Mechanical Engineer of the Malayan Railways, A J Ball, to details likely to affect performance in that country. When finished it was thought to give a little additional publicity to the new power units by naming the locomotives after flowers of the Malayan countryside. As if by magic a cartoon appeared in the *Straits Times* showing the crew of a diesel being ribbed as 'pansies' by the driver and fireman of a steam locomotive drawn up alongside.

In 1955 Westinghouse made another important acquisition, that of Douglas (Kingswood) Ltd. At that time it was engaged principally:

- in the manufacture and sale of Vespa Scooters under licence from Piaggio, of Italy, which licence also covered the importation of complete machines;
- the manufacture and sale of Dragonfly motor bicycles, industrial trucks and engines, and electric vans;
- Sub-contract work of various kinds.

The purchase was made at a key moment in British transport history, for at that same time the great modernisation plan for British Railways was announced, which by its sheer magnitude was going to involve all manufacturers with more work than they had ever been called upon to produce in so short a time. Douglas (Kingswood) had some products that were reasonably profitable; others that were not so, but above all they had spare manufacturing capacity and office space. To make more room for railway brake manufacture at Chippenham, Douglas began sub-contracting for Westinghouse of air brakes for road vehicles, medium sized compressors, and certain signalling apparatus, while the office space that was

Douglas were a very diversified company producing a very wide range of engineering services. The photograph (above right) shows one of the assemblies carried out for the Britannia airliner nearing completion - a front bulkhead with windscreen canopy. The photograph (above left) is captioned: 'This is a complete set of outer and inner flaps for the Britannia. They are the largest flying controls manufactured at Douglas (Kingswood) Ltd.'

(Left) Vespas nearing completion at the Douglas works. (Above) Vespas at Farnborough Air Show. They were found to be invaluable by officials as quick and economical transport over the airfield. (Below left) Seven of a fleet of eleven Vespas which were used for police duties in Cambridge. The drivers are wearing a new type of helmet specially designed for these duties. (An alternative caption in the Westinghouse archive suggested that they were Liverpool police officers, but the machines carry Cambridge registration numbers.)

available in their main administrative block was earmarked for the great expansion of the drawing offices then under my control.

But these developments among subsidiary companies are carrying the story ahead of the main theme, and I must now go back to 1951 when a major reorganisation of the Sales and Engineering Departments took place.

1 Again we have left Nock's country names unchanged, today Burma is Myanmar, Ceylon is Sri Lanka, Malaya is part of Malaysia and Siam is Thailand.

The Railway Signal Company Ltd.

Although not mentioned in this chapter by Nock, one of the most interesting subsidiary companies was the Railway Signal Company Ltd., generally known as the RS Co, based at Fazakerley in Liverpool. As described in Chapter 5 of this book, the RS Co became part of Westinghouse in 1920, and actually remained so until its closure in 1974. Founded as Livesey and Edwards, the company opened as the Railway Signal Company at its premises close to Liverpool in 1881 – the same year that the Westinghouse UK Brake business began. The Memorandum of Association identified the founders as "George Edwards" and "Robert Aurelius King, of 4, Broadlands, Cargreen Road, Norwood, in the County of Surrey, Gentleman". The company thrived on its own for much of its life, working with Westinghouse at London and Chippenham when it was considered appropriate, but largely independently. Indeed there is very little reference to the company at any point

(Above) This 1911 view, signed and dated by Lee Ollerenshaw who was to serve for over 50 years at the RS Co, ending up as MD, shows the Fazakerley works before the First World War.

(Left) The RS Co concentrated on 'traditional' signalling manufacture for much of its existence, as is clear in this view across the shop floor, showing many shunt signals during assembly.

through the tenure of Westinghouse Review from 1949 to 1954, and the company reported its accounts completely separately to the rest of the company, and retained a separate registration.

Fazakerley continued to make traditional signalling equipment right through until the 1950s and 1960s when it diversified into such household objects as 'Raysig' radiant panel heaters and hotplates. It even invested heavily in new office premises in 1956. However by 1974 the company was wound up and Westinghouse's interests liquidated. In a letter to clients it was stated 'We have to advise you that, owing to a change in technology, the demand for the type of equipment which this Company has traditionally manufactured has, over the last several years, progressively declined. It is with regret, therefore, that we have to advise you that The Railway Signal Company Ltd., is forced to cease its operations at Fazakerley. Manufacturing will terminate progressively, with final closure on 3rd May 1974.' With that 39 clerical / managerial staff and 64 factory staff lost their jobs, and the end of an era was reached, just short of a century after it was started.

(Left) The completed office buildings at Fazakerley.

(Left) Long service has been a tradition across the railway industry, and in particular within the Westinghouse companies. This photograph of 17th September 1956 shows Mr L Ollerenshaw laying the foundation stone for the new office building for the RS Co. On the back of the photograph, the staff pictured are identified together with their years of service as:
'J H Burton, Works Manager, 51 years of service, J Williams, Contractor, D J O Kidd, Director and General Manager, 39 years of service, J J Budge, Chief Accountant, 42 years of service, T Jones, Machine Shop Foreman, 43 years of service, Mrs Mandall, Secretary to the MD, 22 years of service, R Johnson, Machine Shop, 50 years of service, J Williams, Fitting Shop, 52 years of service, L Ollerenshaw, 51 years of service and W O'Shaugnessy, Contractor's Foreman.' The combined service is 350 years, and the average is 43¾ years per employee!

(Right) A product of the post-diversification RS Co.

15

Company Reorganisation ~ The British Railways Modernisation Plan and Its Repercussions

T HE SEVEN YEARS from 1951 to 1957 were among the most critical in the history of the parent company up to that time, in the number of major organisational changes that were effected. They had been preceded, a year earlier, by an appointment of much significance to the future. Although the retention in Chippenham of the engineering staffs of the Brake, Signal and Rectifier departments had led, as was hoped, to closer liaison within the works, there had so far been no actual interchange of senior personnel. The appointment in 1950 of N G Cadman, Chief Brake Engineer, to be Deputy Works Manager (Engineering) was thus one of great interest. At New Road, Chippenham, K H Leech, hitherto Chief Design Engineer, was appointed to add the Brake Engineering Department to his existing responsibilities and took the title of Chief Mechanical Engineer.

Cadman's appointment to the works roughly coincided with the launching of a general investigation, by a firm of management consultants, into the general organisation of the company, both inside and outside the works, with the result that in 1951 three virtually autonomous sales and engineering divisions were set up, covering the Signal and Colliery, Brake, and Rectifier activities, each with its headquarters in London. Roughly similar sub-divisions of activity were made in the works, except that in certain cases the divisions were set up to cover manufacturing procedures rather than their end products.

In London the new set-up was designed to give the Divisional Managers a high degree of autonomy and their selection was a matter of vital importance for the future. In the Rectifier Division Leslie Thompson was the natural choice, with Donald Ashby as his assistant; but in the case of the other two the situation was at first not so clear cut. Charles Venning would have been ideal for the Signal and Colliery Division, from his lengthy and distinguished service, and his professional status as one of the leading signal engineers of the whole world; but he had recently suffered a complete breakdown in health, and in 1951 was unable to undertake even the lightest duties.

In the meantime Jack Aldridge had been named as the natural candidate for the Brake Division, from his early training with C C Farmer, and his wide experience in Italy, Poland, Lithuania and, in later years with British Railways. But he was also no stranger to signalling, and when the

From the Westinghouse Review *of January 1951, this photograph is a rarity, showing as it does, most of the major players in the company at the time, all in the same place, as they entertained some visitors. It was captioned: 'Major L H Peter, the Company's Chief Development Engineer, brought a party of Council Members of the Radio and Electronic Component Manufacturer's Federation, of which he is the Chairman, to visit the Works on December 6. In this group, reading from left to right across the picture: Mr J Griffith Hall, Col C J P Hudson, Mr W T Ash (Federation Secretary), Mr W A Jackson (Federation Vice President), Mr A J D Dobie (Federation Trustee), Mr A C Bentley (Federation Assistant Secretary), Mr P D Canning, Mr H A Cruse, Mr Donald Brown, Mr P J Cruse, Mr W F Randall, Mr R G Sell, Mr L E Thompson, Mr N G Cadman, Mr J H Noad, Mr H D Symonds, Mr E M Lee (Federation Vice-President), Mr Mervyn Shorter and Major Peter.'*

difficulty arose over the S&C Divisional Managership he was asked to take it. Having looked forward to the Brake job he was naturally very disappointed and took some persuading to take the alternative; but having done so, no Westinghouse man ever threw himself more energetically and whole-heartedly into his allotted task. Divisional Managership of the Brakes was allocated to J W G Kershaw, son of the Chief Mechanical Engineer of pre-war and wartime years.

The three new Divisional Managers controlled only Sales and Engineering.

Responsibility for production remained entirely with the works management, while Kenneth Leech, retaining his former title of Chief Mechanical Engineer, remained responsible for design. Working under him as Chief Draughtsman, for the next six years I had to serve all three Sales and Engineering Divisions and provide manufacturing information for the works. I must confess that there were times when it was something of a tightrope walk, in satisfying the conflicting priorities with which we, in the Drawing Office, were sometimes faced!

The year 1953, that of the Coronation of Her Majesty Queen Elizabeth II, began auspiciously for Westinghouse in Chippenham, for the 'Grand Old Man' of the works, Herbert Arthur Cruse, Director and General Works Manager, received the award of Commander of the Order of the British Empire in the Queen's New Year's Honours List. As *Westinghouse Review* commented at the time:

> The storybook tale of Mr Cruse's rise from office boy to Director and General Works Manager is known to all of us. He has seen the amalgamation and expansion of our Company during the last fifty years and has entertained many visiting celebrities, including Her Majesty Queen Mary . . .

He was about to be elected Mayor of Chippenham for the third year in succession. The time was not however one of unalloyed happiness for himself and his family, because just over a year earlier his brother Percy, Deputy General Works Manager, had died tragically while on holiday in Switzerland. His deputy for Engineering, N G Cadman, was promoted to be Works Manager as from May 1, 1953. Coronation year will however be remembered among older Westinghouse men for a less felicitous event. In mid July news passed round, surreptitiously at first, of Donald Brown's sudden vacating of the Managing Directorship, and his disappearance from all Westinghouse circles after a family association with the group of more than 50 years. He had climbed to the highest executive office amid the turmoil of the *volte-face* of 1947 and he went out with the suddenness of a thunderclap, though in the silence and mystery of the 'Bermuda Triangle'!

In the *Westinghouse Review* which so faithfully recorded all comings and goings, there was not a line of explanation. Some of us learned in due course however, that before the situation reached flash-point

Mr Mervyn W Shorter, appointed as MD in 1953. Shorter started at the Victoria Street, London Offices of the McKenzie Holland and Westinghouse Power Signal Co Ltd in 1915. Following the war he rose rapidly through the company being appointed Assistant Sales Manager at the end of 1940, Deputy Sales Manager in July 1946, and Sales Manager in 1948. In the same year he was made a Director of the Railway Signal Company, and in 1951 a Director of W R Sykes Interlocking Signal Company, and was later to become Chairman of both. He became a member of the main company in 1950.

there had been increasingly bitter acrimony with some of the other directors, until the situation was summarily ended by the Chairman on July 13 1953. That the Board in general was not prepared for this eventuality is shown by the time that elapsed before a successor was appointed. Then to everyone's pleasure, on October 12 1953, that successor was announced as Mervyn W Shorter. A period of tranquillity within the Company and freedom from further organisational change was certainly needed, because in 1955 the long anticipated plan for the modernisation of British Railways was announced; and from

Euston was typical of the work being carried out by WB&S in the 1950s. The Style L frame commissioned at Euston on 5/10/1952 had been originally built for Preston North, but was never installed. The interlocking was only in use until 1965 when it was taken out as part of the rebuilding and electrification of Euston Station. (Left) Relay Room; (Right) Cabin Interior.

(Above, Right and Below) The installation at Cowlairs in the new Scottish Region, brought into operation in November 1956. A Westinghouse brochure of the time said of the scheme, 'Resignalling, including the supply and installation of a Route Setting Relay Interlocking System (OCS) comprising control desk and illuminated diagram, electro-pneumatically operated points, colour light signals, etc., covering a route mileage of 6½ and replacing eight mechanical signal boxes.'

(Below) In July 1959 Wilmslow was equipped with an OCS control desk and illuminated diagram with 'Westronic' remote control of Handforth Sidings, Chelford and Alderley Edge. A total of 74 routes over 11 route miles were controlled, and connections made to 60 electro-pneumatically operated point ends and 137 track circuits.

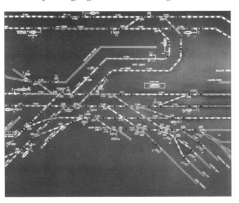

Another large project at the time of the Modernisation was that at Newcastle. The size of the panel is obvious from the first picture (below left), and the complexity of the layout from the second (above). The Westinghouse brochure of the day stated 'Although this new installation at Newcastle cannot claim . . . to be the largest of its kind in the world, it is probably the most complex; including as it does at the eastern end of the Central Section, the intersection of the lines from Gateshead and Tynemouth and the North'. The relay room at Newcastle (below right) was a massive 85ft long by 56ft wide, and occupied two floors. There were 850 lock relays, and 2,000 others for control, indication and release purposes. A total of 641 routes were dealt with by this OCS panel. This photograph shows just part of the upper floor.

the details publicly released it was evident that a tremendous volume of work would be thrust upon all sections of the Company.

In signalling alone, as contract after contract seemed likely to come our way, it was evident that a vastly increased drawing office staff would be needed, while quite apart from railway orientated work the Rectifier Division had some jobs of unprecedented size already in hand. Details of some of the more notable of these, and of new developments arising out of the continuing research work of the London laboratory, are described in a later chapter of this book, while another deals with the ever-evolving practice of modern power signalling. For the Westinghouse group as a whole, enlarged by the recent acquisition of Gresham & Craven, the most demanding production activity arose from the decision by British Railways to equip the entire wagon fleet with continuous brakes.

In 1950, following nationalisation, a decision had been made to standardise on vacuum brakes, using the slipping-band type cylinder formerly used on the Great Western Railway; but in 1956 after further trials the slipping band type cylinder was abandoned and in its place the Gresham & Craven E1 type, with rolling ring seal, was adopted. Although it was only in January 1955 that the outlines of the Modernisation Plan had been announced, within a few months orders had been placed with ten different contractors for no fewer than 46,500 new mineral wagons, and all of these, it was intended, should be fitted with vacuum brakes. The burden of this work was clearly to fall upon Gresham & Craven; but before referring to the plans that were made to deal with it and their catastrophic sequel, mention must be made of developments at Kingswood, to the west of Bristol.

The need to organise a rapid expansion of drawing office facilities was met, so far as office space was concerned, by the ready cooperation of W S McCormack, the Managing Director of Douglas, who put one floor of the general office building at Kingswood at our disposal, and gave every help in the building up of an organisation that was supplementary to that of the main drawing office activities at Chippenham. The location of the offices that were to provide 'back-up' manpower in Bristol was fortunate, in that for this period of rapid recruiting and training of staff in our methods it was much easier to do it there than to try to entice recruits to come to Chippenham. The speed with which they were recruited and the limited experience they had, threw a severe burden on those members of the supervisory drawing office staff who went from Chippenham to Kingswood to build up the new activity. About that time I remember talking to a business associate in the Midlands and telling him how we were taking anyone who could make marks on paper; "Marks on paper," he exclaimed: "Up here, if a chap can sharpen a pencil he's in!"

Hoping that among these new recruits there might be some who would stay with us after the immediate and unprecedented rush was over, we decided to set up at Kingswood sections for each of the main Chippenham activities, brakes, signals, colliery and rectifiers, all of which then came under my jurisdiction. But an element of uncertainty in this began to arise at the beginning of 1957 in view of Kenneth Leech's impending retirement. It was indicated to me that the drawing office would be split into divisions and that I should take charge of the Signal and Colliery section, which by reason of the current British Railway's contracts was becoming larger and larger. In the summer of 1957 the three Sales and Engineering Divisional Managers, Leslie Thompson, Jack Aldridge and J W G Kershaw, together with N G Cadman, the Works Manager, were appointed directors, and so, in my new posting in the Signal and Colliery Division I reported directly to a Director of the Company. Not long afterwards I was appointed Chief Mechanical Engineer. It was however my friends and former colleagues in the Brake Division that were soon to undergo the most shattering of experiences.

In sheer work-load, apart from any technical considerations, the equipping of the British Railways freight stock with continuous brakes would have been in any case a stupendous task, but an incredibly short time limit was imposed upon it. In the programme of modernisation announced in January 1955 it was estimated that the total wagon stock would be 1,141,500 of which a large number would be brand new. Compared to this prospect, Poland, that had involved the fitting of complete brake sets to some 40,000 wagons and through piping to a further 80,000 spreading the work over five years, was a mere drop in the ocean. Although the contracts for supply of the vacuum brake equipment for British Railways were to be spread around several manufacturers, the lion's share would fall upon Gresham & Craven and the delivery programme was going to involve an initial output of 1,000 cylinders per week! No plant existing in 1955 could approach such a require-ment; but the challenge was taken up vigorously. As mentioned previously however, it was not until after further tests in 1956 that British Railways finally decided upon the form of cylinder to be standardised.

Apart from immediate British Railway require-ments, Gresham & Craven were busy developing their AFI system for long freight

trains, with the Indian market particularly in view; and when the magnificent new factory for mass production of vacuum brakes was laid down at Worsley, near Manchester, adjacent to the Eccles to Bolton branch line of the former London & North Western Railway, a demonstration test rack simulating the piping and cylinders on a 92-car freight train was also included. At

(Above) 1950s generation test rig – probably at York Road. (Below) A much later brake test rig.

York Way we had been familiar with the test rack of air brake equipment, skilfully arranged in the confined space within the brake test room in the North Block; but at Worsley, on a virgin site, there was plenty of room outside, where the 4,000ft of piping and the 184 vacuum cylinders could be accommodated in a horizontal layout and running conditions more accurately simulated by all the equipment being exposed to the weather.[1]

In the meantime the new factory was planned on the most spacious modern lines. Never, not even in the USA, had a whole factory been conceived for the single purpose of mass production of brake cylinders. Every feature which the experience of more than 70 years in making vacuum brake equipment had indicated as desirable was incorporated in a superb shop layout. The cylinders chosen were of the E1 type, cast iron, but at the same time consideration was given in planning the layout to the possibility of future production for India. The contract from British Railways for the supply of vacuum brake cylinders was signed on February 13 1958, and provided for the supply of 295,000 cylinders, at an approximate value of £7m.

As previously mentioned the initial rate of output was to be 1,000 cylinders a week, gradually increased to 2,000 with a view to complete the entire contract in about five years. Gresham & Craven, in their fine new works, soon got into their stride, and had already stepped up their output to 1,500 a week, when there came an SOS from British Railways: 'For God's sake stop – we've nowhere to put them!' This cry from the heart was the unofficial prelude to a formal request in April 1959, to restrict

deliveries to 750 a week, revised in June 1959 to no more than 400, and this latter state of delivery to be maintained for a year.

No production engineer will need to be told of the traumatic effect upon a plant exclusively designed for an output of 2,000 per week to be cut back to 400. The entire economics of the great new factory at Worsley was thrown into disarray. The background facts were of course that British Railways had completely miscalculated the other sides of the wagon re-equipment programme, and that the other contracts had either not come up to expectations, or not been placed in sufficient time to fit in with the intensive

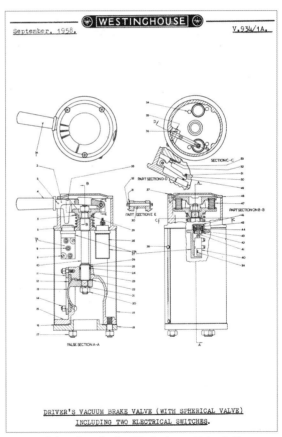

A 1958 datasheet for the Westinghouse Driver's Vacuum Brake Valve with Spherical Valve, showing that the braking systems were every bit as complex as the signalling systems.

delivery requirements imposed upon Westinghouse. But far worse was to follow. On September 7 1961 British Railways terminated this contract, after no more than 119,000 out of the 295,000 cylinders had been supplied. For Westinghouse it was an appalling situation. It was not merely the premature ending of one of the largest single contracts we had ever received, but the throwing into virtual idleness of a factory and its equipment that had been built especially for this job. After urgent consultations, in May 1962 a writ was issued against British Railways, claiming damages for breach of contract.

It can well be imagined that such a step as challenging one's best customer in the Courts was not one that was lightly undertaken, but the feeling that we had been let down was very deep. In the meantime however the curtailments of deliveries from the Gresham & Craven factory at Worsley, and its very serious effect upon the economics of that important subsidiary, led to Gresham & Craven advertising for new projects. No less serious a result of the cancellation of the contract, and the financial losses building up through no more than minimal use being made of the large factory and its modern equipment, was an increasingly bad cash situation. It is true that the cancellation and the inferred lack of cohesion between railway departments, tended to support the poor view that was being taken in many quarters of the progress of the Modernisation Plan as a whole; but that did not help Westinghouse! Within the industry our increasing financial weakness was realised, and when the loss for the year ending September 28 1963 was £1,217,389 we were indeed ripe for a take-over bid.

It came from Thorn Electrical Industries, and was a skilful and potentially most dangerous move. To an outside observer it seemed obvious that we were weakest on the mechanical side, which Thorn did not want. Following a successful take-over that side could have been closed down and only the profitable electrical activities added to their own. In the late autumn of 1963 things were moving towards a crisis. In the High Courts the action against British Railways, claiming more than £3m damages for breach of contract was also nearing a critical stage in which the defendants had made an application to postpone the trial date. Although not known to be so, except by a very few members of the senior staff, December 19 1963 was probably the most crucial day in the entire history of the Company.

Despite the exceedingly bad financial situation the Board felt that to fight off the Thorn bid it was essential to declare a dividend, quickly; but the only way it could be done was by increasing the overdraft facilities, which at that time stood at the frightening total of £6.75m. On that day a letter to all shareholders had been sent off, giving considered reasons for rejecting the Thorn offer and the Secretary of the Company, then Roy Baines, was sent to Lloyds Bank Head Office in the City, to request the Joint General Manager for help. As Baines himself has put it:

> He naturally told me that it was not the role of Lloyds Bank to lend money to a Company in order to allow it to pay a dividend for the purpose of defeating a take-over bid. I told him that whilst I appreciated his view, I was sure that he would still give us the additional facilities – AND HE DID!

That however was not the only hurdle to be surmounted that December day. From the City Baines went hotfoot to the Law Courts, where the concluding stages of an application, by British Railways, to postpone the trial date in connection with our action for damages against them were in progress. This again was a matter of life and death for the Company, because if postponement had been granted the case could have dragged on for a year or more; if that had occurred nothing could have saved us from going into liquidation. Baines entered the Court just as our leading Counsel Sir Stafford Cripps was ending his final speech and happily for us the Judge, Mr Justice Melford Stevenson, refused to allow the trial date to be postponed and awarded us the costs of the application.

Having survived these two 'cliff-hangers' however, our basic difficulties were as grave as ever. We needed cash, urgently. At the beginning of January 1964, taking advantage of our still friendly contacts with officers of the Railway Board, a determined effort was made to agree the terms of compensation and settle the whole distasteful business out of court. Fortunately also, there was a strong disposition on the Railway's side to keep it *sub-judice*, because a revelation of the internal bungling that had made the repudiation of the contract inevitable would have been very bad for their new image.

In 1964 the sole question was the amount of compensation to be paid. Against our claim of more than £3m the first BR offer was for no more than £400,000, which paltry sum one Westinghouse director, mindful of his personal contacts, was actually ready to accept; but the legal people stood out resolutely for much more, and to cut a dramatic story short the figure finally agreed at a meeting between Dr Beeching and our then chairman, P Ewen, was £1,650,000 handed over by cheque dated February 17 1964. To add to the good news in those early months of 1964 the Thorn offer failed, by a very large number of votes of the shareholders, to get the necessary percentages of acceptances, so that another serious danger had been removed. By then however we were deeply in the mire in another direction. (See Panel).

One outcome of the endeavours of Gresham & Craven to secure new projects to take some of the capacity in the Worsley factory made available by the slowing down and eventual cancellation of the British Railways contract for vacuum brake cylinders, was an approach by Hobbs Transmission Ltd who had an automatic gearbox for cars. About that time, with the drastic slowing down of the British

Beeching

Although a name associated with destruction and indiscriminate cuts to railway services across the UK by many who remember the 1960s, history shows Dr Richard Beeching in a rather different light.

At a time at which there was enormous growth in road transport, driven by techno-logical and manufacturing advances which brought family car ownership increasingly in reach of many people, the railways found themselves further endangered by rapidly rising labour and fuel costs. Dr Beeching, already a successful industrialist and a physicist by training, was appointed Chairman of the British Railways Board in 1961.

In his two reports of 1963 and 1965 Beeching advised that the only way to rescue the network was to eliminate loss making services so that the railways could concentrate on the long distance traffic to which they were so well suited. This resulted in the closure of many thousands of miles of secondary and branch lines, and the sending of vast quantities of rolling stock to the scrapyard – giving the photographers the opportunity for many heart-rending photographs of once proud steam locomotives under the torch.

Despite the inevitable loss of jobs associated with this policy, traffic per employee increased by almost 50% between 1963 and 1969. This did not however stem the losses. Beeching returned to ICI in 1965.

The sheer size of what Westinghouse were taking on with the Hobbs Transmission business is apparent from this aerial view of the Blue Streak factory at Manchester.

Railways modernisation plans affecting not only brakes but all other engineering activities and the gloomy state of our finances, the Chairman had asked the three Divisional Managers to explore the possibility of diversifications. The Signal and Rectifier Divisions took a cautious view of this request, but both in due course produced outright winners; but the Brake Divisional Manager seized upon the Hobbs project and presented it to the Board as a matter of such urgency and of such glittering prospects that somewhat reluctantly the first steps towards it were taken, as per the following extracts from minutes of the Board Meeting on May 24 1960:

> After general discussion, whilst it was regretted that an immediate decision did not allow further investigation of this project, it being noted that the amount immediately being invested was only £100,000 and that further capital expenditure would not be

embarked upon until an order was received, it was decided to approve the investment of a half share in Hobbs Transmission Ltd. It was also decided that upon receipt of orders for the Gear Box the necessary attendant capital expenditure envisaged in Mr Kershaw's Report would have to be undertaken, it being agreed that any suitable available capacity within the Group should be fully utilised.

If that Board decision had been followed correctly the £100,000 invested would in due course have become regarded as a write-off, and nothing worse; but unfortunately the enthusiastic presentation of the project to the Board was backed by no market research worth the name. It was to be a diversification of a kind totally different from any that had been made previously – all of which had been from *within* existing activities, putting well proven techniques to new uses. The Hobbs gearbox was a plunge into something totally outside our present experience. As such it needed the most careful specialist examination from every angle. Had that been made it would have been found that the gearbox had been offered to, and turned down by, the leading motor manufacturers of Europe and had met with no success in Great Britain either. Yet the Brake Divisional Manager took the gamble to proceed.

Without waiting for any orders to be received, the Blue Streak factory at Lakefield near Manchester, was leased together with all the necessary plant, at an annual rental of some £350,000. Not a single order was received and, indeed, it was very fortunate that this was so, because there were faults in the design, which motor manufacturers had discerned. Had we blundered into production we should have been plagued with failures that would have been just another millstone round our necks.

After three barren years the shares in Hobbs Transmission Ltd were taken over from the majority of outside shareholders and in 1964 the company was liquidated. Disengagement from the leasing arrangements for factory and plant at Lakefield were negotiated and with the loss on the whole adventure standing at around £4m the dismissal of JWG Kershaw from the Board and from all connection with the Company was inevitable.

But even then the trail of disaster in the Manchester area was not ended. On the collapse of the vacuum brake contract it had been hoped to find other work to fill the Worsley factory of Gresham & Craven; but this was not forthcoming and the sad task ensued of dealing with the many redundancies in staff and eventually of selling the factory and transferring the entire activity of Gresham & Craven to Chippenham. This latter move took place in 1966.

---

1 When E C Sharpe commented on Nock's manuscript he pointed out that a 100 car simulation had also been constructed at Chippenham.

16

The Semi-Conductor Story ~ Some Notable
Applications of Rectifier Equipment

In this chapter, Nock describes the way in which the development of rectifier technology, in particular the exploitation of semiconductor technology, allowed Westinghouse to make progress. This is a complicated topic, based around many difficult ideas of physics. The editors have tried to provide explanatory notes to aid understanding. Clearly this chapter is susceptible to dating, since technology has moved so quickly since the 1980s.

T HE ORIGINAL selenium Westalite rectifiers of Phase 1 (1939) had originally taken over the power applications from cuprous oxide rectifiers by virtue of a greatly increased efficiency at higher temperatures of 70°C to 80°C. Noteworthy applications were the special high reliability rectifier plates for the aircraft industry as exemplified by the Brabazon and Comet aircraft. The large battery charging installation in Faraday House (Post Office) about 1950 has already been referred to, also how the first 'All Metal Television' set was sold as a kit in the post war years – a set in which the only glass was the cathode ray tube and the essential seals in the all-metal hot filament valves of those years!

The second phase of development in semi-conductors began about 1950. It was recognised that the selenium rectifier was susceptible to 'ageing' but not to such an extent as that of the early cuprous oxide rectifier. Workers in other parts of the world had begun using organic chemical layers applied to the selenium surface and

Westinghouse ideas soon resulted in improving the efficiency of the organic layer rectifier, whilst still holding low ageing. Rectifiers of the organic layer type found application in the Services and Post Office where longer term stability was required.

The third phase of development began in about 1955, when the pressed selenium powder was replaced by a high-vacuum deposition method. Other companies, such as Siemens, had already demonstrated the superiority of their rectifiers by this fundamental change. Low forward ageing with high efficiencies were soon in demand and by 1965 Westinghouse was in full production with a brand new plant costing £350,000[1]. This final phase is now fully exploited to cover all the required voltages and special types.

Although silicon rectifiers have taken over from selenium in many areas[2] there is still a substantial market. The characteristics of a selenium rectifier provides naturally the required source impedance that is required in electrical arc

Terms used in this section

Rectifiers work by allowing current to pass in one direction but not the other. In simple terms, if a positive voltage is applied across a rectifier, then current may pass through it. The resistance that the current encounters as it flows through is called **Forward Resistance**. *If a negative voltage is applied across a rectifier, then current is blocked, and cannot flow. Rectifiers frequently demonstrate a characteristic whereby if the negative voltage is great enough, current can flow in that normally blocked direction. The voltage at which this occurs is called the* **Reverse Breakdown Voltage**.

Currents that flow in the reverse (negative voltage) direction, are called **Reverse Creep**, *and are higher (and therefore more of an issue) for older types of rectifier, than for more modern types.*

Rectifiers can be made from a variety of materials, including **Copper Oxide**, **Selenium**, **Germanium** *and* **Silicon**. *Each has different characteristics in terms of the current that they can pass, the way they behave as temperature changes, forward resistance, reverse breakdown voltage and life.*

Modern rectifiers are normally based around silicon **diodes**, *which are in terms of physics similar to half a* **transistor**. *Silicon diodes are constructed from junctions (often called* **point contact junctions**) *of two types of semiconductor, called p and n types – diodes are p-n junctions. Many transistors are made of sandwiches of the two types, pnp or npn.*

Other types of semiconductor device include **Thyristors** *or* **Silicon Controlled Rectifiers**. *These are normally non-conducting, but when voltage is applied to a third terminal on the device, current can flow through the device. These can be constructed to carry very high currents indeed, many thousands of amps. These devices are at the heart of modern power electronics.*

welding, thus enabling low cost welding sets to be produced. Safety requirements for the ever broadening range of electrical children's' toys were more easily achieved with selenium rectifiers, and in this respect they were much less easily damaged by short circuits than silicon rectifiers. The low cost and robustness of selenium rectifiers also meant they were ideal for domestic battery chargers.

Parallel with the selenium programme from 1948 to 1955 three other rectifier materials were being explored. First were the semi-conducting metal oxides. The most promising was based on titanium dioxide and its associated titanates. These were demonstrated to be capable of running hot at temperatures up to 250°C with little change in characteristics. They had high forward resistances and low reverse voltages (up to 20V) but they could

not compete against contemporary types of selenium devices. Second were semi-conducting synthetic lead sulphide crystals, capable of rectifying ultra-high frequency radiation of 3MHz in radar communications. Pilot plant production was demonstrated, but again the device could not compete against silicon point-contact diodes. Third was a diode based on crystalline germanium, with a wire point-contact assembly in miniature tubes. Events eventually overtook this process, and its pilot production line, in favour of the single crystal diode.

While the successful development and applications of selenium rectifiers was in progress in the period 1950 – 60 research into the possible use of germanium had been stimulated by work at the Bell Telephone Laboratories into mono-crystalline rectifiers. Because of its lower melting point than silicon its development for power semiconductors was rapid. In 1950 Westinghouse commenced the manufacture of small germanium point-contact diodes for telecommunications. In these early formative years of the semiconductor industry, no commercial source existed for the raw materials. Thus it was necessary to develop techniques, and manufacture specialist equipment to produce the mono-crystalline germanium of the appropriate quality. Germanium was produced by reduction of a basic germanium oxide, and the metal was then purified by the newly discovered zone refining technique.

The ultra-pure poly-crystalline material was then converted into single crystals by the Czochralski crystal pulling techniques[3]. Wafers were cut from these crystals by diamond impregnated saws and an iridium button alloyed on to the wafer in an inert atmosphere to form the active rectifying junction. Westinghouse started marketing power germanium rectifiers of this type in 1957 with emphasis on high current devices. These products were of prime importance in the manufacture of high power, high efficiency power supplies for the electro-chemical industry, and their reliability is evidenced by the fact that many are still operational. Some of these devices are still manufactured today[4] and are in steady demand for low voltage and high efficiency electro-plating rectifiers.

Germanium has a low voltage drop similar to copper oxide, and it can stand higher reverse voltages and higher current densities than either selenium or copper oxide. However, silicon was showing great

The Works Laboratory was planned during the war years, but built during 1948. The laboratory was set up to carry out Metallurgical, Electrical, Chemical, Mechanical and Physical testing. Each section of the laboratory was set up and staffed to deal with this work for Signals, Brakes or Rectifiers as required.

promise as the future semiconductor material, and although the processing associated with this material generated tremendous technological problems, both in producing the basic material and in transforming it into high current rectifiers – these problems have been gradually mastered and silicon has displaced germanium as the number one semiconductor material. Higher voltages and even higher current densities could be achieved using this new semiconductor material, and this paved the way for a whole revolution in both telecommunications and power equipment. Silicon can also operated at higher temperatures, and this reduces the cooling requirements, resulting in more compact, cost-effective equipment.

By 1957 development work on silicon rectifiers was well advanced in the laboratory in London. As equipment designed in the laboratory was already successfully pulling suitable crystals for use in device development and manufacture and work was in hand on zone-refining techniques. Langridge, heading the laboratory, had developed a satisfactory ¼ inch diode and was planning to make ½ in diameter devices. In the autumn of 1957 a team from England visited Westinghouse Electric in Youngwood, USA, to review and examine the silicon rectifier production that had been running there for 2 ½ years. As a result of that visit it was agreed in December 1957 to set up a full production facility for silicon rectifiers in Chippenham, and a technical exchange agreement was negotiated so that researches of both organisations could be pooled. Some £85,000 was invested in crystal pullers, furnaces, cutting gear and so on to establish the manufacturing areas.

Development continued in the laboratories in London and at Westinghouse USA. Early in 1957 a controllable rectifier was invented in the USA. This new dynamic switching device

was capable of switching many hundreds of amperes from high voltage supplies with no moving parts. This device sounded the death-knell of the traditional mercury arc rectifier for power control. During the late '50s and early '60s great strides were made in the preparation of the basic silicon material. A new chemical industry was born, and specialist chemical companies – Monsanto, DuPont and others – took up the challenge to supply high grade mono-crystalline materials to the rapidly developing semiconductor industry.

But during the '60s the laboratories in London also extended their range of activities and set up a pilot manufacturing plant. This additional activity enabled the

Type B50 Power Diode (left); Type GXB20A1 Finnode, comprising one B20 Power Diode with two cooling fins (right).

A four finnode rectifier unit, comprising four power diodes, each with two cooling fins. One of the diodes is shown in the foreground.

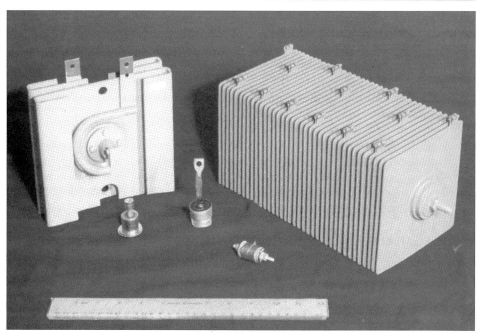

(Left to right). A germanium diode attached to a cooling fin, and several of these assembled on a pair of rods and connected to suit the circuit required. The germanium diode which may also be blast-cooled for igh power output. A heavy current silicon diode, giving 350 amp when fitted with small fins and blast-cooled (three-phase bridge rating). Copper-oxide rectifier for polarising 50v relays. 1.5 kW selenium rectifier designed for air cooling.

rapidly developing new markets to be served, and enabled production processes to be transferred more smoothly and effectively into the full production phase. The success of this plant, together with the rapidly expanding manufacturing facilities at Chippenham established the Company's lead in the power semiconductor industry.

The power semiconductor device wielded tremendous influence on electrical equipment design and in 1966 a joint venture company Westinghouse Brake English Electric Semiconductors Ltd was established between Westinghouse Brake and the then English Electric Company, whereby high power devices and equipment could be developed to a mutual advantage. Low power devices continued to be developed and manufactured separately by each parent company. The joint company was a great success, and with

successive technical breakthroughs, semiconductor products began to set new performance standards required in railway traction, rolling mill drives, inverters, and so on. The product range extended with larger and larger area junction devices, as firstly 1 inch, then 1 ¼ inch, 1 ½ inch and 2 inch diameter crystals became available.

Diode and thyristor ratings extended to several thousand amps and volts and both English Electric and Westinghouse Brake English Electric (WBEES) exploited these leads in their respective fields. Indeed the first and only solid-state High Voltage dc transmission valve in the United Kingdom was constructed in 1970 by English Electric utilising the high voltage Silicon Controlled Rectifiers developed by WBEES Ltd. Throughout the 1960s and for the electrification of British Railways WBEES Ltd provided silicon rectifiers for train-

Diodes under test

borne and trackside equipment. Major equipments were supplied to many overseas companies. Products of such high performance were unique in their time; but they were quickly established and accepted as standard for the traction and electrical power control equipment of today.

In 1972 with the merger of English Electric and GEC, the English Electric Company withdrew from WBEES which then became wholly owned by Westinghouse. In the following years this facility for the design and manufacture of high power devices has been merged with the low power semiconductor activity of the Company to produce a single integrated organisation. One of the most exciting achievements of this new organisation has been the launch of a new range of high power amplifying gate thyristors. The special geometry of the gate configuration, and the process techniques employed, result in very high switching speeds, which improve the efficiency of many equipments such as high frequency induction furnaces. The high efficiency of such products conserve energy, and the use of induction

heating replaces furnaces fired by fossil fuel, thus reducing environmental pollution.

When power semiconductors and in particular thyristors first became available the technology to employ these devices did not exist. A laboratory was opened at Radlett in 1959 with the specific task of developing circuits to use these new products and to assist and advise customers in their application. As basic semiconductor application became more widely known the need for this service decreased and the laboratory was closed in 1972 and the staff were transferred to Chippenham. The London development laboratory was also transferred to Chippenham to form a very powerful team with considerable experience and ability working on one site as a closely knit team to design, develop, produce, market and provide technical support for a very comprehensive range of power semiconductor services under the brand name Westcode Semiconductors.

To appreciate the full significance of the latest techniques in semiconductor design and their application in a very wide variety of equipment it is interesting to set out the power ranges in which it has been found that the four semiconducting materials can most advantageously and efficiently be employed. These can be shown graphically, as in the accompanying diagram. It should be emphasised however that the fields of application thus displayed do not represent hard and fast parameters, applicable to each and every case. The ambient temperature must be taken into consideration, also the current overloads and the space available for the equipment. Operating requirements often justify the use of one type for an output for which another would be the first choice.

One of the earliest uses of Westinghouse rectifiers was for battery charging and, from the simple applications in small and private garages and such like, the practice has developed and expanded enormously over a period of more than 40 years. Using germanium as the semiconductor, automatic vehicle chargers are used by large organisations that run fleets of battery electric fork trucks, tractors and carriers, for transporting goods in factories, stores and warehouses, in dockyards and railway parcel and freight depots. In such applications the traction batteries have to be recharged in daily duty cycles, and these functions were provided for by Westinghouse automatic vehicle chargers. Another interesting and widespread application of automatic charging is to be found in the depots and garages of dairies and bakeries which use battery electric road vehicles of the side-on type for their daily delivery rounds. The batteries are recharged overnight. Another homely application is in recharging the batteries operating the compressor motor of the refrigerator on ice cream vans[5], while a tougher assignment using a larger type of automatic charger is used for the powerful traction batteries of underground locomotives used in mines. These batteries are charged underground, with discharged batteries being exchanged for recharged ones at charging stations in 'safe' areas of the mine, away from explosive gases.

When British Railways decided to adopt 25kV, 50Hz single phase alternating current as the standard traction system for mainline electrification, a dc supply was required for the traction motors of multiple unit trains and electric locomotives. On the first locomotives mercury arc rectifiers were used, but more recently Westinghouse silicon rectifiers have been developed especially for this purpose, and some notable orders were obtained for the Eastern Region multiple unit stock on the London Tilbury and Southend lines, and for the Enfield – Chingford service. This equipments had a continuous rating of 500A at 1500V. Another interesting use has been for dc traction motor supply on the London Clacton express stock, designed for regular running at 100mph and requiring equipments with a continuous rating of 880A at 1250V dc. The battery chargers needed on the above trains to feed lighting controls of the units, rated at 70A 100V were also supplied by Westinghouse; and with lengthy stretches of the routes equipped with Westinghouse signalling and Westinghouse brakes on the trains themselves, these services provided a happy example of the collateral use of the three major products of the Group.

The running of a railway, and of course any modern organisation, depends entirely upon good communication and the part Westinghouse rectifiers have played in the development of modern systems is a massive one. Reference was made in Chapter 13 to the great installation in the Faraday Building of the British Post Office. That however was no more than a beginning, and the overall need, in any system of communication, to provide a stand-by supply of unquestioned reliability, in the event of a failure of the regular main supply of electrical power, has been developed to a remarkable extent.

In referring to this it is appropriate to introduce our one-time subsidiary company of Partridge Wilson & Co Ltd of Leicester, now fully integrated with the Rectifier Equipment Division of the Parent Company, and operating under the name of Westinghouse Davenset Rectifiers. The name Davenset goes back to the earliest days of broadcasting, when the historic transmitter, 2Lo, was operating from Daventry, and Partridge Wilson & Co produced receivers that would pick up the broadcasts – *Daven-sets*. Now the Partridge Wilson works is in the forefront of Westinghouse application of semiconductors in the production of the Constant Voltage Float (CVF) range – an automatic self-regulating, thyristor controlled equipment, designed for various battery charging systems required to supply standing loads and at the same time maintain batteries in a charged condition ready to provide secure dc power supplies in emergencies such as periods of mains failure. Most of this equipment is now made at the Partridge Wilson works at Leicester.

Over the past 25 years rectifying equipment has been used to great advantage for electro-tinning of steel strip. One of the earliest, and still the largest so far as power output is concerned, is that supplied in 1964 for the Velindre plant of the former Steel Company of Wales, now part of the British Steel Corporation. For cleaning, preparing and tinplating on three continuous strip tinning lines, with automatic current control in relation to strip speeds of up to 1250ft per minute, the selenium rectifiers have a capacity of 450,000A dc. Since then however, during the period of the Group's involvement with tinplate producing installations electrical engineering in general and semiconductor technology in particular have been developing at an unprecedented rate, and to maintain the competitive situation our own development needed to be comparably rapid. The power rectification devices have moved from selenium plates, via germanium, to silicon diodes. The power controls have changed from motor driven, moving contact regulators, first to transductors, and now to thyristors, while the electronic controls have developed from thermionic valves to integrated circuits, resulting in a greatly improved accuracy of control.

The No 4 Electrolytic Tinning line at the Ebbw Vale plant of the British Steel Corporation, is typical of modern practice. In this impressively large installation, with a total available direct current capacity of 228,000A, the most important aspect is the control of the current delivered by the plating rectifiers. This current determines the quantity of tin deposited on the strip. With the present high price of tin accuracy of deposition is vital; too much would be wasteful, too little could lead to rejected coil. The plating rectifiers are divided into two groups of eight, one supplying current to the top side of the strip, and the other to the bottom side. The thickness of the tin deposited on each side, and thus the total current used, determines the overall plate thickness and to ensure the degree of accuracy demanded the system as a whole needs to be capable of controlling 72,000A to be better than 0.5%. The actual current to be supplied at any one time is governed by a number of factors, the principal ones being speed, strip width, tin thickness required and plating process efficiency. The system is therefore designed for computer control, in which the variables may be fed, to ensure delivery of the correct current. The computer system is designed to cope with some 2,000 different tin plate specifications that are in common usage and to provide for the even coating of specified thickness across the surface of the strip. The computer system may be set manually if necessary.

Another interesting field of application of rectifiers is for electrostatic precipitation plants in a surprising variety of circumstances. Precipitators are used, for example, for collecting fly-ash; for extracting dust particles from cement, gypsum and magnesium manufacturing processes; for removing particles from gases produced in arc furnaces and sinter plant, and in refuse disposal plants and brickworks. The Westinghouse Davenset thyristor control system is designed to adjust to the continually varying factors that affect the precipitator during gas cleaning processes, and react to any combination of load likely to be met with a particular process. The actual process of precipitation uses electricity to exert a force directly on the dust particles, separating them from the gas stream, feeding high voltage to discharge electrodes, and producing an electrostatic field. When the dust particles flow in the system they become charged and are attached to the earthed and collecting surfaces. For such installations the high voltage transformer and full-wave bridge rectifier are immersed in oil in a tank fitted with cooling tubes as appropriate to the rating of the equipment. One of the largest of such equipments so far constructed provides for an output of 2500mA at 66kV continuous, 78kV peak loading.

It was as long ago as 1952 that Westinghouse first became associated with the protection of oil pipeline in the desert. It was not a case of vandalism or sabotage, but the effects of corrosion. Despite the most elaborate precautions taken when the pipes are laid in deep trenches for hundreds of miles across the desert, the slightest damage to the protective covering can give rise to a point from which galvanic action can cause corrosion. The metal of the pipe is thereupon dissolved, or corroded, at points where electro-chemical or electro-potential differences are set up between the pipe, or other buried structure and the soil – or in the case of submerged equipment, the surrounding liquid.

This effect is neutralised by a process known as Cathodic Protection, and Westinghouse Davenset technology in this field has been extensively developed since the first installation of Westalite oil-cooled sets for the 560 mile oil pipeline of the Iraq Petroleum Company. The principle of Cathodic Protection involves the application of an external voltage to oppose the voltage producing the circulating currents around the buried or submerged equipment, and thus prevent them from flowing from the structure. Some of the major fields in which Cathodic Protection systems are now employed are offshore rigs and pipelines, ships hulls, harbour structures, gas and water mains, telephone and power cables.

---

1 Demand for selenium rectifiers declined over the years, and when the plant was burnt to the ground in a catastrophic fire on Feburary 14th 1987 due to an electrical fault in an air-conditioning unit, it was not replaced.

2 Although Nock wrote this in the early 1980s, this still holds true! Silicon semiconductors are used for the majority of rectifier applications today.

3 A process of obtaining single crystals. This is often used for getting large diameter semiconductor 'wafers'. A single crystal 'seed' is put into the molten material (silicon or germanium), and then slowly withdrawn to make a single crystal. Contaminants or 'dopants' are intentionally introduced into the material, to give the desired characteristics.

4 When Nock wrote this, i.e. 1982.

5 Since Nock's manuscript was written this application has basically disappeared, with power take off from the vehicle engine replacing the separate and heavy motor and generator.

17
Signalling: An Era of Major Development

BEFORE SETTING OUT to record the great advances in signalling practice that followed the launching of the British Railways Modernisation Plan in 1955, with which we in Westinghouse became so deeply and advantageously involved, it is worthwhile to look back a couple of decades, to emphasise the extent to which one of the British Railways, the London & North Eastern, and we, then its principal contractor, were outright world pioneers in the art of relay interlocking.

In 1939 nothing like it was to be seen outside Great Britain. Although some very large new plants were being commissioned in America and interesting developments were taking place on the continent of Europe, all these included lever or slide interlocking frames of the conventional type. After the war, from being the outright pioneer, Great Britain found herself merely one of many countries developing the art of relay interlocking. Nevertheless, in solid fact our installations at Leeds, Hull and Northallerton and that of our erstwhile competitor at Thirsk, were major technological advances; and if we had been able to continue with the installation at York as originally programmed and completion had been possible about 1942, it would certainly have ranked among the railway wonders of the world. As it was, it was not brought into service until 1951. Newcastle Central followed a few years later in the same general

 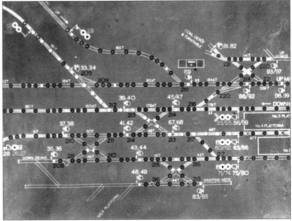

(Left) Operating Switches on York Panel (Right) This panel from Northallerton shows a route set for a train to pass through in white lights

The interior of York Power Box

style; but in their technology they were actually of pre-war vintage – the OCS system.

At the time of nationalisation none of the other British Railways had shown any signs of departing from their earlier ideas on power signalling and with H H Dyer, formerly of the LMS, appointed as the first Signal Engineer of the Railway Executive, little change was at first to be expected; but in 1952 he had been succeeded by J Holden Fraser, formerly of the North Eastern Region and having had continuous experience in the North Eastern Area of the LNER since 1931. He was thus steeped in those pioneer works with which Westinghouse was proud to have been associated; and although when finance for general modernisation was at last made available in 1955 he would no doubt have liked to see the practice of his former railway generally adopted, such was the urgency with which the new work was programmed that the individual regions had to take what the competing manufacturers could supply most quickly.

In such a 'rush' situation, Lewis Boucher and his staff on the Southern would naturally have liked to have the kind of installation with which they were already so familiar and for which they had developed the erection and testing techniques to a fine art – namely the Westinghouse Style 'L' all-electric interlocking frame and its very simple system of control and indication of points and signals. But Boucher, despite all his practical inclinations, felt that in a *modernisation* activity it was time for the Southern to break away from its old traditions, then a quarter of a century old. So, in addition to the Scottish, North Eastern and London Midland Regions, we found ourselves building OCS panels for the Southern.

Fortunately by that time the inventor of the system, Charles Venning, was greatly restored in health and he was able to take executive responsibility once more as Chief Signal Engineer. It was an exciting and inspiring experience to work with him as a close colleague in this very busy period in the Company's history. At first, however, there was little time for much new thinking, and we designed OCS panels in the old style for many new installations. Some of our relatively new recruits in the drawing office, keen though they were, could not understand why the way certain functions were represented, for example on diagrams for the London Midland Region, were not acceptable also to the Southern, and there were variations demanded by other Regions. At first, indeed, the individualities of the old companies remained as strong as ever. On the Southern, in fact, making their first ventures in to panel signal boxes, they tried both our standard OCS arrangement, with an illuminated diagram separate from the control console and an entrance-exit type of control machine at different interlockings in the same installation.

Some of the work we did in that first phase of modernisation like that on the London Midland between Manchester and Crewe and on the Southern in the Beckenham – Chislehurst area, was only the beginning of far more extensive re-equipment of whole areas extending over

hundreds of miles of route. Resignalling on this scale began to take on a new significance. Hitherto the majority of our important contracts had been connected with large individual centres, such as Glasgow, York or great London termini like Waterloo. Now the work began to extend to entire routes.

With this development there arose a need for a considerably smaller type of control machine than had been used up to that time. The OCS system, usually with a separate illuminated diagram, had employed control consoles that were very much smaller than a lever interlocking frame would have been for the same duty; but the diagram itself had to be fairly large for the indications thereon to be seen satisfactorily from the operating position of the console. With the increase in extent of the geographical areas to be controlled from one signal box, a much smaller type of control machine was becoming desirable. The governing factor hitherto had been the size of lamp units, rotary

Train Describers

When block instrument working is used between two signalboxes, a train is described by 'bell-codes'. This means that the first signaller presses a plunger (button), which causes a bell to sound at the second signalbox. By putting sequences together (for example 2 rings, followed by 1 ring, followed by 1 ring) a code can be used to explain what type of train is being sent from one box to the next. This exchange of information takes place before the second signaller accepts control of the train in his / her section of the railway. The description is not comprehensive, the codes identifying trains as for example 'passenger express', or 'fast goods' so, at a junction, the signaller has to route trains in accordance with the timetable – or special supplementary bell codes that were used in some places.

This principle worked very well for a long time, and in many places was used to control complex railway operations. However with the centralisation of control, and larger interlockings being brought into use, a better solution was required. This solution is the 'Train Describer' : a visual reminder to the signaller of which trains are where.

All train describers, of whatever type, aim to provide the signallers with the best possible information about the type and destination of trains and train movements. One of the earliest types was the 'Walker Instrument' which used a rotating arrow on a clockface display, to point to the train description. The magazine type that followed had storage for six approaching trains, and displayed the first three in the order received. Modern Train Describers are, inevitably, computer-based.

A general view of Whitemoor Hump Yard from the Control Tower.

The summit, or hump at Whitemoor

The Control Tower and Number 1 Retarder at Whitemoor

thumb switches and push button circuit controllers, and the first step towards what became known as miniaturisation was to design a completely new range of panel and console equipment. The lamp units, which were made up to a maximum size of six way, consisted of a body formed from extruded brass, housing a perspex light funnel. This latter was the centre piece of the new units, because through it, to use a colloquialism, light could be made to go round corners.

There were also illuminated push-pull switches, very small rotary thumb switches, and a train describer digital display unit. This latter, which included four *very* miniature electromagnetic units gave us some palpitating moments in the course of its development. The basic idea was to obtain maximum compactness by mounting these units actually on the line of the track with the letters and figures of the train description projected on to a ground glass screen. Although the

mechanism by which the stencil discs selected were interposed into the optical system worked satisfactorily, it was not always possible to get a consistently good display on the panel and this type has since been superseded by a cathode ray type of indicator, necessarily mounted on the line of the track to which it refers.

Miniaturised control desks of six different types were built for various requirements of British Railways, and the accompanying cross-sectional diagrams are enough to show the diversity of practice, even in the developing stages of the great modernisation plan. One facet of the plan that brought a great deal of design, development and testing work to my own staff was the equipment of many new fully mechanised marshalling yards. We caused some consternation to the constructional shops in the works at Chippenham in asking for a curved format for the control desks; but these new yards were so much 'show pieces' of the new era on British

Whitemoor Control Panel.

A closeup view of the Point Control Panel for Whitemoor.

Railways that we felt it was necessary to 'play-up' to the situation. Actually Albert Puddle and his men made a magnificent job of the first one, for Perth – at a price; and afterwards we changed to having them moulded in glass fibre. As can be judged from the photograph of Perth the semi-circular format made for a very compact operating layout.

In Chapter 9 of this book I described how we came to install the Eddy Current type of rail brake in the Whitemoor Down Yard of the LNER. Because of that tiresome need to accommodate the occasional wagon with the Mansell type of wheel, those rail brakes were not a success, and in post-war years we had secured at least one contract using retarders of the latest Union Switch type. With the severe competition that was likely to arise for the many yards that British Railways were planning to build, it became clear that direct adaptation of the Union type was going to prejudice our chances because of the high proportion of cast steel

Auto Point-setting drums at Whitemoor

components included. We had no facilities for producing these at Chippenham and the only British manufacturer who was prepared to supply could offer only long and unacceptable delivery dates and in addition prices were going sky-high. Jack Aldridge said that if we were to secure any share of the large market for marshalling yard equipment that was opening up on British Railways the manufacturing costs could not be more than about one half of their present figure. So we had to forget all about steel castings!

An intense and two-fold programme of re-design was begun. The massive levers by which power from the cylinders was transmitted to the longitudinal brake beams were changed to fabrications from steel plate. An immense amount of stress analysis was necessary, later to be supplemented by strain gauge tests, but the bigger problem was that of the main beams. The only way to dispense with steel

The Westardair pneumatic retarder at Perth yard

(Above) The control desk for Millerhill hump yard (Left) Colour Light signals at Carlisle Hump Yard

modern British permanent way. Who would roll such a tremendous section for us? First approaches to some of the steel manufacturers were discouraging; but then I went to the Workington Iron & Steel Company at Moss Bay up on the Cumberland Coast, and I never cease to be grateful to them for the enthusiasm with which they took up the job, nor equally for the staunch backing I had from Jack Aldridge. I was worried about our relatively small quantities. Workington said if we could give them one shift every three months, that was about 250 tons, they would take it on. Even at that it seemed an enormous quantity for us. I telephoned Jack, and his reply was brief and to the point: "You get the beams rolled; I'll sell the retarders!" And that was that.

castings was to make these out of a rolled steel section and preliminary calculations showed that these would require to have a weight of about 300lb per yard – roughly *three times* the weight of an ordinary rail in

The detail design of this enormous beam section was a tricky job, because

Transmission of Information

There are primarily two types of transmission system in use on railways today, Time Division Multiplex (TDM) and Frequency Division Multiplex (FDM).

Multiplexing is the process of combining multiple analogue or digital signals, and passing them all over a single line or channel.

Time Division Multiplexing splits the information into a fixed sequence which is passed over a communication link. The Westinghouse Westronic S2 TDM, for example, is still used widely, typically for passing controls and indications between signalling centres and remote interlockings.

Frequency Division Multiplexing uses a set of carrier frequencies which are coded with the different information streams, and then passed over the communication link. FDM can be used for safety systems, but in the past has not been able to carry as much information as TDM.

cooperative though Workington were, we were just about up to the physical limit of their rolls and in working out the shape we had to modify it more than once to suit their machinery. Eric Harris, now (1981) Chairman and Managing Director of the Rail Transportation Group, who was then my Chief Assistant, was the spearhead of the operation and in a surprisingly short time we finalised a design that came within Jack Aldridge's parameter for cost. It was

Eric Harris also who coined the trade name for them "Westardair" – Westinghouse air operated retarder – and true to forecast, the contracts from British Railways came rolling in. The new yard at Perth was originally to be equipped with the cast steel type, but the first of the rolled steel type was ready in time to be substituted on one of the tracks and a long series of trials were made on it before it was time for the yard to be commissioned. Then there followed

The Westinghouse Brake & Signal Co Veteran Employees Association in 1958

Millerhill, near Edinburgh; Carlisle Kingmoor; Tees yard, near Middlesbrough; Tyne Yard, near Gateshead; and Healey Mills, near Wakefield. In each of these there were two separate yards. There were further installations on generally similar principles in New Zealand, Sweden and in the great yard of the Indian Government Railways at Mughal Sarai, just across the River Ganges from Benares, or Varanasi as it is now known.

The work of the Signal and Colliery Division at that time lacked nothing in variety, from the heavy mechanical engineering of the Westardairs, of which

the beams alone weighed about ten tons, to the miniaturisation exercises in panel signalling equipment. But with facets of the British Railways modernisation plans there came a need for an improved remote control system. CTC of the original American type, with the codes set up by the sequential action of a chain of electro-mechanical stepper switches, was much too slow; and in time for installation on the Styal line of the London Midland Region – part of the first stage of main line electrification at 25kV 50Hz – there was developed the first transistorised time division multiplex (TDM) system of remote

Mosaic Panel

Control Panels in the 21st century are usually computer screens, but state-of-the-art in the latter part of the last century was Mosaic Panels. Large metal panels had been constructed for an extended period of time, with indications laid out in a representation of the railway. Control switches were either mounted on the panel itself, or on a desk in front of it.

Whenever the track layout changed, it was a major exercise to add or remove elements on the panel, and could potentially involve cutting new holes in the panel, or blanking large sections off – whilst all the time maintaining a railway service.

The use of Mosaic Panels, where tens or hundreds of simple panel tiles were made up like a mosaic, greatly simplified things. A standard size of panel tile was constructed, with holes for lamps or switches punched into it specifically for the panel's location on the complete system. All of the tiles were then fitted into an overall framework and wired together to make a complete functional system. Now when a change was required, it was a simple matter of replacing a few tiles with new factory made tiles, and making minor wiring changes.

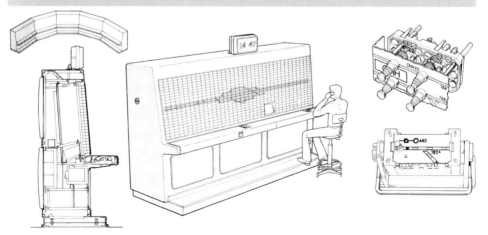

(Left) An example of an illuminated mosaic diagram with route setting controls. (Above right) A typical M3 tile showing switches in place. (Below right) An M3 panel tile held in a special vice which facilitated on-site modification to the tile itself for maintenance purposes.

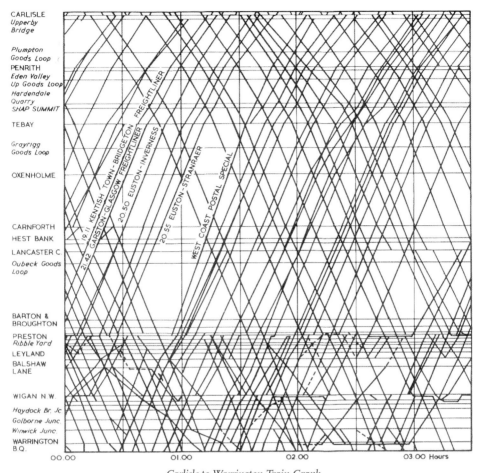

Carlisle to Warrington Train Graph

control (see Panel). It was possibly the first in the world for industrial use and was brought into service in 1957. No more than a single pair of lines was needed to connect each satellite relay interlocking with the parent signal box and, using electronic methods for transmission of the control and indication codes, speed was no longer any problem.

The new system was called Westronic Style 'A' and as a pioneer it was soon superseded by more compact and efficient versions; but so far as Westinghouse was concerned the history of 1925, with the introduction of metal rectifiers, repeated itself. It was soon realised that the Westronic equipment could be used for

purposes other than railway signalling and in the next few years another major diversification was launched to become, in 1965, the Supervisory and Automation Equipment Division. The story of the remarkable development of this is told in the next chapter.

During the Annual Summer Convention of the IRSE in 1957, when we visited Switzerland, great interest was displayed in the mosaic type of control panel (see Panel), then a speciality of the Integra Company of Zurich; and it was thought that this type offered so many advantages in the unit-construction methods that could be used for lamp units, push buttons and such like that we set out

Geographic Signalling

Relay interlockings are generally split into two types – Free Wired and Geographical. Free Wired interlockings generally use standard circuits to construct interlockings based around the selection of individual relays, using contacts in combination to provide the logic that controls the railway.

Geographic interlockings reduce the amount of design that is required, at the cost of some equipment, by using 'building blocks' of relay logic. Units are made up which provide standard functionality for signals, points and so on, and these units are then wired together to provide the interlocking functionality.

The concept is carried forward today to electronic interlockings. Some of these, such as Westinghouse's current WESTRACE interlocking is programmed using free wired relay approaches, whereas many continental systems have all the rules of the railway programmed into them when they leave the factory, and require data to be supplied which defines the geographical layout of the railway.

The Free-Wired approach offers flexibility, adaptability and minimum equipment. The Geographic solution provides reduced engineering time at the cost of a certain redundancy in hardware.

One of first major WESTPAC projects was the rebuilding of Euston Station in 1965. This picture shows clearly the arrangement of relays into groups or functions. (Right) Wolverhampton Westronic Cabinet.

to design a mosaic panel of our own, that would be suitable for British conditions. Our development naturally had many vicissitudes, but it reached one of its most spectacular manifestations in the resignalling of the West Coast main line of British Railways between Weaver Junction, 17 miles north of Crewe, to Kirkpatrick, 13 miles north of Carlisle. In this 135 miles of very busy railway there are only three signal boxes, at Warrington, Preston and Carlisle. There is a large panel box at each of these centres. The distances between them are 26.5 and 90 miles and some of the satellite interlockings with electronic remote control are as much as 50 miles from the parent signal box.

The TDM69, a Time-Division Multiplex system, was used for control of the remote satellite interlockings with separate links for control and indication. As distinct from the TDM69 system used for these controls, a Frequency-Division Multiplex (FDM) system was used to convey indications that did not originate in the remote interlockings, such as track circuits in automatic sections, ground frames and emergency replacement controls for automatic signals.

The success that has attended the introduction of such a remarkable signal modernisation, of a whole route, is shown by the density by night as well as day of the very fast and heavy traffic operated with precision – all trains equipped also with Westinghouse brakes – and by the size and importance of some of the interlockings included, such as Wigan, remotely controlled from Warrington, and Carnforth controlled from Preston.

Reproduced herewith is a timetable diagram showing the occupation of the line between Warrington and Carlisle between midnight and 0330. An examination of this shows that the majority of the north bound trains following each other at such close headway are covering the 90 miles between Preston and Carlisle in 80 minutes, including the ascent from sea level at Carnforth to the 915 ft altitude of Shap Summit. It should be emph-asised that most of these trains are *freights*, and run at their maximum speed of 75mph uphill, on the level, and downhill alike. The heavy night passenger and sleeping car trains run at freight speed, preserving the uniform headway desirable for optimum use of the line.

It was in the resignalling for the electrification of the main lines of the London Midland Region that a notable use

was made of the modern technique of geographical circuitry. The complexity and extent of the wiring in a modern signalling installation would, in the ordinary way, have involved an immense amount of work on site, both in the actual wiring up and in the subsequent testing; but by grouping the relays in geographically associated assemblies standard sets could be mounted on the relay racks, pre-wired, and pre-tested before arrival at the site.

In 1965 Westinghouse went one better in this direction and in carrying out the large installation at Wolverhampton the groups of relays associated with particular operating functions were, for the first time in Great Britain, packaged in completely self-contained cases. The system, aptly named 'Westpac', was used for the first time at Wolverhampton, opened on August 15, 1965, and subsequently at many other large panel boxes. It was in constant course of development and improvement and in the three large installations at Warrington, Preston and Carlisle, the Mark IIIA type was used. In each case it consisted of standard factory-wired and factory-tested units corresponding to the various functions on the ground – points, signals and so on, interconnected by plug-coupled multicore cables in a pattern resembling the track layout. Certain relays that could not be incorporated in the geographical layout were free-wired, but nevertheless mounted on standard chassis.

The 1960s and '70s saw the rapid infiltration of the products of the electronic age into the railway industry, and the success of the 'Westronic' remote control system alone was enough to dispel any early apprehension that might have been felt on the score of reliability. Nowadays in the signalling control field, traditional relay circuits are being largely replaced by solid state equipment; but in particular it has been the advent of the general purpose digital computer that has made the greatest contribution. Small in size and economically priced it has already helped towards an increasing degree of automation in the control, not only of signalling itself, but of important related functions of railway operation. Management of a railway today is a highly complex job, which is becoming even more so with the higher speeds both of passenger and freight trains that are now demanded, with the development of urban mass transit systems, mechanised freight handling and the constant need for commercial and economic planning.

In such an atmosphere, decision-making in virtually all control categories is dependent on the availability and correct interpretation of a mass of information, which by the very nature of the railway business is constantly changing. To say that this kaleidoscopic situation sometimes becomes so involved and inter-related as to be beyond the capacity of a human operator to analyse and interpret at the speed and accuracy with which its presentation is needed for instant decision-making is no exaggeration. The aid of a machine is necessary and the pre-eminent suitability of a computer and the ready availability of certain standard types, has led to the development of a variety of computer based control and supervisory systems. This, of course, is a natural continuation of Westinghouse's long history of innovation in the field of railway signalling. One needs to mention only three ways in which computer based equipment is now in regular use on some of the busiest main lines in Great Britain – and that means busiest in the whole world! – to appreciate its tremendous potentialities: namely train description; automatic train reporting; and automatic train supervision.

In watching the computer based train describers at work in the big panel boxes on the London Midland main line, showing by the cathode ray indications the descriptions of maybe as many as ten trains following each other at close headway through the night on the mountain section of the line between Carnforth and Carlisle, my own mind always goes back to the first Westinghouse train describers; what we would now consider the huge, ungainly electro-mechanical units that Captain Peter put in on the District Railway back in 1905. These were later adapted to marshalling yard use in 1932 for Whitemoor, increasing the capacity to no less than 52 descriptions – 52, on the one drum! Westinghouse were in the forefront then; and now as one watches the description codes on the panel illuminated diagram, automatically following the movements of the trains and being transmitted to the next panel signal box when the train enters the adjoining area, one can appreciate that in this age of computers Westinghouse is still in the forefront. It is good to recall that not only in our own major signalling installations, but also in many of those where competitors have been the main contractors, Westinghouse have supplied the computer based train description apparatus.

Today it seems a far cry to the era when each mechanically operated signal box along the line, often no more than two miles apart, had its own train register book in which the signalmen had to enter, by hand, the time he received every call on the block bells relating to the approach and passage of every train. It was universal procedure on the railways of the United Kingdom at the turn of the century and only slightly less when my own service with the Company began. The automatic reporting of trains today, by computer, makes available, continuously and instantly, all the vital information that is needed concerning their movement – identity, speed, destination and so on. The reporting system provides information for the operating staff, information for passengers on display units at the stations, or where

This fine photograph, dated 1952, was entitled 'Photograph illustrating ease of replacing new type of plug-in relay'

applicable by public address systems. It is also used to give warning of trains having vehicles with overheated axle boxes.

One of the most pleasing features of the new age in the signalling on British Railways has been the continuity of supply maintained at some major centres. The OCS plant at Newcastle put in during the year 1953 may be historic by now, but it was a third-generation Westinghouse job, following upon a very large electro-pneumatic installation at the time of the opening of the King Edward Bridge over the Tyne in 1906, which in itself replaced a huge McKenzie & Holland mechanical plant, extending over several large signal boxes. The new panel box at London Bridge, brought into service in 1977 and one of the largest signalling concentrations in the world, has an even more distinguished ancestor in the history of Westinghouse signalling and that of the company's constituents. Its immediate

predecessors were the large style 'K' frames, with miniature mechanical interlocking at Charing Cross (107 levers), Cannon Street (143 levers), Borough Market Junction (39 levers) and the historic 311 lever frame at London Bridge itself. Then there was the pioneer style 'L' frame with all-electric interlocking, at North Kent East Junction, not to mention many purely mechanical frames of Saxby & Farmer and Evans O'Donnell type on the outlying sections.

At Charing Cross and Cannon Street prior to the resignalling of 1925-6 there were some fine examples of early Saxby & Farmer frames, while at Bricklayers Arms Junction, within the area covered by the North Kent East Junction power interlocking, was at one early time the veritable patriarch of all interlocking frames, a primitive affair but a vital portent for the future installed by Sir Charles Hutton Gregory in 1843.

Another very significant contract, nearing completion at the time of writing, is that on the Midland main line of the London Midland Region, covering the entire first 50 miles out of London, from St Pancras to Bedford, from one large panel signal box located at West Hampstead, four miles out of the terminus. It is indeed symbolic of the ease, speed and reliability of communication made available by modern computer based techniques that a major terminal station with a substantial main line and heavy electrified suburban traffic can be virtually remote controlled. So far as the general running over this busy main line is concerned it need only be added that it constituted a typical example of a 'mixed' railway, on which provision has to be made for operating fast and frequent electric commuter-trains, 90mph expresses and a variety of freights up to 75mph trains – all to the best advantage; a situation that is provided for by modern multiple aspect signalling and trains equipped with brakes appropriate to their performance.

18
Automation and Controls

W ESTINGHOUSE has a notable history of major new activities being born out of diversifications from well-established standard lines of business. In the USA George Westinghouse himself turned his successful use of compressed air as a form of motive power to the operation of railway points and signals. At the end of the First World War in England, the Power Company adapted the principles of railway signal interlocking into coal mines and not long afterwards Major Peter, using some of the earliest metal rectifiers for feeding dc track circuits from ac power supply, realised the enormous possibilities of such rectifiers for a multitude of industrial uses. In the preceding chapter the development of the first transistorised time division multiplex system of remote control for railway signalling, was described. Here again, although a new system was initiated to meet a railway requirement, it was soon realised that this equipment had possibilities for far wider application.

Using electrical engineers of the Signal and Colliery Sales & Engineering Division a project was undertaken with London Transport to use it for the remote supervision and control of electrical switchgear and of other equipment supplying traction power to the London Underground network. This in turn led to application of the remote control system to supervising electrical switchgear and other apparatus on a water pumping and pipeline scheme for the Corporation of the City of Sheffield; and with success in these initial contracts the prospect opened up of applying 'Westronic' in many other fields, such as gas distribution, oil pipelines, electricity distribution and so on, in which the large geographical areas covered by the major authorities operating such activities suggested that sophisticated modern systems of supervision and control would be advantageous.

So, just as early rectifier engineering was separated from signalling in the late 1920s, in 1965 this new activity was separated from the Signal & Colliery Division and the Supervisory and Automation Equipment Division was born. Soon afterwards this rather cumbersome title was very much shortened, simply to Automation Division. It became one of the world's leading suppliers of industrial remote supervisory and control systems. Reference to a few major schemes successfully commissioned will indicate something of the diversity, scale and geographical distribution of the Division's activities.

An early contract was from the Central Scotland Water Development Board for the central control system of the Loch Lomond water supply. The system regulates control of the abstraction of water from the Loch and Ross Priory and measures and controls its flow in two directions via separate treatment works. The latter were situated at Blairlinnans on the pipeline to Old Kilpatrick and at Balmore on the line to Gowanbank. In the latter there is a tunnel in which the system monitors and controls the level of the water.

The Westronic Equipment together with the associated digital computer are installed in the control centre, where in a control room an operator is able to monitor the working of the system as a whole and to control the various pumping stations. Among other functions performed by the computer is that of driving three data-logging typewriters. In such an automated scheme the continuous detailed recording of the performance in all its aspects is very important. The way in which the Westronic remote control can be utilised for additional functions was shown in this installation by the control of the barrage gates across the River Leven, which flows from Loch Lomond to the Firth of Clyde. By measurement of loch level and river flow in the vicinity, control of the gates is imposed to regulate the level of water in the loch and the flow of water in the river.

A fine example of what is termed the 'Distributed Processing System', as applied to the requirements of a great electricity supply undertaking, is provided by the system built for the South Eastern Electricity Board, known within the supply industry as CADEC (Computer Assisted Distribution Engineering Control). To appreciate the extent of this particular plant it should be explained that the South Eastern Electricity Board supplies an area of 3,000 square miles, containing nearly two million customers. It includes all the county of Kent, most of Sussex and of Surrey, together with some of the southern suburbs of London. The Board is divided into three engineering groups with control centres at Dorking, Hayward's Heath and Sittingbourne. These centres are manned 24 hours a day by engineers whose duties are devoted to maintaining the security of the electricity supply, in liaison with other control centres and, of course, ensuring the safety of personnel at all times.

The main benefit of having a Distributed Processing System is that it offers great flexibility for development and expansion in the future. The communication lines linking the primary sub-stations bulk supply points and each control centre radiate in a manner that makes it logical to provide what is termed 'processing power' at the bulk supply points. These take the form of computers that provide communication with the primary substations and perform data reduction functions and have all the flexibility of utilisation inherent in computers. At each of the bulk supply points there is a Data Concentrator, which feeds back electrical system data to the associated control centre, where it is analysed and presented to the control engineers on Visual Display Units (VDUs), printers and what in the automation field is called a mimic diagram – a variation of the familiar signalling track illuminated diagram.

At each centre the control desk has five VDUs and two keyboards. Normally two engineers control the system, each having one keyboard and two VDUs, with facility to share the fifth VDU; but all monitoring and control facilities are available at either of the operating positions. To a railway orientated Westinghouse man such a control desk provides a deeply impressive variation of the equipment in a modern panel signal box.

In Belgium the Authority known by the initials CPTS is responsible for the coordination of the production of electrical energy produced by many individual companies throughout the country. It is also responsible for transmitting this energy in a secure and efficient way, not only in Belgium itself, but via interchanges to neighbouring countries. Early in 1971 it was realised that the network was not only expanding rapidly, but that it was growing far more complex and in order to fulfil its obligations in providing grid security, economical transmission of load requirements to the area control centres, and the security of power supply to the customer it was necessary to build a new National Despatching Centre linked to the 380kV grid and the area control centres by a supervisory system. Here again was an ideal opportunity for the Automation Division of Westinghouse and a contract was secured for the equipment of the new centre, which was sited at Linkebeek.

A Time Division Multiplex supervisory, remote control and telemetry system was installed, the main function of which was to receive data from the telemetry and five telex links, analyse this data and then to present the information to VDUs, mimic diagrams, chart recorders, control desks and printers, the latter in the form of logging typewriters. Three control desks enable the operator to perform national and regional despatching as well as controlling the 380kV network.

In recent years it is a remarkable fact that in industrial circles the Westinghouse Brake & Signal Company has tended to become far better known through some of its diversifications than by its two original basic products. In Qatar the Automation & Controls Division secured a £3m contract for controlling that little, but rich country's power supply. The rapid development of the country has brought a phenomenal increase in electric power demand. In 1954 there were only 500 consumers, yet by 1972 the number had increased to 21,000. It was not until 1963 that the first modern power station at Ras Abu Aboud was commissioned, with a capacity of about 40MW; by the addition of further generator installations this had been increased to 200MW, by the year 1976. Since then the erection of a second power station has more than doubled the capacity.

The Westinghouse contract for the supply and installation of a large computer based Supervisory Control and Data Acquisition system to regulate operation of the state's electrical transmission network ranks among the most advanced systems anywhere in the world today. For the people of Qatar it has resulted in improvements to the stability of supply, making it less vulnerable to interruptions and making maximum and most efficient use of the large generating capacity now available. That it has a spectacularly large mimic diagram and control console goes almost without saying, rivalling in peripheral length and far surpassing in height some of the largest railway signalling control panels made at Chippenham. The diagram, of the mosaic type, consists of no fewer than 132,000 one inch square plastic tiles on which the electrical trackwork is presented. The control desks and consoles are made in afrormosia veneer and hardwood to match the woodwork framing the mimic diagram. A public viewing gallery is planned for the grid control room at Naeeja, so that the people of Qatar can see for themselves this important step forward in their country's development.

Back in the United Kingdom great interest and perhaps some controversy among the conservationists, has been created by the discovery of a large new coalfield, at deep level, beneath the quiet old market town of Selby, above which the gracious 11th Century Benedictine Abbey towers (See Panel). Speeding north towards York the last lingerings of industrialism have been left behind by the time the train slows for the curves at Selby, and one has entered a rich farming area. But now five

Selby

The irony is that it has taken over 20 years to bring this book to the public, during which time Selby colliery has flowered and died. The Selby complex was made up of five mines, Riccall, Stillingfleet, Whitemoor, Wistow and North Selby, and began production in 1983. It was the largest of the deep coalfields in Britain, and certainly the most modern, and generally referred to as a 'Superpit'. At the peak of production the mines employed 3,500 miners and produced some 12 million tonnes of coal each year. The mine also required a new mainline connection with Westinghouse Signalling and a TDM69 system.

In common with all the mines in the UK however, low international coal prices and falling industrial and domestic demand led the pit into huge financial losses as it became too expensive to run. The final load of coal was brought to the surface on Tuesday October 26 2004.

great new pits are being sunk into a coalfield the size of the Isle of Wight. It is a huge industrial enterprise and sure enough Westinghouse is there.

The contract for the 'Wesdac-Minos' remote control and monitoring system, valued at more than £2.75m, is believed to be the largest ever for a coal mining application. Each of the five pits will have control equipment that will enable a few men on the surface, using keyboards and VDUs, to monitor and control the underground coal clearance system, which will consist of a network of conveyors and bunkers.

By the time this book is published it is expected that the equipment at the first pit will be in operation. Then, fed with data from 60 remote underground outstations the surface control desk will also be monitoring coal-face production rates and the performances of equipment such as pumps, ventilating fans and methane gas monitors. It is programmed that the second and third pits, similarly equipped, will be brought into operation in 1981 and the final pair are scheduled for completion in 1982. All coal produced by the Selby complex is earmarked for use in power stations operated by the United Kingdom Central Electricity Generating Board. It goes without saying that the Westinghouse

contribution to this great new activity will not be confined to the "Wesdac-Mino" remote control and monitoring system. British Railways will be cooperating with a service of 'Merry-go-round' coal trains from pits to power stations and these will be fitted with the air brake on locomotives and the coal hopper wagons.

The Marine and Industrial Controls Division, which in 1975 was merged with the Automation Division, was formed in 1965 and the 'controls' side of the present organisation is mainly concerned with fluidic, pneumatic and electromechanical equipment for the marine, oil, bulk handling and manufacturing industries. It is another example of the development of long established Westinghouse expertise in the use of compressed air to further important and profitable new fields. One of the earliest, for the electro-pneumatic control of conveyor ploughs and stops was a fairly close adaptation of railway signal interlocking practice applied to the brewing industry, regulating the movement of beer bottle crates on conveyor belts. At the bottling plant of Ind Coope & Allsopp's at Burton-on-Trent the conveyor network looks more like the track layout at some busy railway junction and the movement of the vast number of crates are controlled with interlocking precision from a

Ind Coope and Allsopp Bottling Plant, Burton on Trent

centralised control panel. Then communication with other parts of the plant is also provided for, in that operators at the receiving ends of the crate routes are able to advise the panel operator at the centre of their future requirements.

The foregoing was one of the earliest applications of electro-pneumatic control to other than railway or colliery tub mechanisation; but more recently compressed air has been applied to conveyor systems in a totally different way. There are many industrial products that are usually bagged up for conveyance such as chemicals in powder form, plastics, minerals, cement and foodstuffs; but nowadays the Controls Division has developed a system of conveying such materials by pipeline, in which these products are suspended in a stream of dry air. As such they can be conveyed over distances up to 1000 ft and in quantities ranging from a few pounds up to hundreds of tons per hour. The Derion blowing seal initiates the action. It is designed to transfer powders and granular solids into the pneumatic conveying systems and the experience now on hand enables the technology to be adapted to a great variety of materials, from fine powders to harsh lumps. Within pressurised, or gravity-discharge systems, Derion rotary airlocks

are used to transfer materials and here again the range of sizes extends from 2 in up to 28 in. It has been said that these airlocks can handle everything from asbestos rock down to mustard seed.

To a Westinghouse man of an older generation like myself, modern adaptations of older standard practice always catch the eye and while the great majority of the applications of power to industrial uses stem from the air brake origins, it is interesting to find also that in one direction the vacuum brake equipment is still in present and developing use. In earlier chapters of this book I have referred to the activities of Gresham & Craven Ltd – for long a thorn in our side – first as a rival to the air and then as a rival in our own development of vacuum braking between the two World Wars. In one respect however we were not serious rivals in the means of creating the vacuum.

All Gresham & Craven's early development was done when steam was the only form of motive power and their celebrated and very widely used SJ Ejector was generally preferred as a means of creating vacuum in the brake system rather than using a pump driven off one of the crossheads of the engine machinery. Westinghouse vacuum exhausters fitted to electric or diesel powered locomotives were of the internal-combustion engine type, usually driven by a separate electric motor.

Nowadays, in modern Westinghouse plants in connection with bulk handling Gresham ejectors are used in many industries, for transporting both liquids and slurries, for moving air and gases and of course for creating vacuum. They are widely appreciated in such applications in having no moving parts. As in the original use on locomotives the action is created by a jet passing through a cone and in present usage the products are entrained by a vacuum and moving fluid stream created by the venturi, which is injected with the

The installation at Tyne Dock

motivating power source, which can be water, air, steam or anything else that is available in this particular plant.

A most interesting use of Derion rotary blowing seals took place during the building of the great road bridge across the Humber Estuary. In its construction some impressive records were established. The main span of more than 4,500 ft was the longest in the world and is carried on towers 500 ft high. Some 500,000 tons of concrete was needed for the sub-structure and the towers and Derion rotary blowing seals were used on both banks to convey cement, sand, fly-ash and dry mud constituents from the back storage hopper by pipeline to the concrete mixer. It was certainly a spectacular use of the conveyance of power and granular material by pipeline.

The name Tyne Dock brings back memories of one of the earliest British installations of electro-pneumatic signalling, dating back to 1902, but by the mid-1950s the use of the extensive dock facilities had taken a complete 'about-turn'. While in the first place they were designed for the export of coal, fifty years later a major activity was the import of iron ore for the great steel works at Consett. An ore handling plant had been installed at the docks, and trains consisting of specially designed hopper wagons were shuttling between the dock and steel works, then conveying about 5,000 tons of ore a day. Westinghouse was closely associated with the mechanised handling facilities both in the ore handling plant at the dockside and on the trains. The latter was an early forerunner of the methods used on the merry-go-round coal trains of today. Pneumatic equipment was used for control of the loading hoppers, but although a first look at the trains and their steam locomotives would have suggested that they were air braked this was not so. At that time

A close up view of the Ore Handling Plant at Tyne Dock

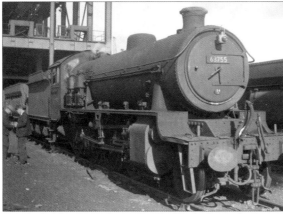

Again Tyne Dock, but notice the Westinghouse Brake Compressor, externally mounted on the loco. Sometime between 1957 and 1959.

British Railways was still using vacuum. The two Westinghouse steam operated air pumps on the locomotives were to provide the air for opening the hopper doors when the train arrived at Consett. The trains consisted of eight cars, each carrying 56 tons of ore and on arrival at the discharge gantry and being 'spotted' exactly in position, the hopper doors throughout the train were opened and 448 tons of ore discharged simultaneously.

Mention of Tyne Dock leads on to the activities of the Automation & Controls Division in the Marine Industry, but in referring to modern applications one must not forget that in the First World War the 'Power Company' supplied electro-pneumatically controlled fore-bridge firing gear to ships of the Royal Navy. Today, with the diversity of skills and experience accumulated in the Division it is a little difficult to imagine any facet of marine activity that could not be assisted by Westinghouse equipment. These can be divided broadly into two categories: navigational controls and control of the cargoes.

The vast size of modern tankers designed for bulk handling and the nature of the loads conveyed, require a variety of safety systems. One needs to mention only such cargoes as crude oil, chemicals and liquid gas to emphasise this. High level alarms providing overspill protection and tank gauging systems are now operated by Westinghouse remote indication systems, an important feature of which is that no equipment other than pipes is installed in the tanks. All working parts are above deck. Main engine controls are now applied alike to ocean-going and offshore supply vessels. They are used for control from the bridge of diesel engines that are direct coupled and have direct reversing also of unidirectional engines driving propellers, while the pneumatic control systems are used for a variety of purposes on vessels ranging from tugs, buoy lifters, sewage disposal dredgers and floating docks. It need hardly be added that control of main engines from the bridge greatly simplifies manoeuvring procedures.

A marine activity today that never fails to stir the imagination is that of the construction and siting of oil rigs. It has been brought home to people living in the British Isles since the opening of the North Sea oilfields. At first however one might well wonder how Westinghouse came to be associated with it. In the case of the Graythorp 1 rig in the Forties Field the rig was secured to the flotation pontoon by 44 clamp and release mechanisms, each weighing about six tons, and they were controlled by pneumatic and hydraulic actuators. This equipment was manufactured by Westinghouse and operated well during the delicate operation of positioning the jacket. After the rig was in position the pontoon was towed clear and with its pneumatic equipment is expected to be used for a subsequent float-out. On station the Graythorp 1 rig is held by nine concrete piles, each having four legs. This was another case for Derion rotary blowing seals, because the piles were secured by liquid concrete fed by pipeline from storage silos by a pneumatic conveying system.

19
Rapid Transit ~ Latest Development in Brakes

IN AUGUST 1962 Parliament passed the Act authorising the construction of the new Victoria Line tube, in London, which was to be equipped for a maximum degree of automation throughout, with automatic driving of the trains. In this, as in so many other features of underground railway working, London once again secured a world first. And once again, as with many previous innovations – illuminated track diagrams, train describers, individual wheel cylinders incorporating automatic slack adjusters – this latest and epoch making development was the result of close cooperation between the engineers of London Transport and Westinghouse. To those of us who were most closely concerned it was an inspiring experience to work with such men as Robert Dell, the Chief Signal Engineer of London Transport and A W Manser, Chief Mechanical Engineer. The drive and speed with which development work went forward is a testimony to the singleness of purpose that animated everyone concerned. Only four months after the passing of the Act the first train trials were made between Acton Town and South Ealing, with empty stock, but early in the following year a passenger train was equipped and was subjected to automatic driving between Ravenscourt Park and Stamford Brook on the District Line.

The completely automatic driving of the trains is actually a dual system, of which one part is based on the traditional safety methods of railway signal engineering used on the London Underground since the first days of the District and Metropolitan line electrification and which, through the agency of the lineside train-stop made an emergency application of the brakes if a train should inadvertently overrun a signal at danger. The principle is maintained through highly sophisticated modern equipment on the track and train; but while this safety equipment is a fundamental necessity to ensure the correct response of automatically driven trains to adverse signals, for an overwhelming proportion of the working hours of the railway the trains are running in their correct timetable paths and under clear signals. Then their progress is controlled so that they accelerate swiftly from station stops and come in smoothly to stop at the correct position alongside the station platform. Another requirement is that if a train should be stopped intermediately by signal it shall restart automatically when the signal clears. Officially the two parts of the dual system are referred to as the 'safety' and the 'non-safety'. This is not to suggest that there is anything unsafe about the latter, which controls the accurate stopping of a train at the station platforms; it is just a method of

Vital and Non Vital

The railway signalling industry often distinguishes between systems as being 'vital' or 'safety' systems, and 'non-vital' or 'non-safety' systems. Vital systems are those that are used to prevent accidents, such as interlockings and ATP systems. Non-Vital systems are those which are part of the signalling system, but not directly responsible for the safety of the railway, such as Train Describers, or control systems. The Victoria Line on-board train-control system used a combination of a Vital System (or Safety Box) and a Non-Vital system to ensure the safe and efficient operation of the trains along the line.

distinguishing between the 'vital' and 'non-vital' part of the controls. (See Panel).

In the first Westinghouse installations of power signalling on the electrified Underground lines in London, the outstanding safety feature was the train-stop, co-acting with every stop signal. On the Victoria Line the train brakes had to be designed to respond to a multiplicity of 'signals' from the track and anything so simple as a plain mechanical contact between a raised train-stop arm and a pendant lever on the train was out of the question. The track circuits are fed with pulsating, rather than continuous, current and the number of pulses per minute are an indication of the state of the line ahead, and these govern the speed at which the trains are allowed to run. While the wheels cut off all the current flowing in the track circuits in the ordinary way, four pick-up coils, mounted *ahead* of the first pair of wheels detect the codes that are flowing in the rails. Two of these coils, one on each side of the train, are used for the safety system and the other two control the automatic driving equipment.

The happy collaboration between Westinghouse and London Transport on this great project was exemplified in March 1965 when Harry Duckitt, then in the London Laboratory and later Divisional Manager Signal & Mining Division, was joint author, with G R Kent, of a paper presented to the IRSE entitled: "Development of Automatic Train Operation on London Transport", in which

the root principles and circuitry for both 'Safety' and 'Non-Safety' systems were fully described. In opening the discussion on that paper Robert Dell paid a very handsome tribute to our Company, thus: 'Mr Duckitt had, to his knowledge, carried out a very great deal of the development work and the laboratory development work leading up to the production of the equipment for that project; but he represented a team of people in the Westinghouse Company who all work together to produce the designs and to produce the equipment, and the effect of that was to produce equipment in an extremely short time.'

When that paper was presented the work had not progressed beyond the inauguration, in April 1964, of a complete service of automatically driven trains between Woodford and Hainault, at the country end of the easterly extension of the Central Line; but it worked extremely well and no more than a relatively few detail improvements were made, to increase further the safety, reliability and long-service potential of the equipment. One very notable feature of the systems as a whole was the change from the telephone-type electromagnetic relays in the circuits of the non-vital part of the system to the 'solid-state' type of switching, using transistors and similar items. It was a momentous step, especially on a railway network like that of London Transport, because these tiny units had not at that time been used to any extent, anywhere, in railway signalling. Although a failure of any one of them could not result in any dangerous consequences, there would inevitably be delay while it was being rectified and the slightest hold-up on London Transport usually produces banner headlines in the evening newspapers! Thus very great care had to be taken in the choice and testing of the many makes of transistor available.

The first section of the Victoria Line, that between Walthamstow and Highbury & Islington, was successfully brought into service in September 1968 and on 7 March 1969 Her Majesty Queen Elizabeth II opened the final section and rode in the cab of the inaugural train. It was the first time ever that a reigning Monarch had opened one of the London Underground railways, though her great grandfather, King Edward VII, when Prince of Wales, had opened both the City & South London and the Central London Tubes. At the inauguration of the Victoria Line, the Company was represented by Jack Aldridge, then Director and Divisional

Jack Aldridge

Manager (Signals & Colliery) and he had the honour of being presented to Her Majesty.

The Victoria Line was no more than the beginning of the Westinghouse connection with Rapid Transit urban railways and their equipment, the latest successes in which are referred to in the final chapter of this book. Automatic driving of trains is a highly specialised development, not necessarily applicable to each and every situation where intense passenger service density is demanded; but in many parts of the world a new philosophy of railway passenger train operation is coming to the fore, not only in rapid transit networks, but in high speed commuter systems and in Inter-City special express trains. Because these categories of passenger train service have the one feature in common, that the rolling stock is separate and is not linked or in common-user service with the rest of the equipment on the railways concerned, the situation gave the brake engineers of Westinghouse an opportunity to develop a new conception of control for dynamic and pneumatic braking. The background to this new development was the 30 years experience in electro-pneumatic braking, in which some 12,000 car sets of equipment had been supplied for railways all over the world. The new system has been given the registered trademark of 'Westcode'.

Apart from the fundamental necessity for providing speedy and reliable operation, two considerations relating particularly to the working of an intense rapid transit service influenced the design of the new equipment. First was the increasing trend to use dynamic (regenerative or rheostatic – see panel) brakes on the motor cars of multiple unit trains to reduce the very heavy wear on brake blocks from frequent stopping from maximum speed. The second consideration is the relatively light weight of the cars used in rapid transit service in relation to their maximum

Dynamic Brakes

Whilst much of this book has been concerned with air and vacuum brakes which are friction brakes, applying a brake shoe directly to a wheel or axle, modern systems rarely use this technique. Modern friction brakes generally apply a brake pad to a disc attached to the axle or wheel – in a similar way to car disc brakes. However on trains which are driven by electrical motors, electrical braking systems, referred to as dynamic brakes, are commonly used.

The most common types are rheostatic brakes and regenerative brakes. Rheostatic brakes take energy from the motors, and feed it into resistors, often mounted on the train roof, where the energy is converted into heat, and dissipated into the atmosphere.
Regnerative brakes feed the energy recovered into the electrical traction system, for use by other vehicles. Whilst this is clearly a very energy-efficient, and therefore ecologically sound technique, it is not straightforward on today's ac traction systems, and has therefore been traditionally applied only to dc railways. This is changing rapidly as power electronics develop.

carrying capacity under 'crush' loading conditions. Although the difference is not so great as in the case of heavy mineral wagons it is the 'empty-load' principle, but in a more difficult context. Furthermore it is a well known characteristic of rapid transit services that even at the peak periods the loading of the cars is not uniform throughout the trains. Passengers tend to crowd into the cars, through the doors near to the platform entrances, from escalators, or to make for parts of the train that will be nearest to the exits at their destination, with the result that some parts of a train will be loaded to crush capacity while in others there will be seating room. For ideal working each car should be braked in proportion to its actual loading and in rapid transit conditions this must be determined automatically.

Referring first, however, to the dynamic brake, where this is fitted the Westcode equipment is arranged to control this directly, but at the same time, through a restricted application limiting valve, air is passed to conventional air brake cylinders. As the speed falls under a brake application, the effect of the dynamic brake lessens and eventually fades out completely and the Westcode equipment provides for a smooth and rapid changeover to the air brake.

When regenerated current is present the limiting valve passes air at 10 lb per square inch to the brake cylinders; this conditions the brake shoes and wheels, and assists in the smooth changeover. This would also take effect immediately in the case of a failure of the dynamic brake.

The valve connected with the variable load feature is regulated either by the pressure in the air suspension system on the cars[1] or by mechanical linkage to the conventional suspension of the car. This arrangement provides for seven different brake cylinder pressures, through the three-wire coded control system that gives Westcode its name. Three magnet valves on the brake unit mounted on each vehicle admit compressed air to three diaphragm chambers of a relay valve, which is arranged to deliver a specific proportion of brake cylinder pressure for each of the seven possible combinations of diaphragms under pressure. This ingenious conception which has provided the fastest and most accurately balanced system of passenger braking yet devised, has already been installed on some of the latest and most advanced rapid transit systems in the world.

As with what could now be called the conventional electro-pneumatic brake however, it is essential to provide against failure of the electricity supply and the cars equipped with Westcode also have the standard automatic air brake. The operation of the driver's handle on the Westcode brake valve is the same whether Westcode or pneumatic operation is used and a given handle position gives the same braking effort with each system. The operation of the all-pneumatic brake is inhibited by a continuously energised magnet valve, while control current supply continues intact; but loss of current, which would imply loss of electro-pneumatic Westcode control, opens the magnet valve and allows the brake pipe pressure to be reduced. Loss of electro-pneumatic control also implies non-operation of the dynamic brake, through absence of control to bring it into operation. When working all-pneumatic the maximum brake force available on each car is in relation to the load carried, but in the interests of simplification graduations are not load controlled.

Two interesting early applications of Westcode were on the subway cars of the Toronto Transit Commission, which operates a fast and intense service and on the Metro in Rotterdam. The former is quite an extensive system with an east-west line some 15 miles long, in addition to an underground loop beneath the heart of the city. The two-car sets, which can be coupled up to make longer trains at the peak periods, are very smart and attractive units. But they had the additional attraction for me in that one could ride abreast of the motorman. He is ensconced in a small compartment at the leading end extending to no more than half the width of the car and the remaining half, on the left hand side, has a passenger seat, from which there is an uninterrupted view of the line ahead. The operation generally is very smart, with rapid acceleration, smooth braking, and station stops sometimes as brief as seven seconds!

In Rotterdam a system of automatic train *control* is incorporated with the Westcode brake and they have gone so far as to dispense with wayside signals and give drivers of the manually driven trains the equivalent of those signals on a console in the cab of the train.

The anticipated difficulties of the transition period was one of the factors that

(Left) The Safety Box for the Victoria Line ATP system is mounted underneath a passenger seat.
(Right) As is the Autodriver box which automatically moves the train around from place to place without driver intervention.

influenced the original decision of the British Transport Commission some 25 years ago to standardise on the vacuum brake, in face of the unanimous recommendation of the technical committee to adopt the air brake. Although the use of rapid transit set trains and the new fixed-formation units like the Inter-City 125 HSTs, has assisted the change from vacuum to what will eventually be an entirely air braked railway, a considerable proportion of older stock, vacuum braked, still remains and Westinghouse has developed its own system to cope with a situation which, although transient, is of considerable concern. At the same time it is always customary for locomotives to be fitted with a brake that is independent of the automatic brake of either kind required when working a train.

Many years ago some of the British railways used steam brakes on their locomotives. Subsquently practice was to install straight air brake for the locomotive itself, operated by a separate brake valve and the train brake system, operated by a second valve which applied and released the brake on the locomotive in unison with the train brake. These systems have been devised to suit either form of train brake. With vacuum stock the locomotive brake is straight air vacuum controlled and with air braked stock there is conventional combination of straight air and automatic brake[2]. It will be appreciated that air brakes are always preferred on modern diesel or electric locomotives, on which space is at a premium on bogies packed with other equipment. Air brake cylinders are so very much smaller.

On railways that are in process of changing from vacuum to air brakes, to secure the maximum utilisation of the locomotives it is essential that they are equipped to work trains fitted with either brake. It is for this purpose that the Dual Brake system has been developed. This

1967 Tube Stock for the Victoria Line – still in service today (2006)

consists of an automatic air brake which operates in synchronism with the train brake, whether this latter be vacuum or air and the usual straight air brake that operates on the locomotive only. When coupling on to a train a manually operated switch, air or vacuum, is set in the appropriate position; and then, by a series of internal connections, the system is interlocked to ensure that the automatic brake on the locomotive is always controlled by the same medium as that in use on the train. More than a thousand sets of this equipment have been supplied to British Railways alone.

The standard automatic air brake, now usually referred to as the direct release air brake, as invented by George Westinghouse in 1872, epoch marking as it was at the time and successful in its world-wide application over the ensuing 70-odd years, had some considerable disadvantages when related to the increasingly demanding traffic conditions of the years since the end of the Second World War. One of its important features is that to release the brakes at the rear of a train it is necessary to raise the pressure in the brake pipe by no more than about 2lb per sq in to cause the triple valve to move to the release position and release of the brake proceeds at a rate controlled only by the timing choke. The auxiliary reservoir is recharged during this time, but its recharging has no connection with the release of the brake. A situation could, and sometimes did, arise that the brakes were fully released, but that the auxiliary reservoir was not sufficiently recharged to give a full application, if one were needed.

In Chapter 10 the changeover gear fitted on the wagons of the Polish State Railways was referred to, in endeavours to equate the release times to the recharge time of the auxiliary reservoirs. But at the beginning of that same chapter mention was made of the development of a graduated release valve for European conditions. This has now been adopted as standard.

Today the Graduated Release Distributor has taken the place of the triple valve as the heart of the automatic air brake. In this modern system each vehicle carries a control reservoir in addition to the brake cylinder and the auxiliary reservoir of the automatic direct release brake. The control reservoir can be described as a 'Standard

of reference'. It is charged initially to brake pipe pressure and, in conjunction with the distributor, enables the brake to be graduated on and off, with no risk of denuding the auxiliary reservoirs of air pressure if it should be needed again quickly for a reapplication.

The original form of the Graduated Release Automatic Brake used a single train pipe as in the original Westinghouse automatic brake. It nevertheless suffered from slow release times because of the need to use the same pipe for both power and control. During release these two functions were in conflict. To release the brakes rapidly a quick increase in brake pipe pressure is needed at a time when large quantities of air are being fed into the pipe to recharge the auxiliary reservoirs, and a single 1 in pipe has been found inadequate.

To overcome this difficulty the 'control' and 'power' functions of the brake have now been separated, and the Two Pipe system of Graduated Release Automatic Brake has been standardised on British

Code Selection and track circuit relays for the Victoria Line.

A Victoria Line Signal Equipment Room, with the electropneumatic interlocking on the left.

Railways. The auxiliary reservoirs are kept continuously cleared from the main reservoir pipe, while to release the brakes it is only necessary to recharge the brake pipe. With this arrangement the brake release times on the last vehicle of a long train are roughly halved – a big advantage in operating traffic such as that on British Railways. The latest development of the Distributor, the 'P4a', while designed for two pipe operation and particularly with British Railways in mind, is equally suitable for single pipe operation to UIC standards. It is a beautiful and intricate piece of modern engineering design, a worthy successor to the long range of eminently successful appliances in the history of the air brake. One feels sure that George Westinghouse himself, that most prolific and ingenious of inventors, would heartily approve!

At the same time it would be wrong to attribute all the honours in brake development in the period 1965-70 to the air brake, because at that time Gresham & Craven were busy introducing an improved vacuum brake system for long freight trains to conform with the appropriate UIC requirements. These had been drawn up solely with air braking in mind on the continent of Europe, whereas Gresham & Craven were looking particularly to India where the vacuum brake was standard. The system in use had indeed been so rigidly standardised over a period of some 40 years as to exclude many developments that had been made elsewhere. Nevertheless in India with the gaining of Independence there was at first a tendency to look outside the British Commonwealth for ideas and new equipment and the French, German and Japanese engineers were not backward in propagating their ideas. It was in this climate that Gresham & Craven developed their vacuum brake system to give a performance fully equal to UIC requirements.

Three stipulations may be noted:

a) On goods trains up to a limit of 200 axles the speed of transmission of brake action during emergency applications must be at least 250m/s.

b) The initial rise of pressure in the brake cylinder during any application must be sufficiently rapid to bring the blocks to the wheels quickly with not more than 10% of the ultimate pressure available.

c) The subsequent build up of brake pressure must be progressive and it must take between 20 and 28 seconds to obtain 95% of the maximum pressure possible.

The Gresham AFI Vacuum Brake System, designed by G C Marsh, using a trainpipe of 3.in diameter, incorporated freight type direct admission valves with inshot chambers and accelerator valves on each vehicle. The DA valve is fitted with a release choke and is also the timing part of the inshot chamber. These ensure an evenness of braking conditions throughout the length of the train. The following results were obtained on the test track at Worsley:

Train Length (ft)	No of 21 in Brake Cylinders	Time lag between front and rear of train (s)
2,000	92	2½
3,000	138	3¼
4,000	184	5

The rate of propagation was thus uniformly 800 ft /sec. It was shown that with a 3 in train pipe the brakes of a train of 3,600 tons, 2,000 ft long could be released in less than 60 seconds after a full emergency application.

Although the AFI system was designed primarily with India in view the first running trials were made on British Railways with a 70-wagon freight train and these confirmed that the AFI system gave application characteristics in accordance with UIC requirements for *air braked*

The Victoria Line Programme Machines which set routes for trains based on a 'pianola' principle of a punched celluloid roll passing over contacts

trains. In 1964 British Railways approved the AFI system and it was subsequently fitted to over 3,000 tank wagons and other

special vehicles for block train workings. British Railways also adopted Gresham & Craven's automatic empty load device for freight vehicles running empty. It was subsequently fitted to many tank wagons. It was in 1963 also that Gresham & Craven developed the EQ self-lapping vacuum brake control system, especially for long freight trains and to handle them on lengthy descending gradients. The new type of valve required that the handle position was the same for any required degree of braking, irrespective of the length of train. It was first fitted to a diesel-electric locomotive of British Railways for trials on passenger, partially-fitted and fully-fitted freight trains. At the same time trials were conducted in India. Five years later British Railways installed the EQ vacuum brake control system on 735 diesel electric locomotives, with 'passenger' and 'goods' timing – the latter controlling the reduction of brake pipe vacuum to a maximum rate of 0.66 in per second that ensured freedom from shocks when working long, loose coupled goods trains.

1 Many modern trains now use a system of air suspension, where the carriages basically ride on a cushion of compressed air, held within a flexible container similar in appearance to a tyre.

2 When E C Sharpe checked Nock's manuscript he commented 'No, no and again no. Auto air controls vacuum which in turn controls loco distribution'.

20
Momentous Evolution ~
Into the Hawker Siddeley Group

SINCE THE TIME of the Newark brake trials in 1875 six crucial years may be singled out in the business history of Westinghouse in the United Kingdom as milestones, either in the successive evolution of the Company, or the surmounting of a major crisis. The six years and their events were:

- 1881 – Incorporation of the Westinghouse Brake Company in England.
- 1901 – Formation of the Consolidated Signal Company (at first called the Pneumatic and Electric General Engineering Company), amalgamating the business interests of once bitterly rival signalling firms.
- 1920 – Formation of the Westinghouse Brake & Saxby Signal Company.
- 1937 – Disposal of American shareholding interests and becoming a wholly-owned British Company.
- 1955 – Defeat of takeover bid by Thorn Electrical.
- 1979 – Incorporation into the Hawker Siddeley Group.

The last named, which took place during the writing of this book might outwardly seem like succumbing to another takeover bid; but actually, of course, it was a highly important development on the long round of steady Westinghouse evolution. It was perhaps significant of the world-wide associations of the present Company that I was in Hong Kong at the time the news broke that negotiations towards it were in progress. In doing research work for this book I had been in the USA and Australia and was visiting the splendid Westinghouse team engaged on that mighty project, the Hong Kong Mass Transit Railway, the equipment and operation of which is described in the final chapter of this book. I must admit we were all a little startled by the news; but by the modern communication system we were put so completely in the picture as to be reassured that it was not a repetition of the Thorn affair.

It was no small business that was about to be incorporated in to Hawker Siddeley: eight Divisions of the Parent Company in England, four subsidiary companies and two associated companies in the United Kingdom; subsidiary companies in Australia, Canada, France, New Zealand and the USA and an associated company in South Africa. The development of the parent company alone is exemplified by there now being *eight* Divisions, against the three when the first Sales and Engineering Divisions were set up in 1951. Just at the

*Westinghouse Decking installation at
Harraton Colliery*

*Westinghouse Tilting Platforms and Articulated Rams
at Hickleton Main Colliery*

*Westinghouse Automatic Decking at Donisthorpe Colliery supplied to Messrs W. H. Baker & son to the
requirements of the National Coal Board*

time of writing their names are being slightly modified to identify their activities more precisely within the Hawker Siddeley Group thus:

1. Railway Brake Division becomes Westinghouse Brakes.
2. Signal & Mining Division becomes Westinghouse Signals.
3. Revenue Controls Division becomes Westinghouse Revenue Controls.
4. Rectifier Equipment Division becomes Westinghouse Davenset Rectifiers.
5. Semiconductor Division becomes Westcode Semiconductors.
6. Automation and Controls Division becomes Westcode Systems.
7. Foundry Division becomes Westinghouse Foundry.
8. Services Division becomes Westinghouse Services.

There was no change in the business conducted by the operating units, except that opportunity was taken to rationalise the mining activity. This was previously split between the Signal and Mining Division, covering the mechanised tub marshalling and associated controls developed from the original electro-pneumatic decking plants of the Power Company 60 years earlier and the purely automation business. All this work is now combined within Westcode Systems.

The change, so far as it affected those formerly in the Signal & Mining Division, coincided with the retirement after 53 years unbroken service of one of the great personalities of the engineering staff, George Gregory, who until 1967 was the Mining Manager. At the age of 14 he joined the staff of the old Signal Estimating Department, under Charles Venning, a chirpy little Cockney office boy; but he did not stay long inside and in two years he was out on installation work and served under such stalwarts as F J Flint, 'George' Stokes and Mostyn Gardner – to such effect

indeed that when only 24 he got his first job as Resident Engineer, in his own right, installing colour light signalling on the LNER branch between Clapton and Chingford. But it was towards the end of the Second World War, in 1944, that his big opportunity came. Fred Rayner, who had installed every colliery decking plant since the very first at Thurcroft, was approaching the retiring age and George Gregory was chosen for training as a possible successor.

He moved house and home to Rotherham, to be in one of the great centres of coal mining in this country and thus began a success story that was to gather momentum and prestige and to last for 32 years, for George proved not only that he could install plant, but he was one of those men who had the facility of getting on with everyone he met; and in so doing, building on the solid foundations that Fred Rayner had laid, he raised the level of Westinghouse prestige in the mining industry to quite unprecedented heights.

It was a time when the whole science of coal mining was in a process of evolution. In Great Britain many of the richest and most accessible seams had long been worked out and in tackling some of the most remote and difficult ones the problems of mechanical handling and transport became acute. Westinghouse became even more involved in the design and installation of mechanised plants to suit the changing circumstances. A notable trend was towards the use of much larger wagons for conveying the coal within the colliery precincts. The old-fashioned and hitherto almost universal 'tub' was a rough-and-ready, rather crude little job; its size had been determined largely by the ability of a man to push two or three of them when loaded, but with the development of the more sophisticated 'mine-car', carrying a much heavier load, the decking plants that had originally been designed for tubs, in

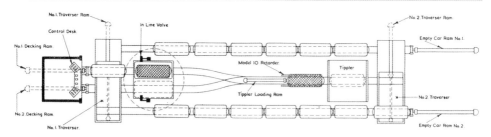

From the May 1954 Westinghouse Review, this diagram shows the decking layout at Donisthorpe.

the old style, were developed to provide a more highly mechanised system of car circulation and unloading at the pit top.

A remarkable compact and efficient pit-top circuit was put in at Donisthorpe Colliery, near Ashby-de-la-Zouch, in which the circulation of mine cars took place entirely within one large building, with no more than 16 cars circulating at any one time. This was indeed a most striking contrast to the old style, in which one had long lines of tubs, sometimes 100 or more, moving slowly between the pit cages and the discharging tipplers. There was inevitably much curvature in the circuit, where tubs running under gravity often stalled, or when running too fast became derailed.

Nevertheless, the introduction of mine-cars brought new problems of their own. With heavier loads in the cages and in many cases deeper levels from which the coal is wound, the stretch on the winding ropes was making it increasingly difficult to 'spot' the cages opposite to the decks, despite the traditional skill of the winding enginemen. To meet this difficulty, instead of running directly from deck or pit bottom level on to the cages, access was provided over a short bridge, or 'tilting platform' as it is known, which takes up the difference in level between cage and deck. As can well be imagined these platforms and their supports are a massive piece of structural engineering. Colliery equipment is always subject to very heavy use and the speed of winding and the power of the

Westinghouse pneumatic decking trains, to give the necessary speed of loading and unloading of the cages, subjects the tilting platforms to severe handling as the heavy mine-cars are rammed forward and over the 'bridge' and into the cages. It is a remarkable sight to see one of these installations in full action, with the operation of each appliance closely coordinated, working in rapid sequence and loading the heavy mine-cars onto the cages in a matter of seconds. No less gratifying to a Westinghouse man is to know how well the equipment, all made at Chippenham, is standing up to this truly punishing utilisation.

As in railway signalling and in all other engineering disciplines in which the Company has become specialists and indeed, among the world leaders, there is no finality in the technology of colliery mechanisation.

The Westinghouse Ticket Machines Company was formed in the 1930s[1] and in appreciation of the already extensive experience gained by several German manufacturers it was appropriate that, in seeking to take full advantage of this experience in launching out into this activity, two of the original four directors of this new company should have been from the Continent of Europe.[2]

The original activity of the Ticket Machine Company and indeed its sole activity, with variations on the theme, for nearly 30 years, was the design and manufacture of machines for printing tickets. This enabled railway administrations to avoid having to carry large stocks of pasteboard tickets and to maintain those stocks by guessing the future demand of tickets from B to Q or from G to L and so on. It was a wasteful and time-wasting survival of earlier railways' days: wasteful in that one inevitably accumulated large stocks of tickets for which the anticipated demand had dried up and time-wasting if a passenger asked for a ticket of which there was no printed one available and one had to be written out by hand.

The subsequent development into a situation from which Westinghouse can furnish systems providing *total management responsibility* for collecting fares from passengers, in a variety of circumstances and deliver audited results afterwards has taken place in the very short space of 15 years and like so many other outstanding Westinghouse developments it arose from the requirements of London

Transport and again by a diversification from basic signalling principles.[3]

The intricacies and problems associated with the whole practice of automatic fare collection were described and discussed at some length at a meeting of the IRSE in January 1967, following a paper by Mr B F Sharp of London Transport, but the mastermind behind this ingenious development, as with the automatic driving of trains on the Victoria Line, was Robert Dell.

Since then the Revenue Controls Division of Westinghouse, at first known as the Ticket Machine Division, has provided more than 1,500 machines to British Railways, including clerk-operated and coin operated ticket machines, while to London Transport alone more than 435 machines have been supplied. To this substantial home market the export business has been considerable including countries on the continent of Europe where the British Company does not normally

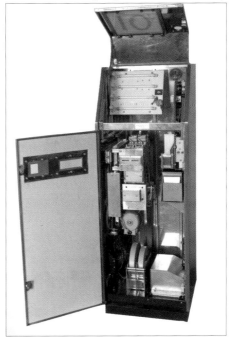

Westomat LT Electronically controlled coin operating heavy usage print and issuing machine, developed to the latest requirements of London Transport

expect to penetrate, such as West Germany, France, Denmark and Greece. At the time of writing this chapter the comprehensiveness of the activity can be appreciated from the following supplies:

- 3,100 Ticket Vending Machines
- 5,100 Automatic Gates
- 280 Excess Fare Machines
- 150 Computer Audit and control systems

The last named adds substantial weight to the assertion that the activity as a whole offers the possibility of total management responsibility.

At Chippenham the Ticket Machine Division, now Westinghouse Revenue Controls, is primarily concerned with the manufacture of equipment as in the case of the earliest developments in automatic fare collection, of which the system engineering was done by London Transport. Then, in 1951, there was established in the USA the Cubic Corporation with headquarters in San Diego, California, to market high technology electronic systems and equipment. From the outset it was concerned in international business and a subsidiary company, Cubic Tiltman Langley, was set up at Merstham, Surrey. This Company and its American counterpart, Cubic Western Data, in a short time achieved unparalleled eminence in the design and production of equipment for Automatic Fare Collection. An alliance with Westinghouse seemed to offer great benefits for both and Westinghouse obtaining an exclusive license to the Cubic technology in Automatic Fare Collection for the United Kingdom, Europe, Africa and the Middle East, a new company was formed, Westinghouse Cubic Ltd, under the Chairmanship of Eric J Harris, Executive Director, Railways of Westinghouse itself.

One of the first fruits of this new joint enterprise was the securing by Westinghouse Cubic Ltd of a multi-million pound contract from London Transport for one of the largest, most comprehensive automatic fare collection systems in the world. The award of it emphasises the distinction between Westinghouse Revenue Controls at Chippenham and the Westinghouse Cubic Company at Merstham. The latter organisation, combining the technical and financial resources and experience of Westinghouse with those of the Cubic Corporation, exists for the system engineering of complete projects for automatic fare collection and the presentation to prospective customers of complete packages, including computer audit and control systems. As such, systems extend far beyond the process of printing and issuing tickets to encompass what amounts to a total management responsibility. The contract received from London Transport is an outstanding example of this, using apparatus developed over many years at Chippenham by the former Ticket Machine Division.

At the time of the incorporation of Westinghouse into the Hawker Siddeley Group in 1979, one of the most noticeable differences between the signalling business then in operation and that of 1920 when the earlier great amalgamation took place, was the almost complete absence of any activity in South America. At the earlier milestone, with most of the Argentine railways and those of other developing countries in that continent British-owned or British-staffed, it was one of the largest and most open areas for export business. But at the end of the Second World War, with political changes, nationalisation of railways and a very difficult financial position in most of the countries involved, the market went dead. The opportunity for revival has come recently, not directly, but through our business associates Dimetal SA in Madrid.

Dimetronic

The Company has gone from strength to strength to become the major signalling supplier in Spain and Portugal, with exports, not only to South America, but also to Central Europe and the Far East. Dimetronic, together with Safetran Systems Corporation in the USA and Westinghouse Rail Systems Australia are sister companies to the current Westinghouse Rail Systems company in the UK. All are part of the Invensys Rail group.

Close collaboration with Westinghouse in the UK has benefited both companies, notably in the supply of automatic train control systems on Madrid and Barcelona Metros, several hundred WESTRACE electronic interlockings throughout Spain, extensive SSI electronic interlocking projects in Portugal and radio-based ETCS (European Train Control System) projects for the Spanish State Railways RENFE.

It was in collaboration with this company that Westinghouse carried out the important CTC signalling on the Madrid – Burgos direct line of the Spanish National Railways, the collaboration on this and other signalling projects was partly by licensing and partly by the supply of equipment. Dimetal was one of five subsidiaries in the Interholding Group, but as from 1 January 1979 the mechanical and signalling activities of Dimetal were separated by formation of a new Spanish company, Dimetronic SA, to deal solely with railway signalling and automation.

---

1 In fact Nock didn't mention when the Ticket Machines company was founded. The editors have, with the help of the Transport Ticket Society, been able to ascertain that the Westinghouse Ticket Machine Co was registered at 82 York Road. Various patents were granted from 1937 to 1939, the first of which was applied for in 1935, before our sources for Chapter 22 identified the company as existing! Further patents were granted to Westinghouse Brake & Signal Co Ltd from 1941 to 1943 and then a number of further patents were granted to Westinghouse Garrard from 1951 onwards.

2 In his manuscript, Nock stated: "In its initial stages the important diversification into the technique of ticket printing machines and automatic fare collection was marked by grievous personal tragedy." He then just noted as a point for further research "Air crash that killed two directors". We have been unable to find any reference to this incident.

3 In his manuscript Nock left a note: '1948 alliance with Garrards'. In 1948 Westinghouse Garrard Ticket Machines Ltd was constituted with Garrard Engineering and Manufacturing Co Ltd with the latter subscribing for 15,000 shares out of a total of 45,000 shares.

21
Into the New Era ~ Mass Transit ~ 200km/h

T HE CENTENARY of the incorporation of the Westinghouse Brake Company in England comes at a very exciting and colourful time in the history of the world's railways. It is not so very many years ago that informed opinion in many parts of the world, quite apart from the neophytes in popular journalism, considered that railways were on the way out. This of course was partly due to the rapid demise of long-distance rail travel in the USA in favour of air; but now the position elsewhere has changed dramatically and it is gratifying to reflect upon the way in which the constantly developing technology of the Westinghouse Group has contributed to this notable trend, both in Mass Transit and in High Speed Inter-City passenger service. Nevertheless on the majority of the world's largest railway networks freight remains the backbone of the activity and to this also, as referred to in the previous chapter, Westinghouse in England and Westcode in Pennsylvania has a massive contribution to make.

In England, the efficiency of the London Transport Railways is now taken for granted, together with the magnificent technology by which the automatic driving of trains on the Victoria Line is safely achieved. Since that memorable March 7 1969 when Her Majesty Queen Elizabeth II opened the final section of the line it has carried Londoners and their visitors in their

millions and to them it has somewhat naturally been regarded as just another tube railway. But the application of the same principles of operation to relieve the ever-increasing traffic congestion in Hong Kong has resulted in one of the most spectacular and successful projects with which Westinghouse has ever been associated.

Taken all round the Mass Transit Railway is the largest and most complex engineering job in Hong Kong's history. While the civil engineering was by far the largest part of the undertaking, with construction of the cross-harbour tunnel involving boring through rock and decomposed granite, excavation of huge holes for the cut and cover construction of stations, and the submerged tube for construction of the cross-harbour section of the tunnelling, Westinghouse was entrusted with the manufacture of the complex and varied equipment necessary for running the trains. This included the signalling throughout, the automatic train control – which includes automatic train operation and automatic train protection – automatic train supervision and also the Power Remote Control System, supervising the 33kV and 11kV transmission lines and, of course, the electro-pneumatic brake equipment on the trains themselves. It was a remarkable example of what can be termed total project control.

As on the Victoria Line in London, the overall job of automatically driving the trains is separated into two distinct parts, consisting of the 'safety' and 'non-vital' features. The former is referred to, in the latest system developed by Westinghouse, as Automatic Train Protection (ATP) and establishes the maximum safe speed on any section of the line by conventional signalling interlocking, conveyed to the train by the fail-safe ATP system. The second controls the speed of the train while running under clear signals and provides for maximum efficiency and effective run-up to precise stopping points in stations. Safety is an inherent feature of the system and appropriate alarms and indications alert the driver to faults. If necessary the train is either brought to a halt at once or prevented from leaving the next station under automatic control.

The Central Control Room for the whole railway is also fully equipped by Westinghouse for completely automatic supervision of train running. For many years now the Company has manufactured the ingenious programme machines used on London Transport, whereby the train working for a whole day can be set in advance. In Hong Kong this principle is also used, with a computer-based central control scheme capable of operating the entire railway in accordance with any one of a number of stored timetables. This system automatically routes and despatches trains at the pre-arranged timetable intervals. On the Line Controller's desk there are closed-circuit television visual display units showing the situation on the platforms of the busiest stations.

At the time the contracts were placed for this very important work it was appreciated that among the teeming population of Hong Kong there would be no personnel having any familiarity with modern signalling technique, either with the equipment itself or in the operation, and an important part of the contract was to supply an Operating Task Trainer. This, in a highly sophisticated way, was following in a Westinghouse tradition set up more than 70 years previously when the first-ever illuminated track diagram was installed on the Metropolitan District Railway, at Acton Town – then known as Mill Hill Park. Associated with it was one of the early electro-pneumatic power interlocking frames. Many years later when I was writing a biographical note at the time of his retirement, Captain Peter told me that the signalmen, used to full-size levers and mechanical semaphore signals, were scared stiff of it and that he had to work the frame for the first week of its service – training the signalmen meanwhile. He did have the advantage, however, that the men

Hong Kong MTRC Control Panel

An ATO Controller for Hong Kong MTRC

(Above) A train to Shek Kip Mei arrives at a Ngau Tau Kok station on the elevated section of Hong Kong MTRC. (Right) A view over a MTRC driver's shoulder, with target speed indicators clearly visible around the speedometer dial.

were fully experienced in the basics of railway signalling. It was not so in Hong Kong.

For the Mass Transit Railway, the Operating Task Trainer uses a model which is about 30 yards square and has a fleet of electric trains which run under full automatic train protection as on the real railway. Each station is equipped with a full-size signalling control console, as in real-life and a full-size line regulator's console allows an instructor or a trainee regulator to supervise the running of the entire system. The trainer is used to demonstrate procedures to overcome such problems as stalled trains, or track circuit or points failures. Trainees are able to see, on the model, how a single incident affects the rest of the system. No more vivid or effective way of inducting trainee operators into the principles of running a modern mass-transit railway could have possibly been devised; and the success with which the railway has run from its very inception is an eloquent testimony to its value.

I shall not forget my own visit to Hong Kong in December 1978, roughly a year before the opening of the first section of the railway. Apart from the utter fascination of the Colony itself and the dramatically beautiful situation of the twin cities of Victoria and Kowloon, some of the open sections of the new railway were sufficiently complete for trial running to be in progress and I was able to experience the precise accuracy with which stops under full automatic control were made at the stations. I was also able to travel on the main line railway of the Colony, the British section of the Kowloon-Canton Railway from Kowloon up to the border with the Peoples Republic of China at Lo Wu. Negotiations were then in progress towards the contract Westinghouse has since received for the re-signalling of this 20 ½ miles of vital connectional railway – so important in the modern context as to be converted from single to double line throughout, and electrified at 25kV. The whole line will be controlled from a Westinghouse panel signal box at the Hung Hom terminal in Kowloon and will not only be equipped with multiple aspect colour light signalling throughout, but will have the British Railways type automatic warning system, with audible signals in the driving cabs of the trains.

What is perhaps even more significant, in this present age of Westinghouse evolution, is that the railway contracts in

A train passes over the Kowloon Bay Depot complex

and subsidiary cables, a telephone exchange, public address system and platform indicators and signal post telephones. The contract also includes a 4-digit, computer-based train describer and a WESDAC microprocessor based system for the remote control of the traction power substations. These systems are to be integrated with the signalling control panel at Hung Hom. Already the passenger and freight traffic flowing over this line has grown to almost embarrassing proportions and the ultramodern systems of signalling and overall control now in process of installation will enable it to be handled with high efficiency.

Hong Kong are not concerned solely with signalling and brakes. In connection with the Mass Transit Railway reference has already been made to the system of Automatic Train Supervision applied to the entire system; but Westinghouse also received the contract for the control and monitoring system for the power supply network for driving the trains. To supervise the 11kV power distribution and the 33kV traction substations a telemetry control is used, based on dual computers, through which fully duplicated telemetry links monitor the outstations located at each passenger station, at the cross-harbour tunnel portal and at the car depot at Kowloon Bay. In the project three master stations scan between them fifteen out-stations and display the information on VDUs mounted on a power regulator's control desk. A mimic diagram mounted immediately above the desk displays what can be termed an 'overview' of the state of the complete network.

On the Kowloon – Canton Railway (British Section) Westinghouse is not only providing the complete modernisation of the signalling, but is also main contractor for a new and comprehensive telecommunications network. This provides trunk

For sheer spectacular operation on railways however the High Speed and Advanced Passenger Trains of British Railways have taken a predominating place in recent years, in the forefront of the railway 'come-back' in inter-city passenger business. The cornerstone on which these remarkably successful services have been built up is once again the vital interface between signalling and brake power. The present-day network of British Railways is outstanding among the world's systems in the remarkably mixed nature of the traffic conveyed, even on its fastest and busiest routes. The maximum speed of the Intercity HST and APT services, of 125mph, is equalled by a few trains in France and slightly exceeded by the Shinkansen 'bullet-trains' of the Japanese National Railways; but there is no comparison in the conditions of working. The French trains run over routes that are relatively sparsely used, while the Japanese use routes that are exclusive to very high speed trains. The standard British multiple-aspect system of colour light signalling; introduced more than 55 years ago, has proved remarkably successful in providing maximum line capacity for a 'mixed' traffic and it was adopted without hesitation when large scale

The Advanced Passenger Train (APT)

To read many contemporary history papers, you would be forgiven for believing that the massive APT project was a complete disaster. This is not the case. Much of the technology that was developed for this forerunner of all today's modern tilting trains, can trace its history directly to this project.

The project was aimed specifically at supplying rolling stock capable of greatly reducing journey times on the West Coast Main Line between London and Scotland. In places this line has series of tight curves, and there are steep gradients to be contended with. Research started in the 1960s into new technologies such as tilting trains, enhanced braking systems, ground-breaking traction systems, increased supply of information to the driver to allow faster trains to use existing infrastructure (including signalling) and very advanced bogie technology.

The train sets were built at British Rail Engineering Limited in Derby, and they were introduced into service in 1979. By 1982-3 however they were still only managing to supply three services a week, due to problems with reliability and the sheer complexity of the vehicles.

APT was never a commercial success, but was clearly responsible for a step change in rolling stock technology.

resignalling of the principal main lines was authorised in the great modernisation plan of British Railways in 1954.

At that time the maximum speed envisaged for passenger trains was 100mph and the signal spacing was designed to accord with the 'W' curve of braking distances in relation to speeds of running. This gives the following basic quantities:

Speed (mph)	Service Braking Distance (Yds)
60	710
75	1,140
90	1,675
100	2,220

The above distances provide for a comfortable retardation, while of course emergency stops could be made in considerably less distances, though not entirely to the comfort of the passengers. The distances show that if the signal spacing is arranged to provide for 100mph running on green aspects, a train running at a maximum speed of 75mph can take the double-yellow aspect as its clear signal, because it needs only half the distance to stop in service braking conditions. This, in

a vastly higher speed range, follows the principle postulated when four-aspect colour light signals of Westinghouse make were installed in the London suburban area of the Southern Railway, at spacings that provided for 70mph running by longer distance express passenger trains using the green aspect and the close-interval suburban trains taking the double-yellow as their clear signal.

Other factors remaining the same, however and increases in maximum speed to 125mph or even more, would have led to an unacceptable situation so far as braking distance was concerned; because the British Railways 'W' curve[1] did not extend beyond a speed of 100mph. It is clear from extrapolation that from a speed of 125mph the service braking distance would have been well in excess of 3,500 yards. And so, modern braking technique has been applied to these very high speed trains to enable them to stop from their maximum speed in the same distance, or less, than the fast express trains of the previous generation stopped from theirs. The brakes on the high speed diesel trains now operating in the Western Region and on the East Coast Main

Line have a service braking distance from 125mph of 2,000 yards in comparison to the 2,250 yards of the 'W' curve for locomotive hauled stock from 100mph.

On the Advanced Passenger Train, designed for a service maximum speed of 155mph and which has attained 160mph on test, the actual retardation is produced by hydrokinetic brakes which use the principle of the water turbine, in reverse. As with every other form of braking with which the Company has been associated through the Century of its existence, Westinghouse, in this latest development, is not responsible for the final link in the chain, that of the physical application of the retarding force – as with the brake blocks in the conventional on-tread type of brake, or in the later types of disc brake. But in engineering the control it is appreciated that the hydrokinetic brake provides a very attractive alternative to any form of direct friction brake, either of the on-tread type, which at the speeds involved would produce excessive temperatures, or of the disc type. It hardly needs to be added that in applying the principle of the water turbine to the braking of a high speed train and its electro-pneumatic control every care has been taken to build in all the safety features that have been established over the past hundred years in railway braking techniques.

A hundred years of speed with safety: the British APT forms a very appropriate culmination to this account of Westinghouse achievement in a century of steady and at times very rapid development. Because of the many ramifications and plain mechanics of book production the manuscript must be produced nearly a year before the actual anniversary of the date of incorporation of the Westinghouse Brake Company in England; and in this breathless age much can happen in a mere twelve months! There is however always a chance to add items of late news at the time of proof correction. In the meantime looking back at Prout's classic biography of the founder and being amazed once again at the astonishing number of companies that he himself set in motion – 76 up to the time of his death in 1914 – one feels that George Westinghouse would approve of the prowess of the English Company, not least in the ultimate triumph of the air brake on the railways of Great Britain.

---

1 As you will recall from Chapter 11, the 'W' curve is a graph which shows required braking distance from a given linespeed for a 'standard' rolling stock, used to design the signalling layout for a railway.

22
Chronology, Facts and Figures

THIS IS THE ONLY CHAPTER in this book that has been added to Nock's original manuscript. It brings together information from several sources to summarise the rapid growth and change of what was to become Westinghouse Brake & Signal Co Ltd over the first century of its existence.

As the first centenary of the Westinghouse name in the UK loomed in the late 1970s, there was increased interest in the history of the Company, and a large number of people invested a lot of effort in trying to write down key events and dates in that history. This chapter takes information from a variety of sources and presents it in a number of different ways.

It should be pointed out that not every date from every source corresponds to every other source, and in particular to Nock's manuscript. We have simply reproduced the data that we have available to us, and

pointed out some of the discrepancies.

The first table is a Chronological History of the development of the Company. Based largely on a history of the Australian Company, this has a distinctly Antipodean feel to it, but shows clearly the global reach of the Company as it developed. References 1 to 21 in the table that follows this Chronology were made from the Australian document, Reference 22 was a similar document constructed in the UK in the early 1970s.

The second table lists the primary trading names of the Company, their principle location, and their date of constitution.

The third table then documents the growth of the Chippenham site from 1894 to the mid 1970s, giving a real insight into the rapid growth of the Company in Chippenham following the Second World War.

Table 1: Chronology of Westinghouse up to 1981

Date	Event	Source

1821   John Saxby born 17th August near Hurstpierpoint, 7 miles from Brighton, Sussex. He became a carpenter and joiner, eventually becoming a shop foreman, Locomotive Department, of the London, Brighton and South Coast Railway until his resignation in April 1862.   1

1825   First steam-worked public railway in England opened between Stockton and Darlington on 26th September, the engine 'Locomotion' driven by George Stephenson.   2

1827   John Stinson Farmer born. He was Assistant Traffic Manager of the London, Brighton and South Coast Railway from 1849 to his resignation in 1862.   1

1841   Mr Hutton Gregory, Engineer to the London and Croydon line, constructed and erected at New Cross in South London the first semaphore signal for railway use, an adaptation of Pasley's apparatus used in the Royal Navy for exchanging messages.   1

1846   On 6th October George Westinghouse was born in Central Bridge, Schoharie County, New York, USA.   3

1856   John Saxby took out his first patent, number 1479 dated 24th June, costing £155, for a mode of working simultaneously the points and signals of railways at junctions to prevent accidents.   2

     Westinghouse's father established an agricultural works in Schenectady called 'G Westinghouse & Co'.   2, 20

1859   A partnership was formed to purchase the Vulcan Iron Works, located on the canal near the railway viaduct in Worcester, comprising of three men:

     Thomas Clunes, newly arrived from Aberdeen, where he had conducted a business of plumbing, brass foundry and gas apparatus manufacture, trading as Thomas Clunes and Co, his partner being his younger brother, James Torrie Clunes.

     Alexander Clunes Sherriff, born 1816 in Leeds, Yorkshire, brother-in-law of Thomas Clunes, General Manager of the Oxford, Worcester and Wolverhampton Railway from 1856 to 1863.

     Edward Wilson, Chief Engineer of the Oxford, Worcester and Wolverhampton Railway.   9

1860   A railway guide book advertisement described Thomas Clunes & Co, as 'Engineers, Millwrights, Brass Founders and Plumbers' of 'Vulcan Works Worcester' and manufacturing 'Iron Girder Bridges and Railway Work in general.   9

     January 5th, an employee of the North London Railway, Austin Chambers, patented (No 31) a device which was the first specification of true interlocking between signals – 'A movement which is dependent on another cannot even commence until such other movement has been fully completed.'   1

     A partnership of Engineer John Saxby and John Stinson Farmer, a man of means, was formed to open a small works near Hayward's Heath, Sussex.   2

     Saxby took out Patent 1754, dated July 19th, for a mechanism which carried out the true principle of interlocking of points and signals. The patent described him as 'Signal Manufacturer'. However this simultaneous motion patent did not include the principle of Austin Chambers' patent, number 31.   1

Date	Event	Source
	George Westinghouse commenced work in his father's factory in May.	2, 20
1861	Walter Holland joined Thomas Clunes in a partnership to make signals, Holland's wealth contributing to the formation of the new company. Up to this time Holland had been an employee of the Oxford, Worcester and Wolverhampton Railway.	9
1862	John McKenzie, Locomotive Superintendent of the West Midland Railway, joined the partnership.	9
	McKenzie & Holland obtained sole manufacturing rights, until 1867, to the locking frame patented by Austin Chambers. McKenzie, Clunes and Holland commenced production of the locking frame at the Clunes works and were so successful that a large new works was built in Worcester to expand the business. Apprentices who became leaders of the firm in later years were S T Dutton, S P Wood and W Griffiths.	3
	Saxby and Farmer moved their works from Brighton to Kilburn Lane, later known as Canterbury Road, Kilburn, London, and traded as 'Patent Railway Signal Works'. Eventually up to 2,000 people were employed including outdoor staff.	1
1863	Formal agreement between Saxby and Farmer signed. Charles Hodgson, aged 21, took charge of the general office and administrative work.	1
	George Westinghouse joined the Union forces in June, and was promoted to the Navy as a junior engineer, in September, aged 17. (The American Civil War had started in 1861).	2, 20
1865	The name of McKenzie, Clunes & Holland changed to McKenzie & Holland.	2
	George Westinghouse returned home after the Civil War finished on April 18th. He attended the Union College, Schenectady, New York, for three months only, then worked for his father. On October 31st he took out his first patent for a rotary steam engine.	2, 20
1866	McKenzie & Holland took out a patent, number 1963, for interlocking between levers, an invention of Thomas Clunes' brother James Torrie Clunes.	9
	James Gresham, a 27 year old draughtsman, formed a partnership with a Mr Heron, wire mattress manufacturer, to make boiler feed injectors, a patent of a Frenchman, Henri Giffard, near Manchester. Domestic sewing machines were also made.	2
1867	Saxby & Farmer purchased outright Patent number 31 of January 5th 1860 from Austin Chambers for £2,000.	1
	On February 12th George Westinghouse invented an 'Improved Railroad Switch for replacing derailed cars.'	2, 20
	Westinghouse conceived the idea of the air brake.	2
1869	Saxby & Farmer sued McKenzie & Holland for infringement of the 1860 patent rights. The case was fought in various courts until it reached the House of Lords in 1874.	3
	Westinghouse, at 22 years of age, was working as a salesman for the firm of Anderson and Cook when he patented the first air brake for railway coaches.	3, 7
	April 13th. The first successful test of the air brake was made on the train 'Steubenville Accommodation' which comprised a 4-4-0 locomotive, tender and three passenger cars of the PRR–controlled Pittsburgh, Cincinnati, Chicago and St Louis railroad, commonly known as the Panhandle Division.	20, 21
	Forming the Westinghouse Air Brake Co in Pittsburgh, Pennsylvania, USA on	

Date	Event	Source
	September 28th, Westinghouse commenced manufacture of the air brake, initially for the Pennsylvania railroad.	3, 7
1870	Tom Craven joined the partnership of Gresham & Heron, and it became Gresham, Heron & Craven.	2
1871	In order to handle export orders from the USA the Westinghouse Continuous Brake Co was formed.	3
1873	Thomas Clunes left the partnership. His brother, James Torrie Clunes, was employed by the firm until 1903.	9
1874	On June 22nd the House of Lords decided in favour of McKenzie & Holland.	3
1875	The Westinghouse Continuous Brake Company opened a depot in Crinan Street, Kings Cross, London.	13
	February 23rd – W R Sykes patented the 'Lock and Block' system of working.	
1876	The Westinghouse Continuous Brake Co established a technical and sales office in Liverpool with small production facilities.	2, 3, 11, 22
1878	An engineer, William J Griffiths, was sent by McKenzie & Holland to Sydney to organise the firm's display at the International Exhibition of 1879 / 1880. The exhibit won the First Degree of Merit. 'The Record' described the exhibit as 'working models of railway station and junction, illustrating the interlocking and working of points, signals and level crossing gates on railways.' The judges reported that 'this arrangement of interlocking, etc., has the merit of great efficiency, combined with moderate cost.'	3
	In England the Westinghouse Continuous Brake Co moved from Liverpool to Westminster, London.	3
	Saxby & Farmer established works at Creil, Department of Oise, France, Saxby directing the works from 1888 until he retired in 1900.	1
1879	September, John Parry of McKenzie & Holland, England, arrived in Sydney to supervise the Firm's exhibit.	15
	Mr Heron of Gresham, Heron & Craven was bought out and the business became 'Gresham & Craven'.	2
	The Vacuum Brake Company formed in London to purchase patents and set up a sales organisation. Gresham & Craven were appointed sole manufacturers.	2
	Thomas Clunes (Senior) died having fathered ten children, three of whom were boys.	9
1880	W Liley was sent to Australia as McKenzie & Holland's representative.	3
	March. John Parry, of McKenzie & Holland, appointed to supervise the installation of an interlocking system at Campbelltown Junction for New South Wales Railways (completed in 1883).	15
	The Westinghouse Continuous Brake Company moved from Westminster to Crinan Street, King's Cross, London.	3
	Saxby & Farmer won an award for their exhibit at the Melbourne International Exhibition of 1880.	1
	Westinghouse invented a pneumatic system of interlocking signals.	2
1881	In November the Westinghouse Brake Co Ltd was incorporated in England and took over the assets and liabilities of the Westinghouse Continuous Brake Co of Pittsburgh. Manufacturing and marketing of the railway air brake system commenced at King's Cross. George Westinghouse appointed President and	

Date	Event	Source
	Managing Director at a salary of £500 per month whilst in Europe, or travelling between Europe and America. Sir Henry Tyler, MP, appointed Vice President and Chairman of the Board.	3, 22
	The Union Switch & Signal Co (US&S) was founded by Westinghouse in Pittsburgh in May to manufacture pneumatic interlocking switch and signal apparatus. He took out his first signalling patent on February 1st.	7
	W R Sykes formed the W R Sykes Interlocking Signal Company at Nunhead, London, later moving to Clapham and Peckham (four miles and one mile away respectively).	22
	The Railway Signal Company Ltd was established with a London office at Caxton House (later at 40 Broadway), Westminster and works at Fazakerley, Liverpool.	
1884	Sidney P Wood, who had served his apprenticeship at the Worcester Engine Works, was sent to Australia by McKenzie & Holland to start up the Spotswood, Victoria, factory, known as 'Semaphore Iron Works', on two acres of land.	3
	Documents for formation of German Branch Company completed.	22
1885	Hannover works purchased.	22
1886	Westinghouse founded 'The Westinghouse Electric Company' on January 8th to manufacture electric lighting apparatus.	7
	The operations of the Union Switch & Signal Co were moved from Pittsburgh to Swissvale.	
1888	The Queensland Government invited McKenzie & Holland to establish a works in Brisbane for manufacture and supply of railway signalling equipment.	4
	Saxby & Farmer partnership dissolved. Saxby took the French works as his share in the business.	1
	McKenzie & Holland exhibited a display at the Centennial International Exhibition in Melbourne.	8
	Nikola Tesla, a Croatian, took out patents in the USA for the alternating current induction motor on May 1st. Westinghouse paid $60,000 on July 7th, to secure exclusive rights to the patents, plus royalties on equipment produced.	16
1889	Samuel Telford Dutton of Marl Bank, Worcester, an employee of McKenzie & Holland, left the UK firm and formed his own company, Dutton & Co Ltd at Worcester.	2
	An area of land was surveyed at Northgate, then the terminus of the Brisbane railway system, and granted to McKenzie & Holland as a site for the new works.	4
	On January 28th 2.035 acres of land at Spotswood, Victoria, was transferred to Walter Holland of Worcester from the Victorian Railway Commissioners for a sum of approximately £216.	6
	McKenzie & Holland were awarded the 'First Order of Merit' on January 31st in the appliance section of the 1888 Melbourne Exhibition.	
1890	A three year contract for the supply of signalling equipment was entered into on July 1st with Queensland Railways by McKenzie & Holland and the Northgate factory commenced operation under the trading style of 'Toombul Iron Interlocking Works' (later 'Toombul Iron Works').	4
	May 28th. Northgate land transferred to Walter Holland of Norton Hall, Worcester, England, engineer, of an area one acre three roods and ten perches. Further land was purchased in 1909.	6

Date	*Event*	*Source*

	Minute appointing George Westinghouse Managing Director cancelled. Albert Kapteyn appointed General Manager and Secretary.	22
1891	February 17th the firm of McKenzie & Holland joined 'Ironmasters Association of Victoria'. A fee of £500 was paid by Walter and Herbert Holland, through their attorney, Sidney P Wood. At this time 83 workmen were employed at 'Spottiswoode' (now Spotswood).	5, 10
	New works purchased at Sevran for French Branch.	
1892	June. Westinghouse Brake Company moved to 82 York Road, King's Cross, London.	2
	John Stinson Farmer died in December at Ifold, Sussex.	1
	Heatley & Gresham Ltd, opened a depot at Entally, Calcutta, India, to handle imports of vacuum brakes to India.	2
1893	Saxby & Farmer became a registered company, Saxby & Farmer Ltd, on May 4th. Charles Hodgson appointed Managing Director and later Chairman of the Board. The Chief Office was at 53 Victoria Street, Westminster, London.	1, 3
1894	McKenzie & Holland took over the patents relating to the electro-pneumatic signalling system owned by the Westinghouse Brake Co Ltd of London, which was a subsidiary company of the Westinghouse Air Brake Co of Pittsburgh, Pennsylvania, USA.	3
	J P O'Donnell, patent agent and representative of Dutton & Co, Worcester and A G Evans, formed 'Evans O'Donnell & Co Ltd' to manufacture railway signal appliances and purchased from Jones & Bayliss & Co a small engineering shop and foundry known as 'The Foundry' in Foundry Lane, Chippenham, Wiltshire. A catch handle type of frame which used a motion designed by F A Atkinson, Patent number 1463 of January 27th 1891, was manufactured. A London office was opened at Palace Chambers, Westminster.	1, 2, 4
1897	Evans O'Donnell built the first shops of the present Chippenham Works in which mechanical signalling, points and rollers and roller bearings were manufactured, some of which were used on 'Big Ben' in London.	2
1898	The Consolidated Pneumatic Tool Co moved into part of the Evans O'Donnell workshops and installed precision machinery.	
	Societe Anonyme Westinghouse formed in St Petersburg, Russia.	22
1899	W R Sykes Interlocking Signal Co became a limited company.	2
	May. J W Cloud appointed Vice President and Managing Director of Westinghouse, A Kapteyn and H H Westinghouse appointed Directors.	22
1900	Westinghouse entered into arrangements with McKenzie & Holland Ltd, which resulted in an amalgamation in 1907.	4
	Northwood and Spotswood (Australia) operated as separate branches of McKenzie & Holland, but combined reports were submitted to London from 1901 to 1918.	4
1901	McKenzie & Holland, Saxby & Farmer Ltd, Dutton & Co Ltd and Evans O'Donnell and Co Ltd, all competitors of each other, joined together to form 'The Pneumatic, Electric and General Engineering Co Ltd' on August 16th. Dutton & Co transferred to Chippenham.	2
	On October 9th, McKenzie & Holland Ltd registered as a Company in England, having an office in London at 61 Sinclair Road, West Kensington Park, and later	

Date	Event	Source
	at 119 Victoria Street, Westminster.	3, 4
	The first of the objects listed in the Memorandum and Articles of Association was 'To acquire the business of Railway Signal Manufacturers, Iron and Brass Founders, and General Engineers now carried on by Walter Holland, William Griffiths, Sidney Prescott Wood and William Thomas Page in partnership as McKenzie & Holland at the City of Worcester and elsewhere in England, and at the Semaphore Works, Melbourne, Victoria, Australia and the Toombul Interlocking works, Brisbane, Queensland Australia and undertake the whole or any part of the assets and liabilities of the said firm in connection with the said business.'	4
	The Heatley Gresham Engineering Co was formed at Letchworth, Hertfordshire, to make small oil engines for India.	2
	Sale to new French company Societe Anonyme Westinghouse of effects and business of French branch.	22
1902	Evans O'Donnell & Co Ltd property at Chippenham was leased by Saxby & Farmer Ltd.	1, 2, 4
	Westinghouse enter into agreement with McKenzie and Holland concerning electro-pneumatic signalling.	
1903	The Pneumatic, Electric & General Engineering Co Ltd changed its name to 'The Consolidated Signal Co'. The Company acquired over 90% of the shares in Saxby & Farmer Ltd.	1
	Saxby & Farmer transferred their operations from Kilburn to Chippenham.	
1904	Saxby & Farmer moved their offices from Kilburn to 53 Victoria Street, Westminster, but retained the premises for subsidiary purposes until 1906.	2
	Terms for manufacture of Morse Chains agreed.	22
1905	Saxby & Farmer Ltd established a works at Entally, Calcutta Ltd, trading as Saxby & Farmer (India) Ltd	1
	Heatley & Gresham Entally depot and works in India sold to Saxby & Farmer of Chippenham.	2
	Agreement with J W Cloud for assignment of his vacuum brake patents.	22
1906	Saxby & Farmer sold the Kilburn Works.	1
	Heintz Heating Company formed. Cia Italiana Westinghouse di Freni formed.	22
1907	McKenzie & Holland Ltd, England combine with the Westinghouse Brake Co Ltd to form the McKenzie, Holland & Westinghouse Power Signal Co Ltd, the office being at 58 Victoria Street, Westminster, London, in order to develop the business of automatic power signalling, first introduced into England by the Westinghouse Brake Co Ltd, pneumatic equipment being made by Westinghouse at King's Cross, London and the mechanical equipment made by McKenzie & Holland at Worcester.	2
	July. Westinghouse Brake Company of Australasia Ltd was incorporated in New South Wales.	3
	Bellamy and Lambie Ltd founded in Johannesburg, South Africa, to supply engineering equipment to the gold and diamond mines of the Transvaal.	19
1909	April 19th. Northgate property (Australia) extended with purchase of four acres of land in the name of McKenzie & Holland Ltd, and included the original one acre, three rood and ten perches.	2, 3

Date	Event	Source
1911	November. Westinghouse Brake Co of Australasia Ltd established at Concord West, New South Wales, for the manufacture of air brake equipment.	
1912	Charles Hodgson of Saxby & Farmer Ltd, died in London, aged 70.	1
	Westinghouse Bremsen GmbH formed to take over business and plant of German branch of London company (excluding the land).	22
1913	John Saxby died, aged 92, at 'North Court', Hassocks, Sussex.	1
1914	March 12th. George Westinghouse died, aged 67, in New York City, of a severe cold caught when fishing. He had been granted 361 US patents and established 60 companies in the US and other countries.	7
	James Gresham, founder of Gresham & Craven Ltd died.	2
1915	51% of capital of Westinghouse Bremsen GmbH sold to Westinghouse Air Brake Co of USA (WABCO). Union Switch & Signal acquired equal number of shares in McKenzie Holland and Westinghouse Power Signal Co, with McKenzie and Holland and Westinghouse Brake Co. H G Brown appointed Managing Director of joint signal company.	
	Control of S A Westinghouse, Paris sold to British Westinghouse Electric and Manufacturing Co Ltd. The Brake business and works at Freinville were excluded from the sale. Cie des Freins Westinghouse formed.	22
1917	The Union Switch & Signal Co became a part of the Westinghouse Air Brake Company.	7
1918	W R Sykes Interlocking Signal Co Ltd became associated with Westinghouse.	2
1919	Company in general meeting agreed to sale of Morse Chain business to Westinghouse Morse Chain Co Ltd of Letchworth. 22,000 shares out of 60,000 were subscribed for by the Company.	22
1920	Dr Lars O Grondahl (born in Minnesota, 1880) was Professor of Physics at Pittsburgh's Carnegie Institute of Technology (now Carnegie-Mellon University) when the Union Switch & Signal company hired him to head their Research & Development Department. One of his first projects resulted in the discovery of the principle of the copper-oxide rectifier.	11, 20
	Westinghouse Brake Co Ltd combined with Saxby & Farmer Ltd, The Consolidated Signal Co Ltd, and McKenzie Holland & Westinghouse Power Signal Co Ltd to form the 'Westinghouse Brake & Saxby Signal Co Ltd' operating at 82 York Road, King's Cross, London. J W Cloud appointed Chairman, H G Brown Managing Director and B H Peter, Chief Engineer.	2
	Manufacture of all signalling equipment except pneumatic items, e.g. signal and point cylinders, was transferred from London to Chippenham between 1920 and 1923.	21
	McKenzie & Holland of Worcester transferred the business and plant to the Chippenham works of Evans O'Donnell & Co Ltd.	2
1921	McKenzie & Holland closed down at Worcester.	3
	A private company was formed, although inoperative, to retain the name 'McKenzie & Holland'.	
	Saxby & Farmer moved from Westminster to King's Cross where their affairs were finally liquidated. A new company with nominal capital was formed to retain possession of its well known name.	1, 2
1922	Westinghouse Brake & Saxby Signal Co Ltd applied for a UK patent, case number

Date	Event	Source
	6194, dated March 7th, for the US&S design of the copper-oxide rectifier.	2
1923	January 9th. The two Australian branches of McKenzie & Holland Ltd were formed into a separate company, McKenzie & Holland (Australia) Pty Ltd, with its head office at Spotswood and a branch at Northgate.	3, 4, 5
	Saxby & Farmer (India) Ltd registered as a company in Calcutta.	1
	Evans O'Donnell & Co Ltd ceased to exist as a manufacturing concern and became ground landlords of the Chippenham premises.	1
1925	Production of copper-oxide metal rectifiers commenced in the Electric Signalling Shop at Chippenham.	19
1926	The York Road foundry moved to Chippenham.	2
	Copper-oxide rectifiers first applied on the Great Western Railway, outside Paddington.	19
1927	McKenzie & Holland (Australia) Pty Ltd installed presses and ancillary equipment at Spotswood to produce plastic mouldings.	12
	Development of the metal rectifier by the Westinghouse Brake & Saxby Signal Co Ltd in conjunction with US&S reached a stage where a private exhibition was held at Chippenham to demonstrate the application of the rectifier not only to railway signalling as first intended but to various branches of electrical engineering.	11
1928	Assembly and Process Shop built at Chippenham for copper-oxide rectifier units.	2
	Foundry at McKenzie & Holland, Spotswood, Australia, closed down. Later re-opened on lease.	
1929	Production of copper-oxide metal rectifiers commenced at Spotswood.	12
1931	J W Cloud resigned as Chairman, but remained on Board. Louth Southborough elected Chairman.	22
1932	London Brake Works transferred to Chippenham from King's Cross.	2
1933	Heatley Gresham Engineering Co at Letchworth transferred to Manchester.	2
1934	John Saxby Ltd, renamed Etablissements Saxby.	
	Polish Brake Contract signed.	22
1935	Westinghouse Brake & Saxby Signal Co Ltd renamed Westinghouse Brake & Signal Co Ltd for simplification.	2, 4
1936	Gresham & Craven of India (Private) Ltd formed with works at Gobra, Calcutta, India (one mile from Entally).	2
1937	March. The Westinghouse Brake Co of Australasia Ltd was registered as a proprietary company and the name changed to Westinghouse Brake (Australasia) Pty Ltd, with Head Office and Works at Concord West, and the Victorian Office at Chancery House, 485 Bourke Street, Melbourne. Agents were appointed in Adelaide, Perth, Brisbane and Wellington, New Zealand.	3, 4
	American interest in share capital disposed of on Stock Exchange.	22
1938	New assembly shops built at Chippenham for worldwide contracts, including the 'Polish Contract' of about £5M of brake equipment.	2
1939	Engineering, Sales and Publicity Departments of York Way, London, office transferred to Hathaways, New Road, Chippenham as a wartime precaution. War declared by Britain on Germany on September 3rd.	21, 22
1940	October 12th. McKenzie & Holland records destroyed in air raid on London, by a	

Date	Event	Source
	bomb falling on the South Block of the Head Office, York Way.	21
1943	Lord Southborough resigned as Chairman, Lord Herbert Scott elected in his place.	22
1944	Lord Herbert Scott died June 17th, Captain A R S Nutting elected Chairman, H A Cruse appointed a Director.	22
1945	H G Brown resigned from Board, D F Brown and E J Fouracre appointed Directors.	22
1946	H Hewins Ltd, Ironfounders, incorporated	22
1947	The Sales Department returned to London from Chippenham.	21
	February. D F Brown appointed Managing Director. Captain B H Peter, Deputy Chairman until his resignation September 30th.	22
1948	Westinghouse Garrard Ticket Machines Ltd reconstituted with Garrard Engineering and Manufacturing Co Ltd with the latter subscribing for 15,000 shares out of a total of 45,000 shares.	22
1950	M W Shorter and J G Hall appointed Directors January 9th.	
1951	A holding company, Westinghouse Brake & Signal Co (Australia) Pty Ltd was formed for the purpose of amalgamating the reporting to London of the trading results of the separate Australian subsidiaries. *(Reference 22 says 1952).*	4
	The US&S Co at Swissvale became Union Switch & Signal Division of WABCO (Westinghouse Air Brake Company).	7
1953	D F Brown resigned from Board July 13th. M W Shorter appointed Managing Director October 12th.	22
	Rights issue of 3 new shares of £1 for each £5 stock held. Issue price 45s per share.	
	Whole of Capital of Gresham Craven and Heatley (Holdings) Ltd acquired in exchange of 255,000 new shares of £1 each fully paid. Gresham & Craven Ltd and Gresham & Craven of India Private Ltd, became wholly-owned subsidiaries.	22
1954	Gresham & Craven, including the Indian firm, taken over by Westinghouse Brake & Signal Co Ltd.	2
	Douglas (Kingswood) Ltd acquired for cash.	22
1955	The Vacuum Brake Co of 137 Abbey House, Westminster, London was bought by the Laycock Engineering Company.	2
	Westinghouse Brake & Signal Co, South Africa, Pty Ltd established.	22
1956	Rights issue of three new shares for £1 for each £10 stock held. Issue price 70s per share.	22
1957	The Salford factory of Gresham and Craven was closed and a new one built at Walkden, Manchester.	2
	Semiconductor process and assembly buildings erected at Chippenham.	2
	Bellamy and Lambie Ltd began developing a new works at Alberton near Johannesburg.	19
	One for one bonus issue made at same time as a rights issue of two new shares of £1 for each £3 Ordinary stock held on April 1st (before bonus issue). Issue price 35s per share.	22
	June 24th. G W H Richardson, T J Aldridge, N G Cadman, J W G Kershaw and L E Thompson appointed Directors, H R Baines appointed Secretary.	22

Date	Event	Source
	East End of King's Cross building North Block rebuilt after war damage.	22
1958	New Centre Block (London) occupied.	22
1960	August. McKenzie & Holland (NZ) Ltd was formed to carry on manufacture of Westinghouse rectifiers from former agents, L M Silver & Co Ltd, at corner of Jarvis Quay and Taranaki Street, Wellington, New Zealand.	
	50% interest acquired in Hobbs Transmission Ltd.	22
	All the issued capital of Heatley & Gresham Ltd acquired for cash.	22
	Lease of Lakefield Factory at Worsley taken for Gearbox manufacture.	22
	Gresham & Craven Brake factory transferred from Salford to Walkden.	22
1961	Westinghouse Brake & Signal (Argentina) SAIYC formed.	22
1962	April 9th. P Ewen appointed Director of WBS, September 17th appointed Deputy Chairman, December 11th Chairman. Captain Nutting resigned from Board December 10th.	22
1963	Shares in Westinghouse Ticket Machine company acquired from Garrard Engineering Ltd. Manufacturing agreement terminated.	22
1964	McKenzie & Holland (NZ) Ltd moved to Rata Street, Naenae, Lower Hutt, 30 km from Wellington.	
	W R Sykes Interlocking Signal Co Ltd of Clapham and Peckham closed and transferred to Chippenham.	2, 22
	Westinghouse Ticket & Business Machines Ltd transferred to Chippenham from Douglas Road, Kingswood, Bristol.	2
	H Hewins Ltd liquidated.	22
	Shares in Hobbs Transmission Ltd taken over from majority of outside shareholders and company closed down.	22
	February 3rd, L E Thompson appointed Managing Director, T J Aldridge, Deputy Managing Director, and M W Shorter Deputy Chairman.	22
	Offer to acquire whole of the issued capital of the Company made by Thorn Electrical Industries December 1963.	22
	Thorn offer lapsed.	22
1965	Manchester works of Gresham & Craven sold and vacuum business transferred to Chippenham. *(1966 according to reference 22)*.	2
	Derion Ltd incorporated at Chippenham to cater for bulk material handling.	2
	Lakefield (Transmission) factory of Gresham & Craven sold. M W Shorter retired December 31st.	22
1966	Westinghouse Brake English Electric Semiconductors Ltd formed at Chippenham. English Electric Co holding 49% of capital.	2, 22
	Marine & Industrial Controls Product transferred from Bristol to Chippenham.	2
	High power research laboratory and pre-production unit at Stapleton House transferred to Avon Works, Chippenham. Worsley (Brake) Factory sold.	
1967	US&S Division of WABCO changed name to Signal and Communications Division.	7
	August. Two divisions were created at WBS Spotswood for rectifier production – Rectifier Sets and Equipment Division, and Semiconductor Division.	5
1967	WBS (Argentina) sold.	22
1968	D Pollock (February 25th) and F R Purcell (December 16th) appointed Directors.	22

Date	Event	Source
1969	Marine and Industrial Control Division consolidated with Derion Ltd	2
	51% of share capital of Westinghouse Saxby Farmer Ltd (India) sold to Government of West Bengal for 1 rupee.	22
	T J Aldridge retired.	22
1970	The manufacture and distribution of brake equipment for road vehicles was separated from the operations of Westinghouse Brake (Australasia) Pty Ltd, and a new company was registered in New South Wales as Westinghouse Road Brake Co Pty Ltd.	4
	Westinghouse acquired 49% interest in Bellamy and Lambie Ltd, and changed the name to Westinghouse Bellambie (Pty) Ltd. This interest was in exchange for the 51% holding in WBS (South Africa) Pty Ltd.	19, 22
	50% of share capital of Douglas (Kingswood) Ltd (renamed to Bendix Westinghouse Ltd) sold to Bendix International.	22
1971	WBS Co Ltd Head Offices premises at 82 York Way was sold to English & Continental Property Co Ltd, on June 12th for £3.4M. *(Reference 22 says 1973).*	14
	An automation section was created at WBS Spotswood, lasting for only two and a half years.	
	WBS stock re-converted into shares of 25p fully paid. Bonus issue of two new shares of 25p for each £1 stock previously held.	22
1972	McKenzie & Holland (Australia) Pty Ltd had a registered change of name to Westinghouse – McKenzie Holland Pty Ltd and opened up a new corporate office at 49–51 Wellington Street, Windsor, Victoria, the following month.	4
	A new company was registered in Queensland on May 10th and named Westinghouse Track & Engineering Pty Ltd, to take over the trading and manufacturing activities of the Brisbane Branch of Westinghouse-McKenzie-Holland Pty Ltd.	4
	Westinghouse Brake & Signal Co (Aust) Pty Ltd acquired Westinghouse Road Brake Co Pty Ltd as a direct subsidiary.	4
	On September 1st the 'S&C division' of WABCO reverted back to the 'Union Switch & Signal Division'.	7
	October. 45% interest in Westinghouse Brake English Electric Semiconductors Ltd repurchased from The English Electric Co Ltd, for £750,000. Company renamed Westinghouse Brake Semiconductors Ltd	22
1973	The manufacturing and trading activities of the subsidiaries in Australia were transferred to divisions of the Holding Company, Westinghouse Brake & Signal Co (Australia) Pty Ltd. Haflinger Sales & Service Pty Ltd was acquired as a new subsidiary.	
	Various Divisional functions of WBS Co Ltd at York Way, King's Cross, transferred to Chippenham, and the Corporate Office moved to John Street, London.	
	Johannesburg office of Westinghouse Bellambie (Pty) Ltd closed and all activities transferred to the Alberton works.	
	Secowest Italia SpA incorporated in Italy.	22
	Westcode Incorporated formed in USA.	22
	Electrical Research Laboratory at Radlett sold for £100,000.	22
	Lea Bridge Road premises sold for £210,000.	22

Date	Event	Source
1974	The Railway Signal Company finally closed down, and WBS investment in it liquidated.	
1975	The Industrial Products section of Railway Brake and Industrial Products Division was sold off in Australia.	4
	Murray & Roberts Group, a South African civil engineering company, acquired a majority interest in Westinghouse Bellambie (Pty) Ltd.	19
1976	McKenzie & Holland (NZ) Ltd sold 75% of the shareholding to Cable Price Downer Ltd, a large NZ owned construction and engineering company.	
1977	Roc Hydraulics, manufacturers of hydraulic telescopic cylinders for truck hoists, became a division of WBS Co (Aust) Pty Ltd.	
1978	McKenzie & Holland (NZ) Ltd repurchased 25% of the share holding from Cable Price Downer Ltd.	
1979	March 23rd. The Westinghouse group was acquired by the Hawker Siddeley Group, as a wholly owned subsidiary, for 994,646 ordinary shares of Hawker Siddeley and £38M in cash.	
1980	December. The Corporate Office of Westinghouse Brake & Signal Co was closed at John Street, London.	
1981	May. Track and Engineering Division of WBS Australia opened a Works at Coffs Harbour, New South Wales to manufacture trackwork.	
1982	June 4th. Divisional business units of WBS became separate limited companies.	

References

1   A Centenary of Signalling, WBS Publication, 1956.
2   The Story of Westinghouse, Report of a Meeting of Westinghouse Supervisors Discussion Group, held at Chippenham, November 14th 1946.
3   Westinghouse Brake & Signal Review September 1950, Article – The Origins of McKenzie & Holland (Aust) Pty Ltd.
4   Internal Memorandum from W G Crowley to S Powell, December 10th 1975.
5   Management Noticeboard, WBS Spotswood.
6   Certificate of Titles.
7   Sundry WABCO publications.
8   Certificate of Award, Centennial International Exhibition, Melbourne, 1888, dated January 31st 1889.
9   Letter dated September 13th 1979 to Mr A C Howker from Mr David Butterworth, Leeds, Yorkshire.
10 Registration Certificate of McKenzie & Holland as member of the Ironmasters Association of Victoria, dated February 17th 1891.
11 Thirty Years Progress in Semiconductor Rectifiers, WBS Publication 30YP/3, March 1958.
12 Datasheet distributed from the McKenzie & Holland exhibit at the Williamstown Industrial Exhibition, 1947.
13 The Works of the Westinghouse Brake & Saxby Signal Company Ltd at London and Chippenham, Catalogue Section S1, May 1922.
14 Chairman's letter to shareholders advising sale of Head Office premises at 82 York Way, King's Cross, London, 1971.
15 Catalogue of Sydney International Exhibition, 1979.
16 Company News, George Westinghouse, Industrialist or Inventor?
17 Evans's Patent Lock and Block Booklet, front page.
18 The Westinghouse Brake Reference Book, Part 1, 1921.
19 Westinghouse News, November 1981, Centenary Issue.
20 The Search for Safety, US&S Centennial Book, M Brignano and H McCullough, 1981.

21   O S Nock.
22   Catalogue – 'Electric Train Staff Instruments' of the Railway Signal Co Ltd.
23   *The Story of Westinghouse*, note, approx 1973.

Diagrammatical History

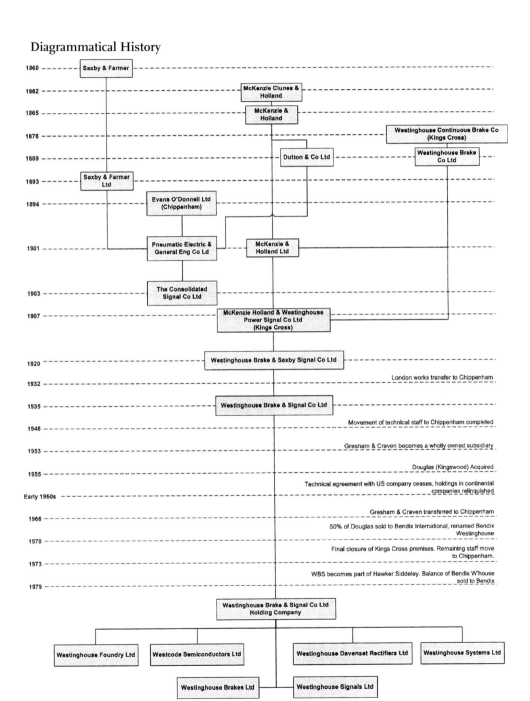

Table 2: Company names and years of formation, together with principle trading locations

Date	Name	Location	Country
1859	Thomas Clunes & Co (Vulcan Iron Works)	Worcester	UK
1860	Saxby & Farmer	Brighton	UK
1862	McKenzie, Clunes & Holland	Worcester	UK
1865	McKenzie & Holland	Worcester	UK
1866	Gresham & Heron	Salford	UK
1869	Westinghouse Air Brake Company	Pittsburgh, PA	USA
1870	Gresham, Heron & Craven	Salford	UK
1871	Westinghouse Continuous Brake Co	Pittsburgh	USA
1879	Gresham & Craven	Salford	UK
1881	Westinghouse Brake Co Ltd	London	UK
1881	The Railway Signal Company Ltd	London & Fazakerley	UK
1881	W R Sykes Interlocking Signal Co	Nunhead	UK
1881	Union Switch & Signal Co Ltd	Pittsburgh, PA	USA
1884	Semaphore Iron Works of McKenzie & Holland	Spotswood, Victoria	Australia
1889	Dutton & Co Ltd	Worcester	UK
1890	Toombul Iron Interlocking Works of McKenzie & Holland	Northgate, Queensland	Australia
1892	Heatley & Gresham Ltd	Entally, Calcutta	India
1893	Saxby & Farmer Ltd	London	UK
1894	Evans O'Donnell & Co Ltd	Chippenham	UK
1898	Consolidated Pneumatic Tool Co	Chippenham	UK
1899	W R Sykes Interlocking Signal Co Ltd	Clapham and Peckham	UK
1901	The Pneumatic, Electric & General Engineering Co Ltd	London	UK
1901	McKenzie & Holland Ltd	London	UK
1901	John Saxby Ltd	Creil	France
1901	The Heatley Gresham Engineering Co	Letchworth	UK
1902	The Consolidated Signal Co	London	UK
1905	Saxby & Farmer (India) Ltd	Calcutta	India
1907	McKenzie, Holland & Westinghouse Power Signal Co Ltd	London	UK
1907	Bellamy & Lambie Ltd	Johannesburg	South Africa
1907	Westinghouse Brake Co of Australasia Ltd	Sydney, New South Wales	Australia
1920	Westinghouse Brake & Saxby Signal Co Ltd	London	UK
1923	McKenzie & Holland (Australia) Pty Ltd	Spotswood, Victoria	Australia
1935	Westinghouse Brake & Signal Co Ltd	London	UK
1936	Gresham & Craven of India (Private) Ltd	Gobra, Calcutta	India
1937	Westinghouse Brake (Australasia) Pty Ltd	Concord West, New South Wales	Australia
1937	Westinghouse Ticket Machine Co Ltd[1]	Bristol	UK
1951	Union Switch & Signal Division (of WABCO)	Swissvale, PA	USA
1956	Westinghouse Garrard Ticket Machines Ltd	Swindon	UK
1960	McKenzie & Holland (NZ) Ltd	Wellington	New Zealand
1964	Westinghouse Ticket & Business Machines Ltd	Chippenham	UK
1965	Derion Ltd	Chippenham	UK

Date	Name	Location	Country
1966	Westinghouse Brake English Electric Semiconductors Ltd		
		Chippenham	UK
1970	Westinghouse Bellambie (Pty) Ltd	Johannesburg	South Africa
1970	Westinghouse Road Brake Co Pty Ltd	Regents Park,	
		New South Wales	Australia
1972	Westinghouse-McKenzie-Holland Pty Ltd	Windsor, Victoria	Australia
1972	Westinghouse Track & Engineering Pty Ltd		
		Northgate, Queensland	Australia
1973	Signal & Rectifier Division of WBS (Aust) Pty Ltd		
		Spotswood, Victoria	Australia
1973	Railway Brake & Industrial Products Division of WBS (Aust) Pty Ltd		
		Concord West, New South Wales	Australia
1973	Road Brake Division of WBS (Aust) Pty Ltd		
		Auburn, New South Wales	Australia
1973	Track Engineering Division of WBS (Aust) Pty Ltd		
		Northgate, Queensland	Australia
1973	Halfinger Sales & Service Pty Ltd	Springvale, Victoria	Australia
1973	Westcode Inc	Erie, PA	USA
1977	Roc Hydraulics Division of WBS (Aust) Pty Ltd		
		Spotswood, Victoria	Australia
1978	WBS (Victoria) Pty Ltd	Springvale, Victoria	Australia
1979	Hawker Siddeley Group Ltd	London	UK
1980	Signal & Rectifier Equipment Division of WBS (Aust) Pty Ltd		
		Spotswood, Victoria	Australia
1982	Westinghouse Signals Ltd	Chippenham	UK
1982	Westinghouse Brakes Ltd	Chippenham	UK
1982	Westinghouse Systems Ltd	Chippenham	UK
1982	Westinghouse Foundry Ltd	Chippenham	UK
1982	Westinghouse Davenset Rectifiers Ltd	Chippenham	UK
1982	Westcode Semiconductors Ltd	Chippenham	UK

Other subsidiary and associate companies not referenced above include:

Douglas (Sales & Service) Ltd, Bristol, UK
Partridge Wilson & Co Ltd, Leicester, UK
Gresham & Craven Ltd, Salford, UK
Westinghouse Cubic Ltd, Merstham, UK
Dimetronic SA, Madrid, Spain
Heatley & Gresham (India) Private Ltd, Bombay, India
Hind Rectifiers Ltd, Bombay, India
Westinghouse Saxby Farmer Ltd, Entally, Calcutta, India

Gresham & Craven of India (Private) Ltd, Gobra, Calcutta, India
Westinghouse Brake & Signal Co South Africa (Pty) Ltd
Westingred Société Anonyme, France
Westinghouse CVB Ltd, Newport, UK
Regent Engineering Pty Ltd, Regents Park, NSW, Australia
Wesdac Systems Ltd

---

1 The 1937 date quoted from this source contradicts information provided to the Editors by the Transport Ticket Society suggesting an earlier date, since patents were being applied for by this company as early as 1935.

Table 3: Development of the Chippenham Site, 1894 to 1973

Date	Company		
1894	Evans O'Donnell	Opened first factory, Foundry Lane	First buildings erected
1901	Dutton & Co	Transferred from Worcester	
1903	Saxby & Farmer	Transferred from Kilburn	
1920	McKenzie & Holland	Transferred from Worcester	Buildings extended
1926	Foundry of Westinghouse Brake & Saxby Signal	Transferred from London	Buildings extended
1928	Signal product of Westinghouse Brake & Saxby Signal	Transferred from London	
1928	Rectifier product	Manufacture introduced	New building erected
1932	Brake product of Westinghouse Brake & Saxby Signal	Transferred from London	New buildings erected
1938	Signal & Brake Products	Growing order book	New buildings erected
1938	Storage Facilities	To service signal and brake products	Acquired the property of Messrs Hathway & Co, New Rd
1947	Laboratory and Plating Shop	For research and improved metal finish techniques	New buildings erected
1953	Semiconductor product	Selenium refinery	New building erected
1955	Semiconductor product	Growing order book	New buildings erected
1956	Rectifier product	Manufacture of plating lines	New building erected
1958	Packing and Despatch facilities	Output necessitates improved facilities	New building erected
1960	Plastic Products	Output necessitates improved facilities	New building erected
1960	Data processing	Space required for computer	New building erected
1964	Sykes Interlocking Signal	Transferred from Clapham and Peckham	
1966	Gresham & Craven	Transferred from Manchester	
1966	Marine and Industrial Controls Product	Transferred from Bristol	
1966	Marine and Industrial Controls Product	Consolidates with Derion	Special Complex provided
1970	Signal product	Growth of Train Description activity	New building erected
1972	Head Office	Transferred from London	New buildings erected

Chippenham Site 1902/3.

Aerial view of Chippenham site, believed to be 1926.

In this 1930 aerial view the 'White House' has now been built, and bears the name "Westinghouse Brake & Saxby Signal Company", also note the new large shop next to the turntable.

1935. There are definite signs of this photograph having been 'touched up' for clarity. Note that the White House now has three stories.

Now the sign on the White House reads Westinghouse Brake & Signal Company Ltd. Note the extensive railway line within the factory. Also note the construction work on the new canteen facilities towards the centre at the top of the photograph.

1948. The Works Laboratory (red brick building to the east of the site) is under construction. Wartime camouflage on the factory roofs is very much in evidence to the left hand side of the picture. A highly 'touched-up' version of this picture appeared in Westinghouse Review January 1949 without the camouflaged roofs! It was captioned "This recent photograph of the works shows the new road which will eventually pass Pew Hill House (top left). The new Laboratory and the Plating Shop under construction are on the right and left of this road."

WESTINGHOUSE BRAKE
& SIGNAL COMPANY, LTD

PROPOSED NEW ENTRANCE
AT PEW HILL, CHIPPENHAM.

SKETCH PERSPECTIVE

From the Westinghouse Review *of 1954, this drawing was captioned 'This is the Architect's perspective drawing of the new Works Entrance which will be situated in the Langley Road near the bottom of Pew Hill. It has been so designed that it will not detract from the amenities of the road. The walls to the gates, which will be set back from the road, will be built from the existing stone wall and as many of the trees as possible are to be left in position.'*

1957, More development at the north of the factory, including the new North Gate from Pew Hill. 'Hathaways' chimney has been lowered. Car parking is now provided for the workers for the first time.

Circa 1973. Most of the sidings on the Great Western Mainline have now gone. The growth of the factory to the north continues.

Circa 1981, this photograph appeared in the Centenary edition of Westinghouse News. The works have not changed much since 1973, but the Great Western mainline has been drastically changed as part of the realignment for the introduction of High Speed Train services.

Fire Engines and Ambulances

Throughout the years, Westinghouse, and the companies from which it was formed, maintained their own Fire Brigade at Chippenham, something that continues to the present day, albeit with a volunteer crew drawn from across the company. The following photographs give an insight to the changing technology in fire-fighting during that period!

Believed to have been taken in around 1905, this photograph shows the Saxby & Farmer Fire Brigade of the time. When published in Westinghouse Review *in 1950, the caption pointed out that the tender carried the monogram of Evans O'Donnell, dating the photo to after 1903. From left to right the men are believed to be: Unknown, Harry Day, Jimmy Spatchett, Percy Marsh, Bill Clifford, "Wantage", Unknown, Unknown and Jack Hillman.*

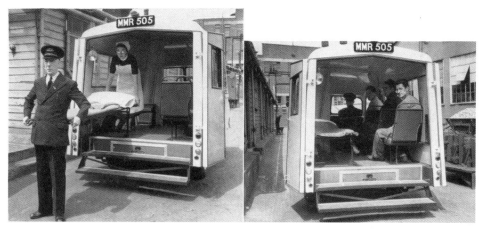

For many years the Medical Staff of the Company had the use of a dedicated Ambulance. These photographs from the Westinghouse Review *of October 1955 show Sister Price and Mr Gist (Ambulance Driver) demonstrating the simple stretcher loading gear. The caption stated 'It will be used when possible for internal medical transport, instead of the trolley which has been used hitherto, and for collecting cases from Old and New Road; also for external transport taking employees home or to hospital. It will be available twenty-four hours a day, as there is a volunteer driver on night shift.'*

In the 1950s there was stiff competition between industrial fire brigades. This photograph from the August 1950 Westinghouse Review was published on the occasion of the works Fire Brigade's appearance at the Annual competitions of the Industrial Fire Protection Association, South Western Branch, held at Filton, Bristol. The Westinghouse Brigade managed to win four cups, and the photograph shows the victorious Firemen with their trophies (including the Westinghouse Cup for Light Trailer Pump Drill for Part-time firemen!), their Chief Officer and the Works Management.

Pew hill house fire brigade 1970s (Jeff Coleman extreme left)

The September 1952 Westinghouse Review *carried a double page spread about 'The Fire and Security Police'. The attached photograph shows the Fire Service men manning a pump for a practice call. From left to right the men are: Deputy Chief Fire Officer R F Hemmings (in Tender), Fireman N W Pond, Fireman R Portlock, Fireman J Smart, Fireman P Bloom, Leading Fireman E Holley and Leading Fireman H Edwards. The article went on to explain that at the time there was a Chief Fire Officer, Mr A L Thomas, his deputy, and thirteen full-time men working on shifts. In addition seven further men were available on a part-time basis, being employed elsewhere but available to report for duty during a fire alarm. It continues to explain that in 1949 there were 24 fires in the factory, but that by 1952 this had been reduced to only (!) seven.*

Appendix 1 – Power Frames

1 Electropneumatic Frames

Frame Number	Brought Into Service	Locality	Railway	Type	Country	Number of Levers
3	Sep 1897	Munich	Bavarian State	US	Germany	11
4	Jan 1899	Granary Junction, Bishopsgate	Great Eastern	US	UK	47
8	Sep 1903	Bolton West	Lancs & Yorks	A	UK	83
9	Jul 1902	Bank Top	North Eastern	A	UK	35
10	Sep 1902	Green Lane	North Eastern	A	UK	71
11	Apr 1903	Pontop Crossing	North Eastern	A	UK	35
12	1904	Selby	North Eastern	Special	UK	1
13	Feb 1903	Cottbus East	Prussian State	German	Prussia	90
14	"	Cottbus Nt	Prussian State	German	Prussia	2
15	"	Cottbus St	Prussian State	German	Prussia	1
16	"	Cottbus Bude III	Prussian State	German	Prussia	2
17	"	Cottbus Bude 172	Prussian State	German	Prussia	2
18	Dec 1903	Harton Colliery Junction	North Eastern	B	UK	23
19	Jun 1906	Cairo A	Egyptian State	B	Egypt	47
20	Mar 1906	Cairo B	Egyptian State	B	Egypt	35
21	Dec 1905	Cairo C	Egyptian State	B	Egypt	11
22	Apr 1904	Mainz	Prussian State	German	Prussia	10
23	Apr 1904	Mainz	Prussian State	German	Prussia	10
24	Oct 1904	Brisbane Central	Queensland	B	Australia	23
25	Jul 1904	Park St Paragon Hull	North Eastern	B	UK	179
26	Dec 1904	Station Paragon Hull	North Eastern	B	UK	143
29	Jun 1905	Mill Hill Park	Met District	B	UK	47
30	Mar 1905	Hedworth Lane Crossing	North Eastern	B	UK	27
31	Nov 1905	Earls Court West	Met District	B	UK	27
32	Jan 1906	Cromwell Road	Met District	B	UK	47
33	Apr 1905	Oberhausen I	Prussian State	German	Prussia	50
34	Apr 1905	Oberhausen II	Prussian State	German	Prussia	50
35	Apr 1905	Oberhausen III	Prussian State	German	Prussia	70
36	Apr 1905	Oberhausen IV	Prussian State	German	Prussia	70
37	Apr 1905	Oberhausen V	Prussian State	German	Prussia	80
38	Apr 1905	Oberhausen VI	Prussian State	German	Prussia	40
39	1906	Worms I	Bavarian State	German	Bavaria	50
40	1906	Worms II	Bavarian State	German	Bavaria	100
41	1906	Worms III	Bavarian State	German	Bavaria	100
42	1905	Wanne Nwt	Bavarian State	German	Bavaria	104
43	1906	Sydney Tunnel	New South Wales Gov	B	Australia	59
44	1906	Sydney Station	New South Wales Gov	B	Australia	203
45	Nov 1905	Earls Court East	Met District	B	UK	27

Frame Number	Brought Into Service	Locality	Railway	Type	Country	Number of Levers
46	Sep 1905	Putney Bridge	Met District	B	UK	15
47	Sep 1905	Parsons Green	Met District	B	UK	39
48	Mar 1906	London Road Depot	Baker St & Waterloo	B	UK	7
49	Mar 1906	Elephant & Castle	Baker St & Waterloo	B	UK	15
50	Mar 1906	Kennington Road	Baker St & Waterloo	B	UK	15
51	Mar 1906	Great Central	Baker St & Waterloo	B	UK	7
52	Mar 1906	Edgware Road	Baker St & Waterloo	B	UK	11
53	Jun 1906	Hammersmith	Met District	B	UK	39
54	Aug 1906	West Kensington East	Met District	B	UK	39
55	1906	Myslowitz	Prussian State		Prussia	80
56	Jan 1906	South Kensington	Met District	B	UK	23
57	Oct 1906	West Kensington West	Met District	B	UK	39
58	Sep 1906	Newcastle Central West End	North Eastern	B	UK	211
59	Feb 1906	Mansion House	Met District	B	UK	35
60	Jul 1906	Minories Junction	Met District	B	UK	7
61	Jul 1906	Aldgate East	Met District	B	UK	15
63	1906	King Edward Junction	North Eastern	B	UK	83
64	1906	Dunedin North	New Zealand	B	New Zealand	47
65	1906	Dunedin South	New Zealand	B	New Zealand	35
66	1906	High St Junction Gateshead	North Eastern	B	UK	39
67	Mar 1907	No 2 Newcastle Central	North Eastern	B	UK	67
68	Dec 1906	Hyde Park Corner	Great Northern, Piccadilly & Brompton	B	UK	11
69	Dec 1906	York Road	Great Northern, Piccadilly & Brompton	B	UK	11
70	Dec 1906	Finsbury Park	Great Northern, Piccadilly & Brompton	B	UK	15
71	1906	Station Howrah	East Indian	B	India	71
72	1906	Junction Howrah	East Indian	B	India	43
73	1906	Ground Frame Howrah	East Indian	Ground	India	3
74	1906	Ground Frame Howrah	East Indian	Ground	India	3
75	1906	Ground Frame Howrah	East Indian	Ground	India	3
76	1906	Covent Garden	Great Northern, Piccadilly & Brompton	B	UK	11
77	Dec 1906	Holborn & Strand	Great Northern, Piccadilly & Brompton	B	UK	19
78	1906	Greensfield Junction	North Eastern	B	UK	55
79	Jun 1907	Hampstead	Charing Cross, Euston & Hampstead	B	UK	11
80	Jun 1907	Highgate	Charing Cross, Euston & Hampstead	B	UK	15
81	Jun 1907	Camden Road Junction	Charing Cross, Euston & Hampstead	B	UK	7
82	Jun 1907	Charing Cross	Charing Cross, Euston & Hampstead	B	UK	11
83	Jun 1907	Mornington Crescent	Charing Cross, Euston & Hampstead	B	UK	11
84	Jun 1907	Golders Green	Charing Cross, Euston & Hampstead	B	UK	31
85	1907	Whitechapel & St Marys	Met District	B	UK	51
86	1907	Glasgow Central	Caledonian	B	UK	374
87	1907	Glasgow Central	Caledonian	Ground B	UK	6
88	1907	Glasgow Central	Caledonian	Ground B	UK	6
89	1907	Glasgow Central	Caledonian	Ground B	UK	6
90	1907	Glasgow Central	Caledonian	Ground B	UK	6

Frame Number	Brought Into Service	Locality	Railway	Type	Country	Number of Levers
91	1907	Glasgow Central	Caledonian	Ground B	UK	6
92	1907	Glasgow Central	Caledonian	Ground B	UK	6
93		Gateshead Junction	North Eastern	B	UK	23
94		Forth Goods Junction	North Eastern	B	UK	79
95		Manors Station	North Eastern	B	UK	43
96	Nov 1909	Newcastle Central No 1	North Eastern	B	UK	283
97	1912	Darmstadt		German	Germany	144
98	1912	Howrah Station	East Indian	Ground A	India	3
99	1912	Howrah Station	East Indian	Ground A	India	3
100	1908	Dudweiler I	Prussian State	German	Prussia	49
101	1908	Dudweiler II	Prussian State	German	Prussia	24
102	1908	Dudweiler III	Prussian State	German	Prussia	47
103	1909	Amsterdam	Dutch State	German	Netherlands	142
104	1907	Haarlem	Dutch State	German	Netherlands	72
105	1910	Linden IIa	Prussian State	German	Prussia	72
106	1910	Linden IIb	Prussian State	German	Prussia	40
107	1910	Linden III	Prussian State	German	Prussia	32
108	1910	Linden IV	Prussian State	German	Prussia	48
109	1910	Linden V	Prussian State	German	Prussia	48
110	1910	Linden VI	Prussian State	German	Prussia	48
111		Park Lane Junction	North Eastern	B	UK	79
112		Cairo South End	Egyptian State	B	Egypt	59
114		Turnham Green	Met District	B	UK	23
115		Korompa No 1	KO	Special	Hungary	23
116		Korompa No 2	KO	Special	Hungary	19
117		Korompa Station Master	KO	Ground B	Hungary	10
118		Liverpool Street	Central London	B	UK	15
119		Illawarra Station	New South Wales	B	Australia	119
120		Illawarra Station	New South Wales	B	Australia	131
121	1912	Junkerath		German		64
122		Caballito Station	Buenos Aires Tramways	B	Argentina	27
123		Rio De Janeiro	Buenos Aires Tramways	B	Argentina	7
124		Slough Bath Road Junct.	Great Western	B	UK	23
125		Shepherd's Bush	Central London	B	UK	11
126		Iglo No 1	KO	B	Hungary	32
127		Iglo No 2	KO	B	Hungary	24
128		Iglo Station Master	KO	B	Hungary	28
129		Poprad No 1	KO	B	Hungary	32
130		Poprad No 2	KO	B	Hungary	28
131		Poprad Station Master	KO	B	Hungary	32
132		Queens Park	London Electric	B	UK	27
133		Southport Station	Lancs & Yorks	B	UK	87
134		St Lukes Road Southport	Lancs & Yorks	B	UK	103
135		Plaza Once	Buenos Aires Tramways	B	Argentina	27
136		Plaza Mayo	Buenos Aires Tramways	B	Argentina	7
137		Wood Lane	Central London	B	UK	31
138		Clapham Common	City & South London	B	UK	15
139		Angel	City & South London	B	UK	11
140		Euston	City & South London	B	UK	15
141	1920	Ealing Broadway	Great Western	B	UK	15
142		Hamilton Square, D	Mersey	B	UK	11
143		Camden	London Electric	B	UK	43
144		Stockwell U	City & South London	B	UK	15

Frame Number	Brought Into Service	Locality	Railway	Type	Country	Number of Levers
145		Plaza Constituçion	Buenos Aires Great Southern	B	Argentina	275
146		Temperley	Buenos Aires Great Southern	B	Argentina	179
147		Morden	London Electric	B	UK	31
148		Tooting	London Electric	B	UK	15
149		Kennington	London Electric	B	UK	31
150		Kings Cross	London Electric	B	UK	11
151		Hounslow West	London Electric	B	UK	15
152		Kilometre 10.2 Main Line	Buenos Aires Western	B	Argentina	51
153		Victoria Terminus A	Great Indian Peninsular	B	India	131
154		Victoria Terminus B	Great Indian Peninsular	B	India	71
155		Federico Lacroze	Buenos Aires Central	B	Argentina	23
156		Callao	Buenos Aires Central	B	Argentina	15
157		Medrano	Buenos Aires Central	B	Argentina	11

At this point the date column is simply a date, not a date of equipment brought into service.

Frame Number	Date	Locality	Railway	Type	Country	Number of Levers
158		Bombay Central	Bombay, Baroda & Central India	B	India	119
160	1930	Plaza Constitucion	Buenos Aires Great Southern	Ground C	Argentina	3
161	1930	Plaza Constitucion	Buenos Aires Great Southern	Ground C	Argentina	3
162	1930	Plaza Constitucion	Buenos Aires Great Southern	Ground C	Argentina	3
163	1930	Plaza Constitucion	Buenos Aires Great Southern	Ground C	Argentina	3
164	1930	Plaza Constitucion	Buenos Aires Great Southern	Ground C	Argentina	3
165	1930	Rancagua	Buenos Aires Central	B	Argentina	27
166	1930	Carlos Pellegrini	Buenos Aires Central	B	Argentina	39
167	1930	Rancagua	Buenos Aires Central	B	Argentina	27
168	1930	Plaza Constitucion	Buenos Aires Great Southern	Ground C	Argentina	3
169	1931	Leandro N Alem	Buenos Aires Central	B	Argentina	7
170	1931	Hyde Park Corner (Additional Frame)	London Electric	N	UK	11
171	1931	Acton Town	London Electric	N	UK	119
172	1931	Wood Green	London Electric	N	UK	15
173	1931	Enfield West	London Electric	N	UK	35
174	1931	Cockfosters	London Electric	N	UK	47
175	1931	Arnos Grove	London Electric	N	UK	59
176	1931	Holborn (New Station)	London Electric	N	UK	11
177	1935	Rayners Lane	London Passenger Transport Bd	N	UK	35
178	1935	Cromwell Road	London Passenger Transport Bd	N	UK	83
179	1936	Finchley Road	London Passenger Transport Bd	N	UK	59
180	1936	Uxbridge	London Passenger Transport Bd	N	UK	59
181	1937	Willesden Green	London Passenger Transport Bd	N	UK	59
182	1937	Neasden North	London Passenger Transport Bd	N	UK	47
183	1937	Aldgate	London Passenger Transport Bd	N	UK	59
184	1937	Neasden South	London Passenger Transport Bd	N	UK	83

At this point the date column changes again to contain date of order.

Frame Number	Date of Order	Locality	Railway	Type	Country	Number of Levers
185	1937	Stanmore	London Passenger Transport Board	N	UK	47
186	1938	Drayton Park	London Passenger Transport Board	N	UK	35
188	1938	East Finchley	London Passenger Transport Board	N	UK	35
189	1938	Park Junction	London Passenger Transport Board	N	UK	83

Frame Number	Date of Order	Locality	Railway	Type	Country	Number of Levers
190	1938	Harrow on the Hill	London Passenger Transport Board	N	UK	95
191	1938	Grange Hill	London Passenger Transport Board	N	UK	83
192	1938	Elephant & Castle	London Passenger Transport Board	N	UK	11
193	1938	Finchley Central	London Passenger Transport Board	N	UK	71
194	1938	High Barnet	London Passenger Transport Board	N	UK	35
195	1939	Leyton	London Passenger Transport Board	N	UK	23
196	1938	Leytonstone	London Passenger Transport Board	N	UK	59
197	1938	Loughton	London Passenger Transport Board	N	UK	59
198	1938	Edgware	London Passenger Transport Board	N	UK	83
199	1938	Ruislip West	London Passenger Transport Board	N	UK	59
200	1938	Newbury Park	London Passenger Transport Board	N	UK	59
201	1939	Neasden North (Repeat)	London Passenger Transport Board	N	UK	47
202	1939	Kings Cross	London Passenger Transport Board	N	UK	35
203	1939	Woodford	London Passenger Transport Board	N	UK	59
204	1939	South Woodford	London Passenger Transport Board	N	UK	35
205	1939	Wood Lane	London Passenger Transport Board	N	UK	47
206	1939	Greenford	London Passenger Transport Board	N	UK	23
207	1939	Northolt	London Passenger Transport Board	N	UK	23
208	1939	North Acton	London Passenger Transport Board	N	UK	11
209	1939	Standby	London Passenger Transport Board	N	UK	47
210	1939	Standby	London Passenger Transport Board	N	UK	47
211	Jun 1943	Standby	London Passenger Transport Board	N	UK	35
212	Jun 1946	Harrow South	London Passenger Transport Board	N2	UK	33
213	Jun 1946	Harrow North	London Passenger Transport Board	N2	UK	44
214	Mar 1948	Chigwell Lane	London Passenger Transport Board	N2M	UK	59
215	Apr 1948	Edgware	London Passenger Transport Board	N2M	UK	35
216	Aug 1948	Epping	London Passenger Transport Board	N2M	UK	47

NB A number of these were special variations of Frames, e.g. Style B Narrow, Full Stroke, Push and Pull. These have not been identified in this table

2 Electric Frames

Frame Number	Date	Locality	Railway	Type	Country	Number of Levers
1	Jan 1908	Praed Street Junction	Metropolitan	M1	UK	7
2	Jan 1908	Aldgate	Metropolitan	M1	UK	30
3	May 1908	Yarnton Junction	Great Western	M1	UK	50
4	Jul 1911	Baker Street	Metropolitan	M2	UK	37
5	Nov 1912	Nordring	Berliner Hochbahn	K	Germany	7
6	Nov 1912	Alexanderplatz	Berliner Hochbahn	K	Germany	15
7	Mar 1914	Spittelmarkt	Berliner Hochbahn	K	Germany	11
8	Mar 1914	Leipzigerplatz	Berliner Hochbahn	K	Germany	19
9	Mar 1914	Gleisdreieck	Berliner Hochbahn	K	Germany	23
10	Oct 1921	Flinder's Street	Victorian Government	K	Australia	55
11	Oct 1922	Otira	New Zealand Govt	K	New Zealand	19
12	Oct 1922	Arthur's Pass	New Zealand Govt	K	New Zealand	19
13	Feb 1923	Rolleston Station	New Zealand Govt	K	New Zealand	19
14	May 1923	Darfield Junction	New Zealand Govt	K	New Zealand	19
15	May 1923	Springfield Station	New Zealand Govt	K	New Zealand	15
16	May 1923	Sheffield Station	New Zealand Govt	K	New Zealand	15
17	Aug 1923	Hendon, AB	Euston & Hampstead	K	UK	11
18	Sep 1923	Brent, AA	Euston & Hampstead	K	UK	11
19	Apr 1924	Baker Street	Metropolitan	K	UK	39
20	Jun 1924	Edgware	London Electric	K	UK	23
21	Jan 1925	Malmö	Swedish State	K	Sweden	83

Frame Number	Date	Locality	Railway	Type	Country	Number of Levers
22	Jun 1924	Colindale	London Electric	K	UK	15
23	May 1925	Paerata	New Zealand Govt	K	New Zealand	31
24	Mar 1926	Papatoetoe	New Zealand Govt	K	New Zealand	31
25	Jun 1926	Charing Cross	Southern	K	UK	107
26	Jun 1926	Cannon Street	Southern	K	UK	143
27	Sep 1926	Edgware Road	Metropolitan	K	UK	39
28	Jul 1926	Piccadilly[1]	Ministry of Transport	K	UK	9
29	Aug 1926	Sao Diogo (reconditioned and reinstalled at Engenheiro Sao Paulo, 1937)	Central Railway	K	Brazil	31
30	Jan 1927	Capetown	South African	K	South Africa	143
31	Oct 1927	London Bridge	Southern	K	UK	311
32	Oct 1927	Borough Market Junction	Southern	K	UK	35
33	Nov 1927	Victoria West Jn (Manchester)	London Midland Scottish	K	UK	95
34	Nov 1927	Deal Street	London Midland Scottish	K	UK	107
35	Nov 1927	Irwell Bridge Sidings	London Midland Scottish	K	UK	15
36	Jan 1928	Whitechapel	East London	K	UK	7
37	Jan 1929	North Kent East Junction	Southern	L	UK	83
38	May 1929	Cascadura	Central	K	Brazil	31
39	Sep 1929	Park Stn Jo'burg	South African	L	South Africa	143
45	Mar 1930	Glasgow St Enoch	London Midland Scottish	L	UK	203
46	Jul 1930	Churchgate (Bombay)	Bombay, Baroda & Central India	L	India	23
47	Jun 1930	Wiri	New Zealand Govt	L	New Zealand	27
48	Jun 1930	Manurewa	New Zealand Govt	L	New Zealand	23
49	Jun 1930	St Leonard's	New Zealand Govt	L	New Zealand	11
50	Oct 1930	Wembley Park	Metropolitan	L	UK	95
53	Jul 1931	Erode Junction	South Indian	L	India	59
54	Nov 1931	Salt River Junction	South African	L	South Africa	71
55	Jan 1932	Brighton Station	Southern	L	UK	225
56	Jul 1932	Cardiff East	Great Western	L	UK	155
57	Sep 1932	Cardiff West	Great Western	L	UK	339
58	Feb 1933	Station WG	Polish State	L	Poland	31
60	May 1934	Wellington Station	New Zealand Govt	L	New Zealand	127
61	Jun 1934	Tawa Flat	New Zealand Govt	L	New Zealand	19
62	Aug 1934	Bandra	Bombay, Baroda & Central India	K	India	107
63	Oct 1934	Salem Junction Station	South Indian	K	India	43
64	Feb 1935	Mahim	Bombay, Baroda & Central India	K	India	51
65	Feb 1935	Cairo No 2	Egyptian State	L	Egypt	35
66	Feb 1935	Waterloo Station	Southern	L	UK	309
67	May 1935	Clapham Junction A	Southern	L	UK	103
68	May 1935	West London Junction	Southern	L	UK	59
69	Sep 1935	Woking	Southern	L	UK	131
71	Jul 1936	Jeppe	South African Railways & Harbours Administration	L	South Africa	47
72	Jul 1936	Langlaagte	South African Railways & Harbours Administration	L	South Africa	79
73	Oct 1936	Norte (Sao Paulo)	Central (State)	L	Brazil	71
74	Oct 1936	5A Parada	Central (State)	L	Brazil	7
75	Oct 1936	Carlos de Campos	Central (State)	L	Brazil	19
76	Nov 1936	No 2 Shan Hai Kuan	Chinese National	L	China	43
77	Nov 1936	No 3 Shan Hai Kuan	Chinese National	L	China	27
78	Dec 1936	Madura Junction	South Indian	L	India	79
79	May 1937	Lumding	Assam – Bengal	L	India	55
80	May 1937	Kilometre 2 (Empalme)	Chilean State	L	Chile	87
81	Jun 1937	Darlington (South)	London & North Eastern	L	UK	155
82	Jun 1937	Badarpur	Assam – Bengal	L	India	55
83	Dec 1937	Battersea Park	Southern	L	UK	31

Frame Number	Date	Locality	Railway	Type	Country	Number of Levers
84	Dec 1937	Victoria Central	Southern	L	UK	225
85	Feb 1938	Huntly	New Zealand Govt	L	New Zealand	55
86	Feb 1938	Papakura	New Zealand Govt	L	New Zealand	47
87	Feb 1938	Drury	New Zealand Govt	L	New Zealand	23
88	Feb 1938	Pukekohe	New Zealand Govt	L	New Zealand	23
89	Feb 1938	Tuakau	New Zealand Govt	L	New Zealand	23
90	Feb 1938	Te-Kauwhata	New Zealand Govt	L	New Zealand	23
91	Feb 1938	Ohinewai	New Zealand Govt	L	New Zealand	23
92	Feb 1938	Taupiri	New Zealand Govt	L	New Zealand	23
93	Dec 1938	Standby	Southern	L	UK	143
94	Feb 1939	Unknown	South African	L	South Africa	95
95	Mar 1939	Crewe South	London Midland Scottish	L	UK	227
96	Mar 1939	Crewe North	London Midland Scottish	L	UK	214
97	Mar 1939	Standby Frame	London Midland Scottish	L	UK	227
98	Apr 1939	Preston North	London Midland Scottish	L	UK	227
99	Apr 1939	Preston South	London Midland Scottish	L	UK	227
100	May 1939	Engenheiro Sao Paulo	Estrada do Ferro Central do Brasil	L	Brazil	47
101	Jan 1940	Liverpool Lime Street	London Midland Scottish	L	UK	95
102	Feb 1940	Lower Hutt	New Zealand Govt	L	New Zealand	23
103	Apr 1940	Otahuhu	New Zealand Govt	L	New Zealand	39
104	Apr 1940	New Plymouth	New Zealand Govt	L	New Zealand	70
105	Apr 1941	Blackfriars Junction	Southern	L	UK	119
106	May 1941	Germiston No 1	South African	L	South Africa	155
107	May 1941	Germiston No 2	South African	L	South Africa	155
108	May 1943	Marton	New Zealand Govt	L	New Zealand	93
109	Jan 1946	Rangoon	Burma	L	Burma	143
110	Jan 1946	Kemmendine	Burma	L	Burma	47
111	Jan 1946	Alameda Station	Chilean State	L	Chile	83
112	Jun 1946	Llai Llai Station	Chilean State	L	Chile	67
113	May 1948	Zwartkops	South African	L	South Africa	47
114	May 1948	New Brighton	South African	L	South Africa	47
115	May 1948	Daljosphat	South African	L	South Africa	31
116	May 1948	Vereeniging	South African	L	South Africa	83
117	May 1948	Nataspruit	South African	L	South Africa	59
118	Mar 1948	Bricklayers Arms Junction	BR Southern Region	L	UK	55
119	Mar 1948	Forest Hill	BR Southern Region	L	UK	47
120	Oct 1949	Clapham Junction B	BR Southern Region	L	UK	103
121	Jan 1949	San Bernardo	Chilean State	L	Chile	23
122	Oct 1949	Balham	BR Southern Region	L	UK	43
123	Oct 1949	Streatham Junction	BR Southern Region	L	UK	79
124	Nov 1950	Vila Matilde	Estrada do Ferro Central do Brasil	L	Brazil	19
125	Nov 1950	Patriarca	Estrada do Ferro Central do Brasil	L	Brazil	23
126	Nov 1950	Engenheiro Artur Alvim	Estrada do Ferro Central do Brasil	L	Brazil	15
127	Nov 1950	Itaquera	Estrada do Ferro Central do Brasil	L	Brazil	27
128	May 1951	Coquimbo Station	Chilean State	L	Chile	39
129	May 1951	La Serena Station	Chilean State	L	Chile	23
130	Mar 1952	Norwood Junction	BR Southern Region	L	UK	107
131	Mar 1952	Gloucester Road Junction	BR Southern Region	L	UK	131
132	Apr 1952	Cairo No 1	Egyptian State	L	Egypt	59
133	Aug 1952	Paine	Chilean State	L	Chile	19
134	Oct 1952	Boksburg East, Transvaal	South African	L	South Africa	55
135	Oct 1952	Unknown	South African	L	South Africa	63
136	Nov 1952	Unknown	South African	L	South Africa	35
137	May 1953	South Croydon	BR Southern Region	L	UK	31
138	May 1953	Purley	BR Southern Region	L	UK	71
139	May 1953	East Croydon	BR Southern Region	L	UK	103
140	Jan 1954	Vereening	South African	L	South Africa	75

Frame Number	Date	Locality	Railway	Type	Country	Number of Levers
141	Jan 1954	Woltemade Flyover	South African	L	South Africa	51
142	Apr 1954	Railway Operations Training Centre, Lahore	UN Economic Commission for Asia and Far East	L	Pakistan	11
143	Aug 1954	Nakuru	East African Railways & Harbours	L	East Africa	39
144	Aug 1954	Booth	South African	L	South Africa	39
145	Aug 1954	Durban Marshalling Yard	South African	L	South Africa	39
146	Aug 1954	Rossburgh	South African	L	South Africa	47
147	Aug 1954	Dalbridge	South African	L	South Africa	55
148	Apr 1955	Longmoor Camp	Ministry Of Supply	L	UK	7
149	Aug 1955	1° De Marzo (Once)	Argentine	L	Argentina	135
150	Mar 1956	Bloemfontein	South African	L	South Africa	147
151	Aug 1957	Talleres (D F Sarmiento)	Argentine	L	Argentina	31
152	May 1958	Unknown	Comission de Los Ferrocarriles	L	Argentina	7
153	May 1958	Unknown	Comission de Los Ferrocarriles	L	Argentina	7
155	May 1958	Unknown	Comission de Los Ferrocarriles	L	Argentina	7
155	May 1958	Unknown	Comission de Los Ferrocarriles	L	Argentina	7
156	May 1958	Unknown	Comission de Los Ferrocarriles	L	Argentina	7
157	Jan 1961	Maidstone East	BR Southern Region	L	UK	47

3 Colliery Frames

Frame Number	Date	Locality	Railway	Type	Country	Number of Levers
1	Apr 1952	Yorkshire Main	National Coal Board	O	UK	11
2	Oct 1952	Ollerton	National Coal Board	O	UK	11
5	Sep 1953	Betteshanger	National Coal Board	O	UK	11
6	Feb 1955	Gedling	National Coal Board	O	UK	15
7	Mar 1955	Astley Green	National Coal Board	O	UK	23

NB Colliery Frames 3 and 4 were originally destined for the Mpopoma Colliery for Rhodesian Railways. These were relatively large frames of 23 and 47 frames respectively. However the order was cancelled.

Appendix 2
Excerpt from Blackwoods Magazine, February 1940

For those interested in reading more of the article referred to in Chapter 12, this is held by the British Library Document Supply Service at Wetherby. Shelf number 2107.710.

THIS IS A SHORT EXCERPT from the amazing story, at which point Stokes, his heroic wife Halka (a Pole) and colleague Cresswell, have managed to get away from Warsaw, and safely return Halka's sister and nephew to their family. Now on the way across Poland towards Lithuania and the boat to freedom, the group were effectively sandwiched between the advancing Germans from the west and the Russians moving from the East. Having travelled on foot, by car, by bicycle and by horse and cart, they were now travelling on one of the increasingly irregular railway services, which was shortly to be the target of a group of ill-disciplined Russian soldiers.

Some distance had been covered before we saw the first Soviet soldier. Soon after seeing him we witnessed a convoy of army lorries, all Fords, on the main road to Brzesc. They stretched as far as they eye could see, and there must have been hundreds of them travelling one very close behind the other towards the west.

As we entered a small cutting someone remarked at the number of soldiers drawn up along the skyline. Halka had just asked one of the railway men if the authorities at Baranowicze had advised all the patrols along the route that we were expected, when the reply came not from within the compartment but from without. The now familiar sound of machine-gun fire sent us all sprawling on the floor and along the seats. Something louder crashed upon us, again and again. The whole carriage shook with the impact. How long this lasted I do not know. It may have only been a few minutes, but to me it seemed like hours. The frenzied shouts of soldiers standing on the slopes of the cutting, pointing rifles through the windows of the train, aroused us from our semi-stupor.

Halka was lying in a pool of blood. One side of her face was a sticky mess of crimson hair. At first she did not speak, and I was terrified lest the worst had happened, but she soon recovered consciousness, and, much to our relief, sat up and assured us that she did not think the bullet had lodged in her head, but only grazed her skull. We could not see exactly where the wound was because of the mess she was in.

The shouts outside had become more persistent, and demanded that we must get out at once or the shooting would start again. The sliding door to our compartment

Stokes pictured in Westinghouse Review, February 1950.

question. Slowly helping the wounded, we stepped down from the coach. The scene that met our gaze was anything but reassuring. We were faced by a hundred or more rifles and bayonets levelled at our breasts, and in the background at the top of the cutting stood a tank with its machine-guns and small cannon trained on our unhappy band. We were made to lie down on the grass, and there seemed no doubt that these were to be our last moments on this earth.

Halka raised herself on her elbow and asked the officer in charge why he was shooting at us; we had done nothing to him. We all admired her courage. The officer, who was livid with rage, replied that it was all a mistake – the soldiers had fired on their own account because they thought the first-class compartment was full of Polish officers. This did not seem much of an excuse to us, but he seemed to think it justified this cold-blooded murder of innocent people. Taking a field dressing from his bag the officer handed it to Halka and called a Polish doctor who was attending the wounded to come and bandage her head.

was jammed, partly by the body of a man lying dead in the corridor and partly because it was splintered in a hundred places. My weight soon settled the door

Index of People

Chapter 22 and the Appendices have not been indexed.

General Index

The major constituent companies have been omitted since there are numerous references to them throughout the text. Chippenham has also been omitted. Chapter 22 and the Appendices have not been indexed.